Also by Robin Furth and published by
Hodder & Stoughton

STEPHEN KING'S THE DARK TOWER:
A Concordance, Volume II

STEPHEN KING'S

THE DARK TOWER

A CONCORDANCE

VOLUME I

ROBIN FURTH

FOREWORD BY STEPHEN KING

HODDER

Copyright © 2003 by Robin Furth
Foreword copyright © 2003 by Stephen King

First published in Great Britain in 2003 by Hodder and Stoughton
A division of Hodder Headline

This edition published in 2005

1   3   5   7   9   10   8   6   4   2

A CIP catalogue record for this title is available from the British Library

ISBN 0 340 89850 X

Typeset in Centaur by
Palimpsest Book Production Limited,
Polmont, Stirlingshire
Printed and bound in Great Britain by
Clays Ltd, St Ives plc

Hodder and Stoughton
A division of Hodder Headline
338 Euston Road
London NW1 3BH

FOR MARK

FOR STEVE

FOR ROLAND

CONTENTS

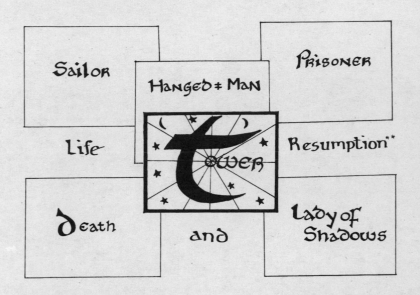

Sailor

Life

Death

Hanged ♯ Man

and

Prisoner

Resumption**

Lady of
Shadows

t ower

FOREWORD

by Stephen King

The tale of Roland of Gilead's search for the Dark Tower is a single novel, picaresque in nature (think *Huckleberry Finn* with monsters, and characters who raft along the Path of the Beam instead of the Mississippi), spanning seven volumes, involving dozens of plot-twists, and hundreds of characters. It's hard to tell how much time passes 'inside the story,' because in Roland Deschain's *where* and *when*, both time and direction have become plastic.[1] Outside the story – in what we laughingly call 'the real world' – thirty-two years passed between the first sentence and the last one.

How long were the lapses between the individual books which make up the entire story? In truth, Constant Reader, I do not know. I think the longest lapse might have been six years (between *The Waste Lands* and *Wizard and Glass*). It is a miracle the story was ever finished at all, but perhaps an even greater one that a second volume ever followed the first, which was originally published in a tiny edition by Donald M. Grant, Publishers.[2] The manuscript

---

[1] This was a demand of the story, but I'd be less than honest if I didn't add that it also helps to foil the often troubling questions of copy-editors such as those asked by Teddy Rosenbaum, who worked on the later volumes of the cycle.

[2] The stories that made up the volume were issued in *The Magazine of Fantasy and Science Fiction*, then edited by Ed Ferman.

of that first volume, wet and barely readable, was rescued from a mildewy cellar. The first forty handwritten pages of a second volume (titled, as I remember, *Roland Draws Three*) were missing. God knows where they wound up.

Will I tell you what happens to a story when it lies fallow over such long periods of time? Will you hear? Then close your eyes and imagine a vast department store, all on one level, lit by great racks of overhead fluorescent lights. You see every kind of item under those lights — underwear and automotive parts, TVs and DVDs, shoes and stationery and bikes for the kiddies, bluejeans and mattresses (oh look, Henry, they're on sale, 40% off!), cosmetics and air-rifles, party dresses and picnic gear.

Now imagine the lights failing, one by one. The huge space grows darker; the goods so temptingly arrayed grow dimmer and harder to see. Finally you can hardly see your hand in front of your face.

That was the kind of room I came to when it was finally time to write *The Drawing of the Three*, except then the store wasn't so big — the first volume was less than three hundred pages long, so it was actually more of a mom 'n pop operation, do ya not see it. I was able to light it again simply by reading over the first volume and having a few ideas (I also resurrected a few old ones; I hadn't entirely forgotten what was in those handwritten pages, or the purpose of the tale).

Coming back to write the third volume (*The Waste Lands*) in the mid-eighties was harder, because the store was once again almost completely dark, and now it was much bigger. Once again I began by reading over what I'd written, taking copious notes, and filling paperback copies of the first two books with yellow highlighted passages and pink Post-It notes.

Another four years passed . . . or perhaps this time it was six. The store had once again grown dark, and by the time I was ready to write *Wizard and Glass,* it was bigger than ever. This time I wanted to add a whole new annex (call it Roland's Past instead of the Bridal Shoppe). Once again out came the book — three of them, this time — the yellow highlighter, and the packets of Post-It notes.

When I sat down to complete Roland's story in the year 2001, I knew that just re-reading and writing myself Post-It notes wouldn't be enough. By now the store that was my story seemed to cover whole acres; had become a Wal-Mart of the imagination. And, were I to write three more volumes, I'd be adding dozens of characters (I actually ended up adding over fifty), a whole new dialect (based on the pidgin English used by the natives of West Africa and first encountered by me in Richard Dooling's extraordinary *White Man's Grave*), and a back story that would — I hoped — finally make Roland's wandering present clear to the patient reader.

This time, instead of reading, I listened to Frank Muller's extraordinary audio recordings of the first four *Dark Tower* stories. Unabridged audio forces the reader to slow down and listen to every word, whether he or she wants to or not. It also lends a new perspective, that of the reader and the audio director. But I knew even that would not be enough. I needed some sort of exhaustive written summary of *everything* that had gone before, a Dark Tower Concordance that would be easy to search when I needed to find a reference in a hurry. In terms of the store metaphor, I needed someone to replace all the fluorescents, and inventory all the goods on offer, and then hand me a clipboard with everything noted down.

Enter Robin Furth. She came to me courtesy of my old friend and teacher at the University of Maine, Burton Hatlen. Burt is a wonderful scholar of poetry and popular fiction. He has written about Roland for several scholarly journals, and was sympathetic to what I was up to with the books (indeed, he seemed to understand what I was up to better than I did myself). So I gave him my list of requirements with some confidence (some hope, at least) that he would find the right person.

Someone who was bright and imaginative.

Someone who had read a good deal of fantasy (although not necessarily the *Tower* books themselves), and was therefore familiar with its rather unique language and thematic concerns.

Someone who could write with clarity and verve.

Someone who was willing to work hard and answer arcane and often bizarre questions (*Who was the Mayor of New York in 1967? Do worms have teeth?*) on short notice.

He found Robin Furth, and my wandering gunslinger had found his Boswell. The Concordance you hold in your hands – and which will surely delight you as it has delighted me – was never written to be published. As a writer I like to fly by the seat of my pants, working without an outline and usually without notes. When I have to slow down to look for something – a name in Volume III, say, or a sequence of events way back in Volume I – I can almost *feel* the story growing cold, the edge of my enthusiasm growing blunt and flecking out with little blooms of rust. The idea of the Concordance was to limit these aggravating pauses by putting Roland's world at my fingertips – not just names and places, but slang terms, dialects, relationships, even whole chronologies.

Robin provided exactly what I needed, and more. One day I walked into my office to discover her down on her knees, carefully sticking photographs to a huge piece of poster paper. It was, she explained, a 'walking tour' of Second Avenue in New York, covering the avenue itself and all the cross-streets from Fortieth to Sixty-sixth. There was the U.N. Plaza Hotel (which has changed its name twice since I started writing Roland's story); there was Hammarskjold Plaza (which did not even exist back in 1970); there was the spot where Tom and Jerry's Artistic Deli ('Party Platters Our Specialty') once stood. That poster eventually went up on the wall of my writing room in Florida, and was of invaluable help in writing *Song of Susannah* (Volume VI). In addition to the 'walking tour' itself, Robin had patiently winkled out the history of the key two blocks, including the real shops and buildings I'd replaced with such fictional bits of real estate as Chew Chew Mama's and The Manhattan Restaurant of the Mind. And it was Robin who discovered that, across the street from 2 Hammarskjold Plaza, there really is a little pocket park (it's called a 'peace garden') that does indeed contain a bronze turtle sculpture. Talk about life imitating art!

As I say, her Concordance was never meant to be published; it was created solely as a writer's tool. But, even with most of my mind preoccupied by the writing of my tale, I was aware of how good it was, how interesting and *readable* it was. I also became aware, as time passed and the actual publication of the final three volumes grew closer, of how valuable it might be to the Constant Reader who'd read the first three or four volumes of the series, but some years ago.

In any case, it was Robin Furth who inventoried the goods I had on sale, and replaced all the dim overhead lights so I could see everything clearly and find my way from Housewares to Appliances without getting lost . . . or from Gilead to Calla Bryn Sturgis, if you prefer. That in no way makes her responsible for my errors – of which I'm sure there are many – but it *is* important that she receive credit for all the good work she has done n my behalf. I found this overview of

In-World, Mid-World, and End-World both entertaining and invaluable.

So, I am convinced, will you.

January 26, 2003

ABOUT THIS BOOK

This book had its first stirrings more than twenty years ago. I was fourteen, and I was spending the summer with my grandparents in Maine. Books have always had an obsessive draw for me, and so that July I arrived with a stack of them. Top of the pile wasn't *The Gunslinger*. No. Not yet. But it was a novel called *'Salem's Lot*.

I can still remember the feeling I had when I read that book. My body was on the tiny, weedy beach of Patten Pond, but the rest of me was in the Marsten House, or crouched by Mark Petrie's side as he held up a glow-in-the-dark cross to ward off the vampire at his window. I climbed on the Greyhound Bus behind Father Callahan – my hand burned and my mouth still tasting Barlow's blood – and the two of us set off for that unknown destination of Thunderclap, a haunted place on the lip of End-World.[1]

I closed the novel, and still caught in that dream-web, I began to walk back toward home. And there, in the pine woods, with my feet deep in leaf mould and my skin still smelling of pond water, I saw myself as an adult. I was grown-up, and

---

[1] Believe it or not, the copy of *'Salem's Lot* that I had as a teenager actually mentioned Thunderclap. I spent years wondering where that place was – it didn't sound like any city in our world. I read the book several times as an adult and never saw this reference again. Recently I asked Steve whether he had deleted Thunderclap from later editions and he told me it was never there in the first place. But it should have been. How can I explain this weird occurrence? I can't.

I was working for Stephen King. I didn't know exactly what I was doing, but I knew it had to do with books, and Father Callahan, and with that dreaded place called Thunderclap. The vision was so vivid, so convincing, and so quickly over. I held onto the feeling of it long enough to write my first horror story (it wasn't very good), but as the vision faded, I began to doubt what I had seen. I buried that vision, lost the story, and didn't think about either for two decades. That is, until one day when I went to check my mail in the English office at the University of Maine. As I was sorting through the grade sheets and memos, I felt a tap on my shoulder. It was Burt Hatlen, one of my professors. Stephen King needed a temporary research assistant, he said. Would I be interested . . .

Sometimes, art imitates life, and sometimes life imitates art, and sometimes the two of them blend to such a degree that we can't figure out where one ends and the other begins. For months before my chat with Burt, I'd been dreaming about roses, moons with demon faces, and huge, imposing, smoke-colored Towers. I didn't think I was losing my mind, but then there was the tall, lanky, ghost-like man pacing at my writing room door. He seemed to want to get through to our world, to NEED to get through to our world, and for some reason he thought I could help him. And every time I laid out my Tarot cards, my future came out Towers.

Ka is a wheel, its one purpose is to turn, and so often it brings us back to just where we started. Twenty years had passed since I boarded that bus to Thunderclap, but in Roland's world, in the world of the Tower quest, twenty years in the past, or twenty years in the future, are only just a doorway apart. I climbed back on that Greyhound Bus only to find myself, as a young girl, still sitting behind Callahan. I'd never really disembarked in the first place.

Pere Callahan waited in Calla Bryn Sturgis, on the border of Thunderclap, and Roland had to reach him. All he needed was somebody from our world to help crack open Stephen King's doorway. I knew many of Steve's other works, I loved fantasy and horror, and I had those rather sinister initials that implied I might be good for writing something other than academic essays. All that remained for me to do was open Roland's biography and read that first, all-important line. *The man in black fled across the desert, and the gunslinger followed . . .*

For over two years I have lived in Roland's world — occasionally surfacing in ours — and during that time I've collected much of the myth, history, and folklore of Mid-World. Just as, when you wake up from a dream, you try to capture what you saw during your night travels, the book that follows is my attempt to capture my journey with Roland. My goal, when I started, was to make a doorway between worlds. I hope that I have, at least, made a small window.

R. F.
March 12, 2003

ABBREVIATIONS AND TEXT GUIDE

I: King, Stephen. *The Gunslinger* © 1982. (London, New English Library, a division of Hodder & Stoughton, 2003)

II: - - -. *The Drawing of the Three* © 1987. (London, New English Library, a division of Hodder & Stoughton, 1997 and 2003)

III: - - -. *The Waste Lands* © 1991. (London, New English Library, a division of Hodder & Stoughton, 1997 and 2003)

IV: - - -. *Wizard and Glass* © 1997. (London, New English Library, a division of Hodder & Stoughton, 1997 and 2003)

E: - - -. 'The Little Sisters of Eluria', in *Everything's Eventual* © 2002. (London, New English Library, a division of Hodder & Stoughton, 2002)

PLEASE NOTE

As frequent visitors to Mid-World know, in 2003, Stephen King rewrote *The Gunslinger*. In the process, a number of characters and places were cut, renamed, or otherwise significantly altered. In this Concordance, I have tried to document these changes, keeping old information (for those who are familiar with the earlier version of the book) but adding the new. Any character, place or term which has undergone change is marked with a double asterisk (**). Since the page references contained within this Concordance correspond to the most recent version of *The Gunslinger*, readers will note that some marked entries have no page references. This is because those characters and places do not play a role in Roland's updated adventures.

2. Page references are as follows:

> III:323
>
> (volume):(page number)

3. Although Mid-World is the name of a specific historical kingdom, in both *Wizard and Glass* and 'The Little Sisters of Eluria' Roland uses this term as a general name for his world. I have followed this practice.

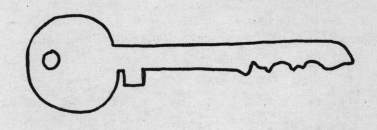

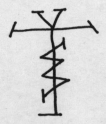

TRAVELLER, BEYOND LIES MID-WORLD

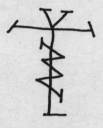

TRAVELLER, BEYOND LIES MID-WORLD

GILEAD FAIR-DAYS

WINTER

WIDE EARTH
Riddling

SOWING
(**NEW EARTH)
(**FRESH COMMALA)
The Sowing Night Cotillion
called Commala
a courting rite dance
celebrating spring

MID-SUMMER

FULL EARTH
Riddling
Full Earth babies born

REAPING
Charyou Tree and burning of stuffy-guys, Reaping lass and
Reaping lad, Reap charms.
In the Outer Arc, a prize is given on Reap Day to the
person or group
that collects the greatest number of rattlesnake skins.
Children planted on Reap come due on Full Earth.

This is the true Year's end.
Reap kisses
Orgy of Reap
Propitiating old gods
Reap Morn: First day of winter

YEAR'S END

MID-WORLD MOONS

KISSING MOON
A perfect disk of silver
Moon of Romance
Shadows of lovers
On its bright skin

PEDDLER'S MOON
Late summer moon
Huge and orange
And the Peddler, who comes out of the Nones
With his sack of squealing souls

HUNTRESS MOON
Last moon of summer, first moon of autumn
Picking apples, cutting hay
Snakes and scorpions wander east from the desert
Day moon
The huntress fills her belly
And becomes
A pallid, vampire woman
Season of Reap
The beginning of endings
Clearer and clearer on each starry night
The Huntress pulls back her bow

DEMON MOON
Blood red
Death moon
Closing of the year
Blade nose
Bone grin
Reap's scythe
Above
He grins and winks
Though a scarlet
shifting
scrim

INTRODUCTION: ROLAND, THE TOWER, AND THE QUEST

Spoiler's Warning: Read this essay only after you have read the first four books of Roland's saga. Otherwise, you'll get more than a glimpse of what is to come . . .

To any reader of *The Dark Tower* series, Roland Deschain is an instantly recognizable character. As I write this, I see him in my mind's eye, striding across the yellowing grasses of the River Barony savannah, his black hair threaded with grey, his body tall and lanky, his holster and gun belt strapped to his hips. Only one of those fabled sandalwood-handled six-shooters is with him; it rests against his left thigh. The other is back at camp, secure in the docker's clutch strapped to Eddie Dean's side. As I stare, Roland turns his head and regards me pragmatically. *If you need to talk to me,* he says, *then come.* Time may be a face on the water, but in Roland's world, water is scarce.

Roland watches as I pass through the doorway of the page. His pale blue eyes really are like those of a bombardier, both cool and assessing. By necessity, this meeting will be brief. I'm another one of Roland's secrets, and he thinks it better to keep me that way. He's not certain what level of the Tower I come from, but he knows one thing. I am mapping his travels.

Finding some shade, Roland hunkers. I hand him one of the rolling papers I've brought, and he accepts it silently. Unlacing the leather thongs of his traveling purse, he removes his tobacco poke and rolls a smoke. Despite the missing fingers on his right hand, he works the paper dexterously, licking the gummed side with a grimace. He strikes a match against the seam of his jeans and lights his cigarette. For a moment his face is illuminated with an eerie glow that makes his features look drawn and more than a little haggard. He has a few days' worth of stubble on his cheeks, and his lips are chapped. Once again I try to show him this Concordance, but he waves the bound manuscript away as he exhales a cloud of smoke. As always, he thinks that my constant revisions waste paper. Besides, he's only interested in the maps. But today I've brought a short piece, and this he has agreed to hear. It's my inter-pretation of his epic journey. Taking another deep drag, Roland rolls his hand in that gesture which means only one thing, in any world. *Get on with it.* So I clear my throat and (rather nervously) begin.

ROLAND, THE TOWER, AND THE QUEST

Roland Deschain is Mid-World's final gunslinger. Like a knight from the Arthurian legends of Our World, Roland is on a quest. His 'grail' is the Dark Tower, the lynch-pin of the Time/Space continuum, and his goal is to climb to its very top and question the god or demon who resides there. Roland's world is unraveling. The Beams which maintain the proper alignment of time, space, size and dimension are breaking down and the Tower itself is foundering. This structural instability affects all worlds, but in Roland's, the symptoms are dramatic. As the fabric of reality wears away, thinnies form and spread. These squalling mist bogs swallow all those that stumble into them, letting their captives fall into the dark no-places between worlds. As the landscape stretches, directions drift. What is west today may be southwest tomorrow and southeast the day after. A goal that lay only fifty miles away can suddenly become a hundred, or even a thousand miles distant.

As the direct descendant of Arthur Eld, King of All-World-That-Was, and as Mid-World's last *dinh*, Roland must rescue his land from annihilation. But his task is gargantuan. He must find a way to safeguard the framework, the loom, upon which the interpenetrating realities are woven. But in order to do so – in order to shore up that central Tower and the Beams which radiate out from it – he must find his way across a landscape so fragmented that neither map nor memory can help him pinpoint his destination. In fact, Roland does not even know where the Tower stands. He realizes that he must head toward a place called End-World, but where does that land lie? How can he find it? During the early stages of his journey, Roland the warrior chooses the path of the ascetic. Believing he can only reach his goal as a solitary traveler, he sacrifices all human relationships, even when it means betrayal, because he thinks such sacrifice will speed him along his way. Comrades and lovers are left behind like abandoned waterskins.

Roland believes that to climb the Tower he must have no ties holding him to Mid-World. He must be isolated, self-sufficient, cut off from the nurturing tides of relation-ship. Thinking in terms of conquest and battle, Roland follows the duplicitous Walter across the deserts of Mid-World, believing that this enemy will eventually lead him to his goal. Similarly, as a boy, he followed the path set for him by Maerlyn's Grapefruit, a magic ball whose evil, distorting visions tricked him into first sacrificing his lover, Susan Delgado, and then murdering his own mother.

What Roland doesn't at first realize is that, like any young knight, he is being tested. The initial path he chooses is a false start, no more than a *glammer* thrown by the enemies who want to thwart him. What their treachery exposes is that the young Roland is driven by ambition, personal glory, and revenge as much as he is by a desire to fulfill his destiny as the last warrior of the White. By tempting him to betray all that a knight should hold sacred, Roland's enemies ensure that Roland will repeat the mistakes of his fathers and either abandon his quest as hopeless or become lost in the deserts and golgothas of Mid-World which, in the end, but mirror the dry wreckage of his heart.

Roland, the young warrior, does not understand the ultimate nature of his quest. He does not realize that, as the trickster Walter says in the golgotha, he already stands so close to the Tower that worlds turn about his head.[1] Because of his own preconceptions, his inherited worldview, he does not understand that his fate, and the fate of Mid-World, are one and the same.

Roland's story is not just an adventure tale; it is one with symbolic meaning. His pilgrimage is intrinsically linked to a legend from our world, a legend which was an important influence upon the Modernists and which formed the basis for a famous poem by T.S. Eliot. That legend is the story of the

[1] I:218

waste land. In its incarnation in *The Dark Tower* series, this legend is bound to another belief, one that dates back to the time when men and women thought that their kings and queens were appointed by God. According to this worldview, the body of the king is the body of the land, and the well-being of one is indivisible from the well-being of the other. If the king is sick, in body or in mind, then the land falls to ruin. To cure the land, you must first cure the king. The one will only flourish if the other is in balance.

As above, so below. The disease of the larger is the same as that of the smaller, and they both progress according to the same principle. To understand what dries and devastates the land, what threatens the very fabric of the universe and the stability of the interpenetrating worlds, one must also understand what ails the king. All are affected by the same illness, but to cure this illness we must discover its underlying cause. And this is the true purpose of Roland's journey.

We all know that as the Beams snap, the Tower falters. But what is its equivalent on the human plane? What malaise weakens the bonds of Mid-World's culture? What disease affects Roland, the foremost representative of his fragmenting world?

High Speech, the tongue of gunslingers, is a subtle and complex language. Its words are difficult to define because they are so full of nuance. Each word has multiple meanings which refer, simultaneously, to ordinary human interaction, to the web that joins the interacting individuals, and the greater pattern of humanity's past and future movements. No human interaction, then, is meaningless. They all reflect both individual and cultural *ka*.

Ka, we know, resembles a wheel. In fact, it looks much like the wheel Roland draws in *The Waste Lands*, a wheel meant to represent the Tower, the Beams, and the Portals in and out of Mid-World. In Roland's map, the hub of the wheel is the Tower, the spokes are the Beams, and the rivets are the Guardians who are the Portals' sentries. Some Guardians, like the Turtle, are protective, while others, like the Bear Guardian Shardik, are downright dangerous. But they all serve the Beams, the Beams serve the Tower, and the Tower is what keeps the universe united. And perhaps these Beams work like batteries, with positive and negative charges, the one balancing the other. That would explain why the Turtle is kind and the Bear — the opposite end of the Beam — is negative. Even polarity has its place, like light and darkness. That is, as long as the whole remains in balance.

Although it would be difficult to map the wheel of *ka* in this way — it is much too big — we can, at least, map the forces of *ka-tet*, remembering that the small is a miniature of the larger. As *dinh* of his *ka-tet* and as *dinh* of Mid-World, Roland sits at the center of the wheel. The Guardians of his present *ka-tet* are his companions Jake, Susannah, Eddie and Oy. The sorcerer Walter — who plays a large part in the drawing and binding of this *ka-tet* — can also be placed as one of the Guardians, though his polarity is negative.

Just as there is a word for the pattern of *ka-tet*, there is a word for the bonds (or Beams) which hold the *tet* together. This word is *khef*. Like almost all the words of High Speech, *khef* has multiple meanings, including birth and life-force, but perhaps the most ubiquitous of these meanings is also the simplest. And that meaning is water.

As Roland knows all too well from his journey in the Mohaine Desert, a human will die much sooner from dehydration than he will from lack of food. The same can be said about the land, about society, and about the individual soul. Once again, the patterns and forces remain the same, what changes are the superficial forms. *Khef* can be literal water, the essence of life, but it can also mean emotion, the essence and bond of relationship. Whether this bond is one of loyalty or hatred, it always binds. That is, as long as the forces of the positive and the negative remain in dynamic balance. A certain amount of conflict is necessary for growth and change, but too much of the negative – too much repellant – and the *ka-tet* ceases to exist.

The patterns of *ka-tet* can be used to describe the subtle interactions which hold a society together. Without these emotional interactions which create dynamic and forceful cohesion, society devolves and disintegrates; it becomes a mass of warring individuals, or warring clans. The beneficial interconnectedness of the whole is lost.

The bonds of *khef* are reciprocal. Both parties must contribute or else the connection is at best unstable, at worst illusory. Each side must give of itself. The unity of *ka-tet* depends on the forces of *khef*. In order for the *ka-tet* to survive, the Guardians of *ka-tet* must remain true, but their loyalty depends, in turn, upon the truth and honesty of the center. When the center does not hold true, the fabric begins to unravel, and this is exactly what has happened to Roland's world, and what has, in turn, happened over and over in Roland's life.

Ka is a wheel; its one purpose is to turn. The spin of *ka* always brings us back to the same place, to face and reface our mistakes and defeats until we can learn from them.[2] When we learn from the past, the wheel continues to move forward, towards growth and evolution. When we don't, the wheel spins

---

[2] As Stephen King mentioned when he read this essay, he first began to articulate this idea in *The Stand*.

backward, and we are given another chance. If once more we squander the opportunity, the wheel continues its rotation towards devolution, or destruction. While the High Speech terms for life and relationship have multiple meanings and subtle nuances, *char*, the Tongue's word for Death, has no other meaning. *Char* is bleak and final. The wheel continues to turn, but we are forcefully removed from it. Since we each have a place in the greater pattern, breaking of *khef* rends the fabric of the All.

What can be said of individuals can also be said of societies, and Roland's society is no exception. Although Mid-World enjoyed periods of stability, its history remains predominantly a story of sacrifice and bloodshed. Although High Speech shows that unity and relationship were valued, in the everyday of life they were, more often than not, forgotten. Many of Mid-World's sins were sins against *khef*, the bonding force of *ka* and culture. In Mid-World-That-Was, the balance between positive and negative was lost; creating and maintaining *khef* became less important than the propagation of *char*. Just as the Beams began to weaken, the *khef* which was meant to unite began to repel. The waters of life withdrew, and Mid-World became a desert. The result? Fragmentation and dehydration on all levels of reality, and on all levels of the Tower.

In 'The Little Sisters of Eluria,' Roland says that the religions of his world taught that 'love and murder were inextricably bound together — that in the end God always drank blood.'[3] Upon intensive scrutiny, Roland's statement certainly seems to hold true. The Druits, the most ancient of Mid-World's people, raised the stones of the Speaking Rings in

[3] E:157

order to have temples devoted to human sacrifice. Although these practices may have drawn some of the people together, giving them a sense of unity and strength, they would have also created a blood-debt to the victim, and the victim's *ka-tet*, rending the fabric of the All. Even at this early stage of Mid-World's cultural evolution, the negative energy released by these acts began to thin reality. The forces of *char* became more powerful and the forces of *khef* were weakened. Within these circles doorways formed, but the sentries of these lesser portals were demons, not Guardians.

Although technologically advanced, the later generations of Mid-World gave little more thought to the forces of *khef*, or life-water, than their ancestors. The Great Old Ones created computerized wonders, such as Blaine, and accomplished amazing engineering and architectural feats, such as the building of Lud and the laying of the train lines deep below the Cyclopean Mountains, but even these seemingly 'good' things were eventually tainted by the death-drive of their makers. Blaine developed a psychotic personality and drove the people of Lud onto Mid-World's oldest practice – human sacrifice. The city of Lud, once the gem of the Imperium, fell into the hands of diseased and warring gangs, and the train lines of the mountains seethed with Slow Mutants, those terrible creatures who were once human but who had been completely mutated by the Old Ones' poisons. No matter what grand plan they had for the future of the interpenetrating universes, the Old Ones worshipped the gods of *char*, the gods of destruction. The Old Ones' technological wizardry was focused on one endpoint, and that endpoint was the creation of more and more dangerous weapons. In this they succeeded. In fact, they succeeded so completely that they wiped out their own civilization and transformed Mid-World into a poisoned, desiccated waste land.

As Susan Delgado says to Roland when they stand, horrified, by a line of resurrected war tankers, the ways of the Great Old Ones were the ways of death.[4] But over the course of the series we learn that the ways of death are, and always have been, the ways of Mid-World. Even during the time of Arthur Eld, Mid-World's greatest hero, human beings were thrown onto Charyou Tree fires to appease the gods of Reap, and in Roland's day those old ways were not completely abandoned. As we see when Susan Delgado is made into such a scapegoat, having the blame for her town's sins heaped upon her innocent head, such sacrifice and hypocrisy undermine all human relationships. No matter what their stated aims might be, such practices breed duplicity and mistrust and treachery, all of which are the opposite of *khef*.

In the more central parts of Roland's world, stuffy guys were usually burned in lieu of men and women, but life was still harsh and leaders were bred to be killers before they were taught to be statesmen. All that the ruling gunslingers had to do to justify this sacrifice of *khef* was to point west to the lands that were already torn apart by anarchy and rebellion. In Gilead, the light of civilization was championed, but its ideals of fairness, justice, compassion — of fundamental human worth whatever class or land that person might come from — were left to the gentle and the lame, like Roland's old tutor Vannay, to promulgate. Although Roland loved Vannay, by far his most influential teacher was Cort, who taught him how to survive in a world where a knife would constantly be at his back, or at his throat.

In Gilead, the sons of the aristocracy trained to be an Eye and a Hand, an aim and a trigger, before they were trained to

[4] IV:382

be a heart and a mind. And often, as Roland found to his later distress, such training meant that the hand could act before the mind had time to think. Gilead's coming-of-age battles were brutal, and the cost of defeat was banishment, a complete destruction of the *khef* that linked the young gunslinger to his society. The end — the creation of a strong, fearless, hardened gunslinger elite that could keep the anarchic darkness at bay — justified both the violence and the humiliation of the means. But *ka* makes no exceptions. As one sows, so one reaps, and the harvest is not always pleasant. Those trained killers — such as Eldred Jonas — who were banished from their society became the foot soldiers of Mid-World's next apocalypse.

The gunslingers could not see that the rot eating away at the fabric of their world was also at work upon the *khef* of their city, and upon the *khef* of their personal relationships. Roland's father, Steven Deschain, is a prime example. Trained in the ways of *char*, the waters of *khef* dried up in him, and around him. He was bound to his fellow gunslingers, his fellow human hawks, but the bond he had with his wife became arid and his relationship with his magician (who also happened to be his foremost councilor) was duplicitous. Even his relations with Roland — whom he obviously loved — were gruff and distant. The situation was no better in the castle, or the kingdom. Hax, the head cook, turned traitor, as did at least some of the guards. All bonds of loyalty were broken, there was no longer a sense of cultural *ka-tet*, so many turned away to serve the forces of the enemy. Farson's propaganda about equality and democracy was only effective because it contained the grains of truth and exploited the alienation and anger of a society out of balance.

In the end, the gunslingers were destroyed and their city

razed, its former castles becoming the filthy nest of a band of Slow Mutants. The forces of dissolution gained their coveted ground, and the universal waters of *khef* drew back a little more. With the fall of Gilead, the *ka-tet* of the Affiliation finally collapsed, and another part of the world stretched and unraveled.

As we have seen in the case of Steven Deschain, the reserved and isolated ruler who does not serve the greater *ka-tet* does not create the reciprocity and empathy needed to bind the parts of society into a whole. He is not behaving as a true *dinh* should. Although the disease predates him, and though he is, ultimately, another victim of the universal malaise, as the heir to the throne he carries the sins of both past kings and past kingdoms. As the center of cultural *ka-tet*, he must choose; either he must become the stable center of his kingdom and combat the malady of fragmentation or he must suffer the ultimate fate of his ancient forefathers. He can either perpetuate a cycle or pay penance, atone, and change. The disease of the land, and the disease of society, mirror the king's *ka*. In order to reverse the spin of the wheel and halt the process of dissolution, the king must look into the world-mirror but see the reflection of his own face, and the faces of his fathers.

When we first meet Roland in *The Gunslinger*, he is an anti-hero every bit as much as he is a hero. He is a man willing to sacrifice the members of his *ka-tet* in pursuit of his personal vision, just as his ancestors justified the drying of *khef* in the name of 'progress' or 'necessity.' Susan Delgado, Roland's first and only true love, burns on a Charyou Tree fire because he will not be swayed from his quest long enough to save her. Jake Chambers falls into the abyss beneath the Cyclopean Mountains because Roland refuses to pause in his pursuit of the Man in Black. Even Roland's mother dies under his guns, those symbolic weapons of his fathers. As the trickster Walter hints during Roland's Tarot Reading in the golgotha, unless he, the Hanged Man, occupies the symbolic, central place of the Tower — unless he surrenders to the need of the world and focuses on the forces of *khef* which unite him to The Prisoner, The Lady of Shadows, The Sailor — his *ka* will only encompass Death, not Life. Unless he reclaims his humanity — which is, by its very definition, benevolence and respect for the needs of life — he will never reach the Tower, he will only be oppressed by its weight.

Roland, the isolated individual, is a survivor, but he is no more than a fragment of a larger, lost mosaic. He has no meaning. Like the landscape he travels, his soul has become a waste land. As we see in both *The Gunslinger* and the beginning of *The Drawing of the Three*, every time Roland betrays *khef*, he finds himself in an increasingly barren landscape. After his misadventures in Tull, Roland is almost killed by the parching dryness of the Mohaine Desert. After he lets Jake fall into the abyss, he finds himself first in the golgotha, an ancient bone-strewn killing ground, and then on the purgatorial beach of the Western Sea where lobstrosities devour two of his fingers and a chunk of one of his toes. It is only when Roland draws companions to him — first Jake, then Eddie and Susannah — that the landscape becomes more hospitable. At these points Roland, the isolated warrior focused only on himself and his desires, rediscovers his humanity. Significantly, it is at these points that he actually moves closer to the fulfillment of his quest. It is no accident that Roland discovers Jake at the Way Station, the place where he finds the water he needs to survive, and that with Jake he catches up with the man in black. Similarly, it is only after he has drawn Eddie and Susannah into his world (and out of their own personal hells), that he escapes the lobstrosity-infested beach of the Western Sea. And it is with Eddie and Susannah that he discovers the Bear-Turtle Beam which will eventually lead him directly to his destination.

Unlike his ancestors, Roland is beginning to understand the relationship between his world and himself. He is beginning to learn from both his personal past and the past of Mid-World. Throughout the series, Eddie Dean accuses Roland of being a Tower-obsessed killing machine, but as Roland progresses on his journey, this accusation becomes less and less accurate. This Roland is determined to maintain his humanity despite the perils along his path. This Roland wants to live honorably, to live well and to live justly. And this is, in large part, what he strives to do over the course of the series.

In *The Gunslinger*, Roland lets Jake fall into the abyss beneath the Cyclopean Mountains, but in *The Waste Lands*, he risks his own life to save him from the Dutch Hill Mansion Demon and then from the boy-hungry gangs of Lud. When the wheel of *ka* turns and brings him back to a thinny so like the one he knew as a boy in Hambry, Roland tells his new companions about his betrayal of Susan Delgado, and then about the murder of his mother. It is almost as if he needs to confess his own sins against *khef* before he can move beyond them. This later Roland is conscious of himself and acknowledges his past mistakes. He recognizes his potential for treachery and fights against it. He is evolving, despite the twittering, goading, vindictive voice of the man in black. He is evolving from a mere warrior into a king.

Ka is destiny, but it is not just individual destiny. The sins Roland must expiate are not just his own, but those of all the rulers and cultures that came before him. *Ka* encompasses the past. Hence Roland's pilgrimage through the waste lands is also a penance for the human sacrifice of Arthur Eld's time, and for the time of the Speaking Rings. It is for the Great Old Ones and their hunger for power and their hubris which drove them on to destroy the very fabric of the world. It's for the hierarchical inflexibility of Gilead-that-was, and the violent, destructive rebellion staged by Farson's army. It is his penance for, and his weapon against, the fragmentation generated by that gloating Prince of Chaos, the Crimson King.

Khef is what unites *dinh* and *ka-tet*, what unites king and kingdom, but it is also, ultimately, the force of the Beams and the force which keeps the multiple universes spinning like sequins around the needle of the Tower. In order to save the Tower, and in order to save all of the worlds that depend upon it, Roland must preserve the waters of *khef*. He must re-envision the world, redefine the cultural meaning of progress, and return to his lands a sense of what is truly sacred. In order to maintain the purity and strength of *khef*, he must, somehow, lessen the atrocity of Mid-World's history.

If each decision – personal, national, global – has a thousand different possible outcomes, each of those outcomes presents another possible future. Each of those futures will be different, and each will spin a unique timeline which exists only in that new-born world. But each of those future worlds remain linked, though they have no awareness of each other. Their link is the seed-moment that they came from, a seed held in the Eternal which encompasses every moment that ever has been or ever will be. They are all linked by the Tower.

In order to save the Tower, in order to ensure that there is a future for all these worlds and to ensure that more and more worlds are born, Roland must journey into the mythic history of his world — he must journey into Our World. His quest, in the books to come, will be to save not a king or a kingdom but a single rose. A rose which sits in a vacant lot of a city which will someday become the technological Oz of the Great Old Ones, the foundation of their pride and the seed of their Fall. Before Roland, the great Warrior of the White, can save the Tower, he will have to risk his life to save a delicate flower whose yellow center is the womb of all worlds, and whose voice is the voice of *Yes* and of *Always*. He must save a simple rose which is, in our world, the symbol of unity and the symbol of love.

In their very imagery, the Tower and the Rose unite the symbolic male and the symbolic female, the two parts that join to give birth to the universe, and to life. In this unity they become One, which is simultaneously the center of all existence and the center of the integrated self. These two polarities, which seem so separate, bring together aggressive adventuring and passive nurturing, that within us which strives to conquer, to hold fast to high ideals, and that which is flexible enough to allow for human foibles, in ourselves and in others. They unite us with ourselves, our personal pasts, but also with the greater world. Although the Tower may reach higher than the heavens, and though the rose may sing a single aria that rises from the deepest well of the universe, both are — as Roland sees and hears in his visions and his dreams — woven of many voices and faces. The Tower and Rose unite to form the self's axis, but they also function as a brutally honest mirror, exposing where we have betrayed both ourselves and the world. The two, which are One, contain the voices and faces of Roland's betrayed loves, the reminders of his sins against *khef*. And it is these, in the final reckoning, that Roland will have to face.

Roland journeys through the purgatorial waste lands of his world as both sinner and redeemer. He is simultaneously the king, the land, and the Everyman. Through the course of his journey he must come to Know Himself. And only in this way can he begin to approach the Tower.

DEIRDRE THE MAD

She was Roland's grandmother. It was from her that he inherited his particular combination of dry pragmatism and wild intuition.

III:500

DELEVAN, CARL

Carl Delevan was the overweight, cigarette-loving New York cop who patrolled the area around CLEMENTS GUNS AND SPORTING GOODS. He and his partner GEORGE O'MEARAH were fooled and then humiliated by Roland. Years later, Delevan died of a stroke while watching *The Terminator*. The reason? The Terminator reminded him of Roland.

II:388, II:391 *(indirect)*, II:392–404, II:421–29, II:430, II:432

DELGADO, CORDELIA

Cordelia Delgado was SUSAN DELGADO's skinny maiden aunt. Susan's widowed father, PAT DELGADO, took her in when she had nowhere else to go, but this act of goodwill proved to be quite unwise. Within a few years Pat was dead – betrayed by one of his friends. His lands and possessions were stolen by the traitorous members of THE HORSEMEN'S ASSOCIATION and his daughter's maidenhead was essentially auctioned off by Cordelia. It seems unlikely that Cordelia participated in the plot against her brother, but she most certainly knew about it.

Although Cordelia was herself a prude, she didn't seem to have any qualms about acting as a kind of pimp for her niece. After Susan was burned on the Charyou Tree fire, Cordelia died of a stroke.

IV:156, IV:157, IV:163, IV:164, IV:166–67, IV:169, IV:174, IV:188, IV:190, IV:197, IV:207–12, IV:221, IV:241–64 *(Seafront party. Cordelia present – mentioned or at least within earshot – on following pages: 246–53, 254–55, 259),* IV:265, IV:266, IV:295–300, IV:302, IV:303–5, IV:308–9, IV:313, IV:314, IV:315, IV:322, IV:350–51, IV:354, IV:361–62, IV:371, IV:383, IV:386–87, IV:389–97 *(391–95 listens to Susan's story about Thorin),* IV:410, IV:414–18, IV:422, IV:429, IV:446, IV:453–54, IV:457–60, IV:466–69, IV:470–72, IV:474, IV:483, IV:499, IV:500, IV:507, IV:520, IV:525, IV:537–38, IV:539, IV:541, IV:547, IV:548, IV:577, IV:579–81, IV:588–89, IV:624–27, IV:635, IV:647 *(aunt),* IV:649, IV:693–97, IV:711–13, IV:739, IV:766–68, IV:787

DELGADO, HIRAM

Hiram was SUSAN's grandfather as well as PAT and CORDELIA DELGADO's father.

IV:696

DELGADO, PAT

Red-haired, red-bearded Pat Delgado was SUSAN DELGADO's 'da.' He also happened to be the best drover on the WESTERN DROP. By the time Roland and his first *ka-tet* arrived in HAMBRY, Pat had already been dead for five years. Unlike many of the important men of Hambry, Pat Delgado was loyal to the AFFILIATION. FRAN LENGYLL maintained that Pat was killed by his horse, **OCEAN FOAM**, but he was actually murdered for daring to stand up to Lengyll and CROYDON's plans to turn traitor. Though honorable in life, Pat's memory was desecrated. The men who were supposed to be his friends stole his lands, and his money-hungry sister, CORDELIA DELGADO, tried to sell his only daughter's maidenhead to the highest bidder.

IV:154, IV:155, IV:156, IV:163, IV:169, IV:172, IV:173, IV:174, IV:177, IV:178, IV:180, IV:182, IV:183, IV:188, IV:192, IV:196, IV:197, IV:198, IV:209, IV:210 *(indirect)*, IV:212, IV:255, IV:258, IV:261, IV:266, IV:294, IV:295, IV:296, IV:297, IV:298, IV:300, IV:301 *(favorite cuss)*, IV:302, IV:314, IV:315, IV:316, IV:317, IV:320, IV:322, IV:323, IV:351, IV:355, IV:368 *(father)*, IV:369, IV:370, IV:371, IV:372, IV:373, IV:376, IV:380, IV:390, IV:396, IV:397, IV:398, IV:458, IV:459, IV:567, IV:568, IV:576, IV:577–81 *(Susan in his office)*, IV:585, IV:587, IV:588 *(Cordelia's dead brother)*, IV:624, IV:626, IV:636, IV:637, IV:639, IV:683, IV:696, IV:763

DELGADO, SUSAN

Although we hear of Susan Delgado, 'the lovely girl at the window,' as early as *The Gunslinger*, we don't find out much about her love affair with Roland until *Wizard and Glass*. Susan was Roland's only true love. He met her in HAMBRY, after he and his first *ka-tet* were sent east by their fathers who wished to keep them far from the dangerous machinations of THE GOOD MAN, otherwise known as JOHN FARSON. At the time of their meeting, Roland was fourteen and Susan sixteen. Roland had just won his guns and had only recently lost his virginity. Susan, a drover's daughter, had lost her father and was about to lose her honor as well, thanks to her AUNT CORDELIA's financial deal with the randy mayor, HART THORIN.

Susan was probably descended from 'The Friendly Folk,' a sect that seemed quite widespread in Mid-World before it moved on. Like them, she used the terms 'thee' and 'thou.'

It's quite possible that the Friends were somehow related to the MANNI, though we do not know this for certain. Although she was an excellent horseback rider (her beloved horses, **PYLON** and **FELICIA**, are also characters in the book), Susan was uncomfortable with guns. This, too, may have been because of her family's background.

Roland first met Susan while she was on her way home from her disagreeable and embarrassing meeting with the nasty old witch RHEA OF THE COOS. Rhea was to check Susan's 'honesty,' in other words, her virginity. In order to fulfill her upcoming duty as Mayor Thorin's gilly she had to be pure — unsullied by either man or demon. Ostensibly she was to bear the mayor a child (his own wife was barren) but Thorin was actually much more interested in the planting than in the cultivation of his seed.

With her waist-length golden-blond hair and gray eyes, Susan is the most beautiful woman found in the Dark Tower series. She is also 'honest' in every sense of the word and gives Roland her heart freely and completely, despite the fact that her prissy and hypocritical maiden aunt has already squirreled away much of the gold given for Susan's maidenhead.

Susan's devotion to Roland did not end happily. Branded a traitor, she was burned as a Charyou Tree sacrifice. Although she didn't know it, Roland had already abandoned her, though he was forced to witness her death while lost in the nowhere dreamtime of MAERLYN'S GRAPEFRUIT.

In the years following her death, Roland frequently dreamt of Susan, often in association with the rhyme, 'bird and bear and hare and fish, give my love her fondest wish.' Her scent of jasmine, rose, honeysuckle and old sweet hay was evoked by the ORACLE OF THE MOUNTAINS when she wanted to seduce him.

I:48–49, I:71, I:92, I:93, I:115, I:128, I:130, I:134, I:140, I:144, I:162, I:170, II:260 *(girl at the window)*, II:448, III:55, IV:79, IV:81, IV:84, IV:122, IV:123, IV:140, IV:144, IV:150–51, IV:152, IV:153–72 *(Rhea)*, IV:173–200 *(with Roland)*, IV:202, IV:205–7, IV:207–13, IV:221, IV:239, IV:241–64 *(Seafront party. Susan appears on the following pages: 244–53, 254–55, 258, 259–62, 263–64)*, IV:265–66, IV:267, IV:280–81 *(Roland thinks about her)*, IV:293, IV:294–325, IV:342, IV:343, IV:344, IV:345, IV:350–55, IV:356–57 *(corvette)*, IV:358–59, IV:360, IV:361–62, IV:364, IV:365–85 *(366–67 Rhea's glass)*, IV:386–414 *(405–10 hair)*, IV:415–18 *(415–16 Cordelia discusses her with Jonas)*, IV:423, IV:429, IV:431–33, IV:442, IV:443, IV:446–47 *(Rhea plans revenge)*, IV:448, IV:449, IV:452 *(indirect)*, IV:453–54, IV:457–60, IV:464–65, IV:469, IV:470–71, IV:472, IV:474, IV:475 *(Thorin's autumn treat)*, IV:493, IV:499, IV:502, IV:503, IV:504, IV:510, IV:511, IV:518, IV:519, IV:520, IV:522, IV:523, IV:524, IV:527, IV:536–50, IV:554–60, IV:566–68 *(and Sheemie)*, IV:570, IV:573 *(the girl)*, IV:576–81, IV:584–87, IV:588–89 *(Cordelia makes stuffy guy)*, IV:599, IV:604, IV:605–8, IV:622–29, IV:633–54, IV:659–64, IV:667–68, IV:670, IV:672–73, IV:677–80, IV:681–82 *(Sheemie worries)*, IV:681–89 *(Jonas's prisoner)*, IV:690, IV:692–93, IV:694, IV:697 *(Cordelia wants revenge)*, IV:708–10, IV:712–13 *(blamed by Rhea and Cordelia)*, IV:713–19 *(Sheemie follows)*, IV:721–26, IV:730–31, IV:732, IV:733, IV:734–37, IV:739–42, IV:751, IV:760 *(indirect)*, IV:761–69 *(burned)*, IV:770, IV:778, IV:780, IV:784, IV:818, IV:824, IV:836, E:172, E:179, E:183, E:216

AMY: Susan's childhood friend. IV:413

GRAMMA: Susan inherited her singing voice from this grandmother. IV:154

MATERNAL GREAT-AUNT: She ran crazy, set herself on fire, and threw herself over the DROP. IV:190

MOTHER: The only thing we know about Susan's mother is that her maiden name was MANCHESTER. IV:395

DEMONS/SPIRITS/DEVILS

Mid-World is a desolate land littered with the ruined machinery and leaking poisons of THE GREAT OLD ONES. However, it is also a landscape haunted by the magic of a more primitive but equally dangerous people – ones who knew more about demonology than they did about technology.

In each of the novels, Roland and his friends encounter 'thin' places – areas where the division between the spirit world and the physical world is almost nonexistent. These places – whether circles of DRUIT STONES or cellars where men have been murdered and their bodies hidden – are the sites of human sacrifice. Hence, they function like evil magic circles. Unfortunately for unwary travelers, it is not just the magician who can conjure demons and spirits in these 'in-betweens.' Because of their history of violence and blood, these evil places are portals where thirsty demons can manifest whenever they scent possible prey.

Like the demons of our world, Mid-World demons seem to feed on human blood and human energy. Locked in the circles or buildings they haunt, they wait for unwary men and women to chance upon them. Drawn by the *khef*, or life-force, of human beings, they come to drink. Lucky people chancing upon these beings will be able to entice a prophecy from them. Unlucky ones will lose their lives.

I:5, I:7 *(dust devils)*, I:44, I:45, I:59, I:60, I:69, I:91, I:97, I:99, I:136, I:142, I:167, I:228, II:17, II:27, II:36, II:40,

II:76, II:124, II:409, II:416, III:25, III:47, III:337, III:435, IV:5 *(Blaine as goblin)*, IV:18, IV:77, IV:144 *(Musty)*, IV:165 *(and proving honesty)*, IV:406, IV:412 *(in mind)*, IV:478 *(in conscience)*

DEVIL GRASS/DEVIL WEED: Devil Grass grows in the waste lands of Mid-World. It is often the only fuel in these desolate places but burning it brings its own dangers. Devils dance in the greasy flickering flames and those who watch them can be drawn into the fire. Roland thinks that the **DEVIL POWDER** (cocaine) of our world is very similar to Devil Grass. I:3, I:5, I:6, I:7, I:9, I:25, I:31, I:32 *(weed-eater)*, I:33, I:37, I:45, I:76, I:129, I:152, II:36 *(and heroin)*, II:67, II:75, II:108–9, II:156, II:448–49, III:332, III:340, IV:337

**INTERLOPER/SATAN/ANTICHRIST: The Bible-bashing lunatic SYLVIA PITTSTON believed that Roland was the Interloper — in other words, Satan himself. In the new *Gunslinger* Roland shares this dubious honor with his eventual nemesis, THE CRIMSON KING. I:51, I:52–55, I:63, I:64, I:67

MANSION DEMON/DOORKEEPER (PLASTER-MAN/DUTCH HILL DEMON): This is the demon-of-place that haunts the DUTCH HILL MANSION in BROOKLYN. It is the animating spirit of an evil house but it is also a DOORKEEPER, or a spirit that guards the passageway between one world and another. The DUTCH HILL MANSION is paired with the SPEAKING RING DEMON that Roland, SUSANNAH and EDDIE encounter while traveling along the PATH OF THE BEAM toward LUD. Although the demonic doorkeepers are evil, they also serve a purpose: they prevent people from leaping from one level of the TOWER to another.

Because of these two demons, JAKE CHAMBERS' second entry into Mid-World is doubly dangerous. Not only does he have to elude this Mansion Demon but he must also escape the Speaking Ring Demon who waits for him on the other side. Luckily, he had his *ka-tet* to help him. III:262 *(monster)*, III:268–70, III:273–77, III:280–81, III:282–85, III:287–88, III:289, III:290–91, III:293, III:299, III:349, III:361, III:364, IV:123

**ORACLE (SUCCUBUS): This female demon haunts a circle of DRUIT STONES in the WILLOW JUNGLES of the CYCLOPEAN MOUNTAINS and is the first such creature we meet in the series. Like others of her kind, she feeds on desire. This weeping, sighing presence who is described as a 'demon with no shape, only a kind of unformed sexual glare with the eye of prophecy,' first lures JAKE to her cold embrace and then, when she is thwarted, takes Roland. (Roland is probably the one she wants anyway.)

Unlike Jake, Roland enters the Oracle's circle willingly, and with the aid of mescaline (what Cort once called the Philosopher's Stone) makes conscious contact with the haunting presence. Roland's desire is to force the spirit to prophesy, but in order to do this he has to have sex with this star-slut and whore of the winds. During their encounter, the Oracle takes on the voice and scent of Roland's dead love SUSAN DELGADO. In the new version of *The Gunslinger*, the Oracle warns Roland to watch for Roses and Unfound Doorways. I:127, I:132–33, I:135–36, I:138–44, I:152, I:236, II:17, II:36, II:355, III:238

SPEAKING DEMON (WAY STATION): When Roland descended into the WAY STATION's cellar, he heard this demon moaning. The sound, which soon turned into

labored breathing, came from behind one of the cellar's
crooked sandstone walls. Roland addressed the creature in
High Speech and it responded in a low, dragging voice
which resembled that of his dead lover ALICE from the
town of TULL. After hearing the demon's warning about
the DRAWERS and about JAKE ('Go slow past the
Drawers, gunslinger. While you travel with the boy, the man
in black travels with your soul in his pocket'), Roland
punched the wall, reached in, and pulled out a human
jawbone. Though this action seems violent to us, it was
one of the things Roland had been taught to do when
dealing with demons. As the old proverbs said, 'Take the
dead from the dead; only a corpse may speak true prophecy.'
From the moment he heard that initial moan, Roland knew
that a body lay behind the sandstone. Such corpses can be
possessed by spirits and can prove to be powerful mojo
when dealing with other demonic beings. I:96–99, I:132,
III:59, III:62, III:65, III:134, III:188

SPEAKING RING DEMON: Like the MANSION
DEMON, this invisible male monster is a Doorkeeper.
Roland, EDDIE and SUSANNAH have to outwit it in
order to draw JAKE CHAMBERS from his version of Our
World into Mid-World.

Like all such sexually-charged Druit Stone spirits, this
invisible creature's weakness is the same as its weapon. Hence,
the only hope our *ka-tet* has of 'drawing' Jake successfully is
first to capture the Doorkeeper and then to keep him in a
sexual snare long enough for the boy to pass through.

As soon as our *ka-tet* enters the circle, this raging, hungry
demon senses their presence and comes toward them,
disturbing the grasses to the north as it rushes forward.
Since Eddie is the one drawing the magical picture of the

door itself (and hence the one transgressing that ancient law against passage between worlds) he is the lightning rod drawing the force. However, as the demon rushes toward him, Susannah Dean traps it, quite literally, between her legs. Though it is agonizingly painful, Susannah manages to hold the demon long enough for Jake to be 'born.'

Sex with such demons has its risks, as Roland is all too aware. As the novel progresses we find that Susannah is probably pregnant, but it is all too likely that this demon – whose engorged sex is like a giant icicle – is the baby's father. III:260 *(indirect)*, III:261–62, III:265–67, III:271–73, III:277–79, III:284, III:286, III:289, III:293, III:356, IV:85, IV:115

SUCKERBATS: These strange creatures live in the WILLOW JUNGLES of the CYCLOPEAN MOUNTAINS. Many of them are vampire bats. Those bitten in the night do not wake to the world of the living. I:128

SUVIA: Suvia is a female demon with eight or nine arms. II:202

DENBY, TOM
JAKE CHAMBERS uses this alias during his NEW YORK wanderings.
III:232–33

DENNIS
See FLAGG, RANDALL

**DESCHAIN, GABRIELLE (GABRIELLE OF ARTEN, GABRIELLE VERISS, GABRIELLE OF THE WATERS)
Born Gabrielle of Arten (IV:752), Gabrielle Deschain was Roland's mother. Despite her standing as the wife of STEVEN

DESCHAIN – the last Lord of Light and the direct descendant of ARTHUR ELD, King of ALL-WORLD – she broke GILEAD's codes of honor and had an affair with the court enchanter, MARTEN BROADCLOAK. Gabrielle is quite a sad character, since this affair was, at least in part, a trap set for her by the enemies of the AFFILIATION.

Despite her dislike of guns and her gentleness toward her son, Gabrielle had a dangerous side. In MAERLYN's glass, Roland saw his mother scratch his father with a poisoned knife. This terrible deed was to be done after Gabrielle falsely repented her affair and made love with her husband. Roland prevented this disaster, but later on, blinded by a different kind of *glammer*, he committed matricide by shooting her.

In the new *Gunslinger*, we learn that Gabrielle's given name was GABRIELLE VERISS, and that she was the daughter of ALAN. She was also known as GABRIELLE OF THE WATERS.

I:76, I:82, I:92, I:115, I:139, I:150, I:164–65, I:174–77, I:180, I:183, I:188, I:191, I:225, III:579, IV:8, IV:133–34, IV:138, IV:204, IV:205, IV:207, IV:280–81, IV:323, IV:325, IV:347, IV:401, IV:409 *(drawing of her in Roland's locket)*, IV:553–54, IV:752, IV:781, IV:821, IV:823–27, IV:828, IV:832 *(Roland's responsibility for her murder)*, IV:835, IV:836–37, IV:838, E:216

**ALAN (GABRIELLE'S FATHER): I:164
ROLAND'S NURSE: III:44, III:53, III:54

DESCHAIN, HENRY
See HENRY THE TALL

**DESCHAIN, HORN OF
See HORN OF DESCHAIN

DESCHAIN, ROLAND

Roland Deschain, Mid-World's last gunslinger, is the central character of the Dark Tower series. Son of STEVEN DESCHAIN and GABRIELLE DESCHAIN, he is thirtieth on a side-line of descent from ARTHUR ELD, the mythical king of ALL-WORLD. Like the rest of his line, Roland is a warrior of the White. His quest is to find the DARK TOWER, the lynchpin of the Time/Space continuum.

Since Roland is the main character of the series, his presence is implied in all other entries. For specific information about Roland's adventures, look up the other characters or places involved. For example, page references for his love affair with Susan Delgado are listed under DELGADO, SUSAN. Also see the introductory essay entitled 'Roland, the Tower, and the Quest,' located at the beginning of this Concordance.

**DESCHAIN, STEVEN (STEVEN OF GILEAD)

Steven Deschain, the last Lord of Light, was twenty-ninth, on a side-line of descent, from ARTHUR ELD, King of ALL-WORLD. (In other words, he was descended from one of Arthur's side-wives, or gillies.) Before Roland gained his guns at fourteen, Steven Deschain was the youngest apprentice to prove his manhood and win his weapons. (Steven bested Cort when he was sixteen.) After he was murdered, and after the final gunslingers were defeated at the battle of **JERICHO HILL, the last vestiges of Mid-World's decaying civilization collapsed into complete anarchy.

Steven Deschain (also occasionally called **ROLAND THE ELDER**) was the leader of NEW CANAAN's gunslingers. Tall, painfully thin, and with a heavy handlebar mustache, the elder Deschain's gruff looks belied his actual nobility. Like all the gunslingers, he was an aristocrat, and it was in part this class division that turned many common people against the AFFILIATION and toward the cause of the traitorous GOOD MAN, JOHN FARSON. Like his fathers before him, Steven Deschain wore the true gunslinger's six-shooters – the ones with sandalwood grips – against the wings of his hips. He passed them on to Roland after the younger man proved himself in HAMBRY.

In the new *Gunslinger*, we learn that during Roland's childhood his father managed to take control of his *ka-tet* (the *tet* of the Gun), and was on the verge of becoming *dinh* of Gilead, if not all of IN-WORLD. He was betrayed by the serpent in his bosom – his own counselor and sorcerer, MARTEN – who first seduced his wife and then raised the forces of anarchy in his lands. Although Steven didn't know it, Marten was actually a shape-shifter of multiple identities. Some of his other names were John Farson and WALTER O'DIM. In all of his incarnations, Walter/Marten/Farson served the chaotic force of THE CRIMSON KING. Hence he opposed the White and all who championed it.

I:4 *(father)*, I:6 *(and guns)*, I:76, I:112–15, I:117, I:119, I:121, I:143, I:150 *(parents)*, I:164–65, I:172, I:175, I:176, I:177, I:180, I:183, I:184, I:188, I:189, I:203, I:224, I:225, I:226, I:234, II:113, II:342, III:13, III:68, III:379, III:521, III:524, III:576, III:579, IV:5, IV:8, IV:10, IV:11, IV:23, IV:32, IV:59, IV:123 *(indirect)*, IV:133, IV:136–40, IV:179 *(indirect)*, IV:189 *(father)*, IV:193, IV:201, IV:204–5, IV:227, IV:230, IV:238 *(indirect)*, IV:248, IV:325, IV:330, IV:339, IV:340, IV:347 *(father)*, IV:360, IV:361, IV:381 *(Roland's father)*, IV:385, IV:401, IV:548, IV:550–53, IV:557 *(da)*, IV:558 *(father)*, IV:585 *(father)*, IV:629 *(father)*, IV:669, IV:670, IV:720, IV:752, IV:781,

IV:782, IV:783, IV:819, IV:821–22, IV:825, IV:835, IV:837, E:229 *(father)*

DESMOND
Desmond was one of Roland's original gunslinger companions. When Roland sees the neon sign for BALAZAR's headquarters, THE LEANING TOWER, he calls out this old friend's name. For a moment, Roland believes that he has reached his final destination.

II:131

DEWEY
See DEAN, EDDIE: EDDIE'S ASSOCIATES, PAST AND PRESENT

DEWLAP
See GRAYS: GRAY LEADERS: TICK-TOCK

DIANA'S DREAM
Diana's Dream is a Mid-World story very close to that of 'The Lady or the Tiger.'

II:114

DOCTOR BUGS
See CAM TAM under ELURIA CHARACTERS

DOLLENTZ
See KATZ

DORFMAN
See MORT, JACK

DORFMAN, STAN
See PIPER SCHOOL CHARACTERS

DORNING, JANE
See DEAN, EDDIE: DELTA FLIGHT 901 CHARAC-
TERS

DOROTHY (OF OZ)
See OZ, WIZARD OF

DOUGLAS, SUSY
See DEAN, EDDIE: DELTA FLIGHT 901 CHARAC-
TERS

DRABNIK, CSABA
See DEAN, HENRY: HENRY DEAN'S *KA-TET*

DRETTO, CARLOCIMI ('CIMI)
See BALAZAR'S MEN

DUGARELLI, FRANK
See DEAN, HENRY: HENRY DEAN'S *KA-TET*

E

EARP, WYATT
See GUNSLINGERS (OUR WORLD)

EASTWOOD, CLINT

Clint Eastwood starred in a number of spaghetti westerns including *A Fistful of Dollars* and *A Few Dollars More*. He also directed and starred in such great gothic westerns as *Pale Rider* and *High Plains Drifter*. Roland looks a bit like Clint and is an even better shot.

III:251

ELD, ARTHUR

Roland is thirtieth on a side-line of descent from one of Arthur Eld's forty gillies. Despite his many wives and side-wives, Arthur represented the White. In story and tapestry, Arthur is often depicted as riding a white stallion and brandishing his great sword Excalibur. In fact, he was popularly known as 'he of the white horse and the unifying sword.' After his death, Arthur's sword was entombed in a pyramid.

In Arthur's time, Mid-World was unified; hence, he wore the crown of ALL-WORLD. His original kingdom lay in the western part of Mid-World, in the Baronies destroyed by FARSON. Despite the glory of its memory, Arthur's reign was a brutal time. In the days of ELD, people, not stuffy-guys, were thrown on the Charyou Tree fires.

I:102, I:162, I:183, I:184, IV:214 *(Rest)*, IV:226, IV:230 *(Roland's ancestor)*, IV:243, IV:266, IV:280, IV:315, IV:316, IV:336, IV:340, IV:382, IV:401, IV:439 *(line of Eld)*, IV:452 *(Jewels of Eld)*, IV:476, IV:480, IV:641, IV:705, IV:711, IV:733 *(Arthur's cup)*, E:229

ELI

See CHAMBERS, JAKE

ELURIA CHARACTERS

Eluria was a small town in the far west of Mid-World; it was also the setting for the story 'The Little Sisters of Eluria'. At the time of this tale, GILEAD had already fallen but Roland had not yet managed to track down his enemy, the evil sorcerer WALTER.

Like so many Mid-World villages, Eluria resembled one of the tumbleweed towns of the Old West. When Roland arrived, it seemed to be deserted save for a CROSS DOG (also known as a JESUS DOG), a single corpse, some SLOW MUTANTS (called the GREEN FOLK) and some strangely disturbing singing insects. After being attacked by the Green Folk, an injured Roland found himself in the hospital-tent of the *glammer*-throwing LITTLE SISTERS OF ELURIA – a tribe of female vampires. Roland fell in love with SISTER JENNA, the youngest of these strange demonic women, and she, in turn, betrayed her sisters in order to help him escape.

BOUNCER, THE BUSTLING PIG: By the time Roland reached Eluria, the only sign of this man was his nail-spiked club, wielded by one of the Green Folk. E:165

CAM TAM (DOCTOR BUGS): The vampiric Little Sisters posed as a religious order of hospitalers. Hence, the doctor bugs – which were only a little smaller than fat honeybees – were an important part of their disguise.

Despite the sisters' evil habits, these insects were actually healers. Although ugly and disturbing to watch, the *cam tam* ate disease and knitted broken bones. E:155 *(like crickets)*, E:157, E:163, E:170, E:171, E:172, E:173, E:182, E:183–87, E:188, E:189, E:190, E:195, E:196, E:197, E:199, E:200, E:203, E:213, E:218, E:219–20, E:223, E:225, E:230, E:231–32

CHAS: A free-born cattle thief destined to be tried in

Eluria. However, the Little Sisters got to the town first. E:161

CROSS DOG/JESUS DOG: The Cross Dog takes its name from the black cross upon its white chest fur. This coloration oddity saves its life, since the vampiric Little Sisters can't touch it. Despite its superficial relation to religious good, this crippled animal is a rather unpleasant creature. In fact, the first time Roland sees it, it is chewing on the bloated leg of dead JAMES NORMAN. At the end of the story, the Jesus Dog redeems itself by attacking the evil SISTER MARY. It kills her. E:162–63, E:165, E:168, E:170, E:172, E:173, E:199, E:216, E:226–28, E:229, E:230–31

GREEN FOLK: Like many other tribes of SLOW MUTANTS, the Green Folk are the descendants of human men and women exposed to the OLD ONES' toxic pollutants. In the case of the Green Folk, the poison was radium. In fact, Roland is fairly certain that the ones who attacked him still hide from sunlight in the old radium mines.

Despite their unnerving color and their tallowy skin, these shuffling, snuffling, fluorescent green Slow Mutants have a more human shape than the group Roland and JAKE met under the CYCLOPEAN MOUNTAINS. Roland thinks of them as both animate corpses and toadstools with brains. Like other Slow Mutants, the Green Folk sometimes eat human flesh. For more information about Slow Mutants, see entry under MUTANTS. E:155, E:161, E:165–70, E:175, E:186, E:189 *(slow mutants)*, E:193, E:195–96, E:210, E:213, E:228

LUMPY BALD HEAD WITH RED SIZZLING SORES: E:166–70 *(present for action)*

MALE WITH MELTED CANDLEWAX FACE: E:166

MR CLUB-WITH-NAILS: This creature probably stole his nasty weapon from the BUSTLING PIG's dead BOUNCER. E:165–70 *(present for action)*, E:172

MR TOAD: Mr Toad looks like a toad-mouthed troll. E:167–78

RALPH: One-eyed Ralph wears a bowler hat and red suspenders. He is one of the mutants who attacks Roland soon after his arrival in Eluria. It seems likely that Ralph is the leader of his tribe. He is also the one that the Little Sisters try to bribe into removing JOHN NORMAN's Christian medallion. E:166–70, E:196, E:209–12, E:213

RED VEST WOMAN: Her saggy breasts are visible beneath her vest. E:166–70 *(present for action)*, E:172, E:196

SMASHER: He gave Roland's guns to the Little Sisters without telling Ralph. E:212

TWO-HEADED MALE: This nasty creature is the one who sneaked up behind Roland and mounted a surprise attack. Roland shot him. E:168–70, E:189 *(one who yelled 'booh!')*

LITTLE SISTERS OF ELURIA: *See* ELURIA, LITTLE SISTERS OF (below)

NORMAN, JAMES: James Norman was a young, towheaded cowboy between the ages of fourteen and sixteen. He was the brother of JOHN NORMAN and the son of JESSE NORMAN. Roland came across his drowned corpse early in his wanderings around Eluria. James wore a medallion which read, 'James, Loved of Family, Loved of God.' SISTER JENNA placed it around Roland's neck and he continued to wear it throughout his time among the Sisters. They could not bleed him while he wore it. E:162–65,

E:167, E:170, E:175, E:178 *(medallion)*, E:188, E:189 *(indirect)*, E:192, E:193, E:194, E:202, E:203, E:207, E:213 *(bloated body)*, E:215 *(Jimmy)*, E:217 *(Jimmy)*

NORMAN, JASON ('JASON, BROTHER OF JOHN'): The Little Sisters call Roland 'Jason, Brother of John' to try and trick him into proving he is not really JAMES NORMAN. Perhaps that would have made the magic of his medallion less potent. Roland doesn't fall for the trick. E:202

NORMAN, JESSE: Father of John and James. E:207

NORMAN, MRS: Mother of John and James. Wife of Jesse. E:175 *(indirect)*, E:207 *(parents)*

NORMAN, JOHN: John Norman was the brother of JAMES NORMAN, and was in the bed next to Roland's in the Little Sisters' hospital tent. John warned Roland about the Sisters' evil natures. Like his brother JAMES, John wore a Christian medallion around his neck. The sisters eventually forced one of the GREEN FOLK to tear it from him. E:175–76, E:178, E:183, E:188, E:192–97, E:199, E:200, E:201, E:202, E:205, E:206, E:207, E:210–12, E:213, E:214, E:215, E:217, E:221, E:224

SHERIFF: By the time Roland reached Eluria, the Sheriff had long since disappeared. Like everyone else in the town, he was probably drained dry by the Little Sisters. E:160, E:166

UNCONSCIOUS MAN: Roland sees this unconscious man dangling from one of the Sisters' white slings. Like JAMES and JOHN NORMAN, this unfortunate fellow was attacked by the GREEN FOLK while protecting a long-haul caravan. The three men were later given to the Little Sisters. This man never completely regained consciousness while under the Sisters' care. They drank his blood anyway. E:175 *(indirect)*, E:176, E:178, E:184–85, E:196 *(indirect)*, E:198, E:199, E:201, E:219

ELURIA, LITTLE SISTERS OF: This tribe of vampires posed as a holy order of hospital nuns. They dressed in billowing white habits and their crones' faces were framed by white wimples. Hanging from the bands of silk imprisoning their hair were lines of tiny bells which chimed when they moved or spoke. Upon the breast of each habit was embroidered a single, blood-red ROSE – the *sigul* of the DARK TOWER. Roland barely escaped their clutches. A few of them are still wandering around Mid-World.

These strange sorceresses were not actually human. When Roland grabbed SISTER MARY by the throat he found her flesh repellent. It didn't feel like solid flesh at all but something both *various* and flowing.

In their true form, the Little Sisters looked like the ghastly siblings of RHEA OF THE COOS, the ancient hag-witch we met in *Wizard and Glass*. Like Rhea, they were creatures of magic and could cast a *glammer* which made them appear young and lovely. But this illusion faded quickly, especially when they were hungry. Like their own loveliness, the airy white silk pavilion in which they kept their victims – first to cure them, then to bleed them – was only a *glammer*. In reality it was a fraying canvas tent. The only truly beautiful creature ever existent in the dream-realm woven by the Little Sisters was SISTER JENNA, a twenty-one-year-old woman bound to these others by the cruelty of *ka*.

The Little Sisters were – and are – a strange order, and the reader cannot help but wonder whether they, like the mutants of Mid-World, were originally something good. Although their *cam tam* were ugly, their purpose was to heal, and the

Rose they wore was a *sigul* not only of the Tower but of the White.

However, not all things that serve a purpose are comfortable to contemplate. The dark bells which Sister Jenna wore, and which Roland thought were the true *sigul* of the order, are described as *charry*. Since the High Speech root-word *char* means death, it seems likely that these quasi-mortal women were originally death-angels, or beings meant to help men avoid (or less painfully reach) death. Perhaps, as Sister Jenna said, before the world moved on, they really were an order of hospitalers, albeit supernatural ones. But sadly, the evil of the Great Old Ones poisoned not only the air and water of Mid-World, but the magic as well. Although they may have begun as creatures of the White, the evil Little Sisters now have cause to fear all religious *siguls*, even their own dark bells. E:179–82, E:188 *(indirect)*, E:189, E:193 *(old biddies)*, E:195, E:196 *(indirect)*, E:197–200, E:201, E:202 *(dark bells)*, E:205, E:207, E:209–12, E:213, E:216, E:221, E:222, E:223, E:224, E:228, E:229, E:230

SISTER COQUINA: E:180–82, E:189–93, E:197–200, E:210–12 *(present)*, E:216, E:218–20, E:221, E:223

SISTER JENNA: Sister Jenna was a young black-haired beauty of twenty-one or twenty-two. Unlike that of her sisters, her youth was real, not the result of *glammer*. Although Jenna was a vampire and participated in her order's grisly meals, she wished to rebel against her destiny.

Sister Jenna appeared to be a kind of vampire royalty. Although the other sisters wore bells of bright silver, the ones Jenna wore looked as though they had been smoked over a fire. These dark bells – also called charry bells – are the true *sigul* of the order, and gave Jenna special powers over the doctor bugs.

Jenna fell in love with Roland and betrayed her Sisters in order to help him escape, but human love was forbidden her. After she helped Roland flee from the hospital pavilion and then elude the evil clutches of SISTER MARY, Jenna's body became *cam tam*. E:172–74, E:175 *(indirect)*, E:179, E:180–89, E:190, E:191–92, E:193–94, E:196, E:197, E:201, E:202, E:203, E:204, E:205, E:208, E:215, E:216, E:218–33

JENNA'S MOTHER: Like her daughter, Jenna's mother tried to escape her fate. She deserted her order and bore a child, presumably to a human man, though it is possible these creatures reproduce by parthenogenesis. Unfortunately, escape was not possible. Without blood to sustain her, Jenna's mother began to sicken. She returned to her sisters along with her small child. Jenna's mother died, but the Sisters kept and raised little Jenna. E:182, E:201, E:202, E:224, E:229

SISTER LOUISE: E:180–82, E:186, E:197–200, E:201–4, E:210–12, E:216, E:221–23, E:228

SISTER MARY/ BIG SISTER: Sister Mary, also called Big Sister, was the head of the Little Sisters' order. Like the others of her kind, she was actually more shade than substance.

Although she did not wear the charry bells as did JENNA, Sister Mary's dominance over her order was complete. Whenever one of them disobeyed her wishes, Sister Mary sent them to the nearby cave called THOUGHTFUL HOUSE. She even sometimes had disobedient sisters whipped.

Out of love for Roland and despair over her fate, Jenna rebelled against Big Sister. However, outside of the *glammer*-filled pavilion, not even the charry bells were strong enough to defeat this enemy. In the end, it was the *sigul*-bearing CROSS DOG – not Jenna or Roland – that destroyed Sister Mary. E:180–82, E:184, E:191, E:192, E:194, E:197–200, E:201–4, E:206, E:210–12, E:214–15, E:217, E:218, E:221, E:223, E:224–28, E:229, E:232

SISTER MICHELA: E:180–82, E:186, E:197–200, E:208, E:210–12, E:216, E:221–23, E:228

SISTER TAMRA: E:180–82, E:186, E:192–93, E:197–200, E:210–12, E:216–17, E:221–23, E:228

ENGINEER BOB
See CHARLIE THE CHOO-CHOO

ESTEVEZ, JULIO
See DEAN, SUSANNAH: DETTA/ODETTA'S A TRAIN' ACCIDENT

EVANS, BERYL
See CHARLIE THE CHOO-CHOO

F

FANNIN, RICHARD
See entry under R.F.

FARDO
See CORT

**FARSON, JOHN (THE GOOD MAN)

John Farson was a bandit who justified his thefts and murders with talk of democracy and equality. He wanted to overthrow the AFFILIATION and IN-WORLD's aristocracy of gunslingers. However, it seems fairly certain that Farson had no intention of setting up a democratic government in place of Mid-World's reigning order. Like the CRIMSON KING** whose *sigul* he used and whom he ultimately served, Farson gloried in chaos, and chaos and destruction were exactly what he brought to the civilized lands Roland knew as a boy. At the beginning of *Wizard and Glass*, Farson had MAERLYN'S GRAPEFRUIT, one of Mid-World's magic balls. Luckily for In-World, Roland stole it from him, though Roland paid a great price for this theft.

Farson began as a harrier and a stage-robber in GARLAN and DESOY. Late in his career he was known for his cruelty. According to ELDRED JONAS, Farson was dangerously insane; one of his favorite pastimes was playing polo with human heads as the balls.

Farson pretended to represent the people, and part of his appeal was religious. In *The Gunslinger*, HAX equated him with Jesus, but there was little of the savior in the Good Man. Unfortunately for Mid-World, Farson resurrected the Old Ones' robots and killing machines so that he could use them against the Affiliation. By so doing, he destroyed what was left of Mid-World's cohesion.

In *Wizard and Glass*, we found out that WALTER worked for Farson. However, in the new *Gunslinger* we find out that Farson was just one of Walter's many masks. Roland, as a soldier of the White, actually has one single enemy. But his name is LEGION.

I:110, I:114, I:121, II:138, III:102, III:331, IV:137,

IV:139, IV:176, IV:186, IV:189, IV:204, IV:205, IV:218,
IV:230, IV:243, IV:247, IV:250, IV:256, IV:259, IV:330,
IV:331, IV:348, IV:381, IV:382, IV:436, IV:440, IV:461,
IV:474, IV:475, IV:478, IV:484, IV:506, IV:508, IV:509,
IV:511, IV:512, IV:530, IV:532–35 *(Jonas and Latigo discuss
his desires)*, IV:541, IV:542, IV:543, IV:544, IV:545, IV:552,
IV:558, IV:614, IV:616, IV:617, IV:618, IV:621, IV:625,
IV:631, IV:653, IV:655, IV:656, IV:659, IV:670, IV:679,
IV:685, IV:737, IV:738, IV:740, IV:745, IV:746, IV:759,
IV:771, IV:780, IV:781, IV:782, IV:785, IV:796

FARSON'S MEN: Final battle between Farson's men and
Roland's *ka-tet* can be found on IV:746–57

> **FARSON'S NEPHEW:** Disguised as a wandering singer,
> this young man smuggled a poisoned knife into GILEAD.
> The knife was meant to kill STEVEN DESCHAIN.
> IV:782
>
> **HENDRICKS, RODNEY:** IV:746–57
> **LATIGO, GEORGE:** One of Farson's chief lieutenants.
> IV:292, IV:461, IV:465, IV:474, IV:478, IV:509,
> IV:530–35, IV:593, IV:610, IV:631, IV:659, IV:666,
> IV:684, IV:737, IV:738, IV:745–58
> **RAINES:** Bugler. IV:747–58 *(final battle)*

FEATHEREX (GRAND FEATHEREX)
The Grand Featherex is a winged being that supposedly lives
in the mythical Kingdom of GARLAN. Like the stork, the
Featherex brings babies. In Stephen King's novel *Eyes of the
Dragon*, we learn that this creature is related to the phoenix.
II:68, IV:188

FEENY, ANDREW
See SUSANNAH DEAN: ODETTA HOLMES

FELDON, AMY
See TULL

FELICIA
See DELGADO, SUSAN

FLAGG, RANDALL
See entry under R.F.

FRANCESCA (AND ROBERT)
See HAMBRY CHARACTERS: HAMBRY LOVERS

FRANKS, JOANNE
See PIPER SCHOOL CHARACTERS

FREDERICKS, TOMMY
See DEAN, HENRY: HENRY DEAN'S *KA-TET*

FREEDOM RIDERS
II:255

FRIENDLY FOLK
The Friends were a sect of the OLD PEOPLE. Like the MANNI, they spoke using the terms 'thee' and 'thou'. SUSAN DELGADO may have been descended from them, since her family used these words in their daily speech. The Friendly Folk remained in IN-WORLD throughout Roland's youth.
IV:314

G

GALE, DOROTHY
See OZ, WIZARD OF

GARBER
See HAMBRY CHARACTERS: HORSEMEN'S ASSO-
CIATION

GASHER
See GRAYS: GRAY HIGH COMMAND

GHOSTS IN THE MACHINES
See NORTH CENTRAL POSITRONICS: BLAINE

GILEAD STABLEHAND
When Roland was a young boy, this man was badly burned
in a kerosene fire. Like the patient-prisoners of THE LITTLE
SISTERS OF ELURIA, he was suspended above his bed rather
than placed directly upon the sheets. He eventually died, but
only after two days of shrieking.
E:173

GILEAD WHORE
After his coming-of-age battle with CORT, Roland went to
one of Gilead's brothels and lost his virginity. This was the
lucky gal.
I:191, IV:134–37, IV:819

GINELLI
See BALAZAR'S MEN

GLUE BOY
See ALLGOOD, CUTHBERT

GOOD MAN, THE
See FARSON, JOHN

GRAND FEATHEREX
See FEATHEREX

GRAYS

The Grays were one of the two bands of harriers warring over the city of LUD, and were the sworn enemies of the PUBES. Although the Grays lived in the mazes and old silos below the eastern part of the city and the Pubes lived above ground in CITY NORTH, the Grays were the more powerful. With the help of BLAINE, the city's mad computer brain, they convinced the Pubes that they had to appease the vindictive and flesh hungry GHOSTS IN THE MACHINES with a daily ritual of human sacrifice. The Grays signaled this horrid event by playing the god-drums (actually no more than the backbeat of the ZZ Top song 'Velcro Fly') over the city's loudspeakers.

Originally, the Grays were the city's besiegers. They were led by DAVID QUICK, the outlaw prince. In our story, the Grays are led by ANDREW QUICK, also known as TICK-TOCK, who is David Quick's great-grandson.

Tick-Tock and his band don't really understand why the god-drums work, but are eager to try to control more of Lud's computers. In the end, the computers (à la Blaine) destroy both of Lud's warring factions.

The easiest way to tell the difference between a Pube and a Gray is by checking the color of their headscarves. The Pubes wear blue ones while the Grays wear yellow ones. The Grays also have a taste for young boys.

III:317, III:318, III:325, III:326, III:329, III:334–35, III:411, III:419, III:424, III:426, III:439, III:440, III:444, III:485–96, III:497, III:499, III:501, III:506–16, III:517, III:518, III:519–22, III:524, III:525, III:527, III:570, IV:70.

GRAY LEADERS (GRAY HIGH COMMAND): III:485–96, III:506–16

QUICK, DAVID: Also known as the outlaw prince, David Quick was the original leader of the Grays. He was also the harrier who organized the sundry outlaw bands besieging the city of LUD. Roland's *ka-tet* finds his giant, mummified body in a wrecked German Focke-Wulf airplane a few days' walk outside of the city. He was TICK-TOCK's great-grandfather. III:329, III:334–35, III:375–78, III:492–93, III:498, III:529, IV:26 *(indirect)*, IV:813

TICK-TOCK (ANDREW QUICK): Tick-Tock was the leader of the Grays at the time of Roland, JAKE, and OY's little visit to the CRADLE OF THE GRAYS. He was also the great-grandson of DAVID QUICK, the outlaw prince. Tick-Tock looked like a cross between a Viking warrior and a giant from a child's fairy tale. He had a heavily muscled upper body, dirty gray-blond hair that reached halfway down his back, and green eyes. He had a refined sense of cruelty and wore a coffin-shaped clock around his neck. The clock ran backward. III:410–11, III:421, III:432, III:433, III:450, III:452, III:465, III:467–70, III:486–96, III:498, III:506–16,

III:520, III:526, III:529, III:535–42, IV:812–15, IV:819, IV:834

DEWLAP: Once upon a time, a scrawny old man named Dewlap worked the cider presses located in a park on the far western side of LUD. In the later chaos of that city, even the cider houses were probably destroyed. By the time our tale takes place, Dewlap and his companions were no more than memories in the damaged brain of the injured ANDREW QUICK. III:536

FATHER: After he was scalped by JAKE's bullet, Tick-Tock had a memory of his father taking him to see the cider presses of Lud. III:536

GRAY HIGH COMMAND:

BLACK HAIRED WOMAN: This unnamed woman had an annoying laugh so TICK-TOCK threw a knife at her. The blade stabbed her in the chest and she died in front of JAKE. III:487, III:488–89 *(killed)*, III:493

BRANDON: Brandon was a short, bandy-legged man. III:490–96, III:506–16, III:519, IV:813

COPPERHEAD: Copperhead was a tall, bespectacled man in a white silk shirt and black silk trousers. He looked like a college professor in a late nineteenth century *Punch* cartoon. III:432, III:506–16

GASHER: The first time Roland's *ka-tet* met Gasher, he was wearing patched green velvet pants and looked like a dying, but dangerous, buccaneer. Since he was in the late stages of the nasty venereal disease known as mandrus, his face was covered with oozing sores. Gasher had gray eyes, and was bald except for a few black hairs that stuck out of his head like porcupine quills. He usually covered his head with his yellow scarf. III:408–16,

III:417, III:419–23, III:431–33, III:434, III:435, III:449–53, III:455, III:463–70, III:473, III:485–96, III:497, III:498, III:503, III:506–16, III:520, III:532, III:558, IV:29, IV:74, IV:125–26, IV:807, IV:813

GASHER'S FATHER: When he died, he was so rotten with mandrus that the dogs wouldn't even eat him. III:491

HOOTS: Hoots was Gasher's former lover. When we see him in the Cradle of the Grays, he is a tall skinny man in a black suit. He has a terrible, itchy rash on his face, caused by mandrus. III:468, III:487–96, III:506–16, IV:813

TILLY: Tilly was one of the two female members of the Grays High Command. (Unfortunately, Tick-Tock murdered the other one.) She looked like a red-haired female truck driver. III:489–96, III:506–16, III:518–19, IV:813

OTHER GRAYS: After Blaine set off the city's alarms, Roland and Jake saw a number of unnamed Grays fleeing through the gang's kitchens. III:519, III:524

SCRUFFY MAN IN KITCHEN: Blaine killed this guy by dropping open an oven door and directing a blast of blue-white fire at his head. III:522, III:523

GREAT OLD ONES
See OLD ONES

GREEN FOLK
See ELURIA CHARACTERS

**GUARDIANS OF THE BEAM (TOTEMS OF THE BEAM):

In *The Waste Lands*, Roland draws a metaphysical map of Mid-World. The map is circular and looks like a clockface, but its circumference contains twelve X's rather than twelve numbers. Each X designates a PORTAL, or a doorway into, and out of, Mid-World. Just as the minor portals in and out of Mid-World are guarded by DEMONS, these major portals are guarded by animal totems. These twelve Guardians (divided into six pairs to guard the ends of each of the six BEAMS) are not mortal, and so exist either beyond, or outside, *ka*.

During Roland's youth, many people maintained that the Beams and Portals were natural. Others (such as HAX) stated that they were created by the OLD ONES in atonement for the great wrongs they had done to one another, and to the earth. When Roland was young, the Guardians were still revered. He sees them depicted outside HAMBRY'S MERCANTILE and then later upon the imposing CRADLE OF LUD, where they march along the roof in their Beam pairs. We are told the names of eleven of the twelve Guardians. They are BEAR, TURTLE, FISH, EAGLE, LION, BAT, WOLF, HARE, RAT, HORSE, and DOG. We also know that the DARK TOWER is guarded by a thirteenth totem, known as THE BEAST. (However, in the new version of *The Gunslinger*, we find out that it is the CRIMSON KING, and not the Beast, that Roland will have to face when he reaches the Tower.)

As the Dark Tower fails, the Guardians sicken and die. When we meet the Bear Guardian (also known as SHARDIK, or MIR), he is coughing up white worms, a disease which (if we take a look at *The Talisman* by Stephen King and Peter Straub) concurs with the breakdown of the time/space continuum.

Although the original Guardians may have been magical creatures, the one that Roland, SUSANNAH and EDDIE find is a giant cyborg. Shardik's body was created by NORTH CENTRAL POSITRONICS, the same company that made BLAINE. When Roland was a child, he was told that each Guardian had a thinking cap, or a hat upon its head which contained a second brain. This somewhat apocryphal story was based on the fact that the North Central Positronics Guardians all had small radar dishes coming out of their skulls.

Two Mid-World sayings invoke the Guardians. They are 'Bird and bear and hare and fish, Give my love her fondest wish,' and 'Bless the Turtle.' (PLEASE NOTE: References to these two sayings are not always recorded under the individual Guardians.)

GENERAL INFORMATION: III:39, III:45, III:50–54, III:79, III:235, III:458, III:461, IV:279, IV:282, IV:308, IV:445, IV:839

**BEAST, THE: In the original version of *The Gunslinger*, we learned that the Beast was the Thirteenth Guardian, that he stood watch over the DARK TOWER, and that he was the final enemy that Roland would have to face before attaining his goal. The Beast (so WALTER said) was the originator of all *glammer*, and was an even more powerful force than MAERLYN. However, in the new version of *The Gunslinger*, the Beast is not mentioned and neither is Maerlyn. Instead we learn that Roland will have to slay the AGELESS STRANGER, whose other name is LEGION, before he meets his final enemy who is THE CRIMSON KING himself. It seems likely that the Ageless Stranger is a great sorcerer (perhaps another incarnation of the shape-shifter Walter) and that the Beast is the ugly form of the Crimson King. III:72, III:357, III:358, IV:564

BAT: III:53, IV:279
BEAR (SHARDIK/MIR):
>DESIGN 4 GUARDIAN
>SERIAL # AA 24123 CX 755431297 L 14
>TYPE/SPECIES: BEAR
>SHARDIK
>**NR**SUBNUCLEAR CELLS MUST NOT
>BE REPLACED**NR**

Shardik was made in the dim, unknown reaches of OUT-WORLD, where we can assume the factories of NORTH CENTRAL POSITRONICS operated. Standing seventy feet high, Shardik was the largest creature ever to walk the GREAT WEST WOODS. He was so huge that he seemed to be a moving building or a shaggy tower rather than a bear. Although he had roamed the woods for eighteen centuries, Roland believed that he was actually two or three thousand years old. By the time Roland and his friends met the great bear, he (like the rest of Mid-World) was dying.

The primitive people who came across Shardik in the years following the destruction of the OLD ONES' world renamed the great bear MIR. In their language, Mir meant 'the world beneath the world' (III:43). They believed him to be both a demon incarnate and the shadow of a god.

In *Wizard and Glass*, Eddie Dean had a dream-vision in which he and his friends stood before the fence surrounding the magic LOT. Written in dusky pink letters upon the fence was the following rhyme:

>See the BEAR of fearsome size!
>All the WORLD'S within his eyes.
>TIME grows thin, the past's a riddle;
>The TOWER awaits you in the middle.

Shardik is paired with the TURTLE Guardian. III:24 *(indirect)*, III:25–27, III:33–47, III:50, III:53, III:54, III:68, III:72, III:73–80 *(warning – shutting down)*, III:86–98, III:99, III:103, III:109, III:112, III:116, III:211, III:222, III:339, III:356, III:358, III:360, III:363, III:449, III:480, III:546, III:564, IV:51, IV:125, IV:279, IV:282, IV:333, IV:414, IV:606, IV:723

SERVOMECHANISMS: These nasty little mechanical creatures served Shardik. Like the Guardians, they each had a radar dish coming out of their heads. After Shardik's destruction, our *ka-tet* came across this pathetic but dangerous little retinue walking round and round in a circle. The five described resemble a **TONKA TRACTOR**, a **RAT**, a **SNAKE**, a **BLOCK**, and a **BAT**. III:90–98, III:99, III:100, III:102–3, III:109 *(bat)*, III:115 *(bat)*, III:211, III:212, III:356

DOG: The Dog is paired with the HORSE Guardian. III:449

EAGLE: IV:279

FISH: The Fish is paired with the RAT Guardian. When JAKE ran through the CRADLE OF THE GRAYS (prodded ever onward by the malicious GASHER), he saw a huge chrome and crystal fish statue. Upon it was written a single word of High Speech. That word was DELIGHT. III:53, III:420, III:449, IV:279, IV:723

HARE: IV:723

HORSE: The Horse is paired with the DOG Guardian. III:449

LION: III:53, IV:279

RAT: The Rat is paired with the FISH Guardian. III:449

TURTLE: The Turtle is one of the most important Guardians, and seems to be the major totem of the city of

LUD. (The STREET OF THE TURTLE, with its sculptured Turtle, leads to BLAINE'S CRADLE.) Although we have not seen him yet, we have heard the following two poems about him:

See the TURTLE of enormous girth!
On his shell he holds the earth.
His thought is slow but always kind;
He holds us all within his mind.
On his back all vows are made:
He sees the truth but mayn't aid.
He loves the land and loves the sea,
And even loves a child like me.

See the TURTLE of enormous girth!
On his shell he holds the earth
If you want to run and play,
Come along the BEAM today.

The Turtle is paired with SHARDIK, the BEAR Guardian. III:53, III:169, III:178, III:362–63, III:365, III:427, III:428, IV:279, IV:333, IV:414, IV:535, IV:606, IV:722–23 *(voice of the Turtle)*
WOLF: IV:279

GUNSLINGERS (OUR WORLD)

Individuals from our *when* and *where* who come in contact with Roland Deschain are usually reminded of one or more gunslingers from the Old West of the late nineteenth and early twentieth centuries. Here is a short list of those gunslingers, including a brief bio of each.

BILLY THE KID: Billy the Kid (William H. Bonney) was

one of the Old West's most famous outlaws. Although he was born in New York, the Kid became one of the notorious gunslingers involved in New Mexico's cattle wars. Legend has it that he killed twenty-one men before his twenty-first birthday. True to his nickname, the Kid died young. He never saw twenty-two. II:208

CASSIDY, BUTCH AND THE SUNDANCE KID: Butch Cassidy was one of the most celebrated outlaws of the American West. Born Robert Leroy Parker, he took his last name from Mike Cassidy, a cowboy rustler who taught him the horse thieving trade. His first name came from his stint working for a butcher in Wyoming.

Butch Cassidy and Harry Longbaugh (known as the Sundance Kid) formed the Wild Bunch Gang, also known as the Hole in the Wall Gang. Cassidy was sometimes called a 'gentleman bandit' because he claimed never to have killed anyone during his raids. II:405

EARP, WYATT: Wyatt Earp was one of the Old West's most famous lawmen and was a wiz with the six-shooter. He earned a reputation as a hard caliber man in towns such as Tombstone and Dodge City. He and the other Earp brothers took part in the famous shootout at the OK Corral. (They fought the Clinton clan.) Earp actually wore the famous lawman's star for less than a decade. His other careers were as gambler, teamster, buffalo hunter and railroad man. He was friends with the equally famous DOC HOLLIDAY. II:405

HOLLIDAY, DOC: Doc Holliday was born John Henry Holliday. Although he trained as a dentist, Holliday moved west to try to ease the tuberculosis that was killing him. Unfortunately, the dryer climates didn't help much and his constant coughing drove away his clientele. As a result, he took up a new profession – gambling – and was remarkably good at it. He eventually diversified and also took up train robbery, despite the fact that he was friends with the lawman WYATT EARP. (Interestingly enough, the Doc occasionally served as Earp's deputy.) Like so many of the other famous gunslingers of our world, Holliday was a deadly shot with the six-gun. However, in the end it was the TB, and not the gun, that killed him. Holliday died at age thirty-six. II:405

OAKLEY, ANNIE: Although Annie Oakley was a woman, she could shoot like Roland. From 1885 to 1902, she starred in Buffalo Bill's Wild West Show. Although she stood just under five feet tall, her aim could make a huge man tremble. As part of her act, Annie shot cigarettes from her husband's lips. She could even shoot through the pips of a playing card tossed in the air. Too bad she never met our *ka-tet*. II:416

H

HACKFORD, DR MORRIS
 See TOPEKA CHARACTERS

HALVORSEN, JIMMY
 See DEAN, SUSANNAH: OTHER ASSOCIATES: MACY'S EMPLOYEES

HAMBRY CHARACTERS
 HORSEMEN'S ASSOCIATION: All of Hambry's large

ranchers, stockliners, and livestock owners belonged to this local, but powerful, association. Many of the farmers belonged as well. FRAN LENGYLL — distant friend and later murderer of PAT DELGADO — was its president. Not surprisingly, SUSAN DELGADO thought them a cold lot. This Association owned the BAR K RANCH, where Roland, CUTHBERT and ALAIN stayed during their time in MEJIS. Although they pretended to be loyal to the AFFILIATION, the Horsemen's Association actually supported THE GOOD MAN. In reality, they were the FARSON Association. IV:235, IV:250, IV:265, IV:315, IV:317, IV:318, IV:478, IV:534, IV:655 (*Farson Association*), IV:658, IV:684, IV:704

CROYDON, JOHN (PIANO RANCH): John Croydon owned THE PIANO RANCH and a good part of THE DROP. He also owned some small orchards. IV:234, IV:235, IV:239, IV:241–64 (*Seafront party. Mentioned on 250 and 257*), IV:316, IV:427, IV:579, IV:588, IV:593, IV:689, IV:705 (*killed*)

GARBER: This is the family that owned Bar K Ranch before it passed to the Horsemen's Association. IV:235, IV:315, IV:328 (*Garber place*)

LENGYLL, FRANCIS (ROCKING B RANCH): Fran Lengyll, President of the Horsemen's Association, was a blocky man with pale eyes, a net of wrinkles, and wind burned cheeks. His handshake was strong and quick.

Lengyll owned the ROCKING B RANCH. He also owned the biggest Honda generator in Hambry. Although he pretended to be loyal to the AFFILIATION, he was one of the first of Hambry's residents that Roland caught lying in aid of FARSON's rebel forces.

Lengyll's service to the GOOD MAN extended to

murder. According to Lengyll, PAT DELGADO – a loyal Affiliation man – was killed by his horse. However, this proved to be a lie. Lengyll killed him. IV:233, IV:234, IV:235, IV:241–64 (*Seafront party. Part of action on following pages:249–53, 254, 255, 256, 257*), IV:315, IV:320, IV:321, IV:322, IV:396, IV:445, IV:484, IV:563, IV:578, IV:579, IV:580, IV:584, IV:585, IV:588, IV:593, IV:596–604, IV:609, IV:610, IV:630–33, IV:658, IV:666, IV:667, IV:675, IV:676, IV:683–89, IV:698–704 (*Roland's ka-tet attacks the riding party*), IV:705 (*shot*)

RENFREW, HASH (LAZY SUSAN RANCH): Hash Renfrew (also known as RENNIE) was the owner of the LAZY SUSAN RANCH. He was also a big boozer. Not surprisingly, he was even larger and blockier than FRAN LENGYLL. Renfrew's place was the biggest horse ranch in MEJIS. Like the other members of the Horsemen's Association, Renfrew was a secret supporter of THE GOOD MAN. Like Lengyll, Renfrew lied to Roland and his friends about the number of MUTIE horses born in the area. IV:234, IV:241–64 (*Seafront party. Mentioned on following pages: 250, 255–62*), IV:280, IV:297, IV:320, IV:321, IV:445, IV:579, IV:658, IV:665–67, IV:671–76 (*in riding party*), IV:678–80, IV:683–89 (*Jonas's party*), IV:703–4 (*killed*), IV:735

RIMER, LASLO: Laslo Rimer was KIMBA RIMER'S older brother. He looked like a stony-hearted preacher. Laslo owned the ROCKING H RANCH, where he secretly kept oxen. They were for FARSON's use. IV:370, IV:580, IV:708, IV:739–42, IV:763

WERTNER, HENRY (BARONY STOCKLINER): Henry Wertner was the Barony's stockliner as well as a

horsebreeder in his own right. He took PAT
DELGADO's job after he died. IV:234, IV:241–64
(Seafront party. Mentioned on following pages: 250, 257), IV:265,
IV:427, IV:579, IV:689

WHITE, JAKE: White owned some of the apple
orchards north of Hambry. IV:241–64 *(Seafront party.
Mentioned on page 250)*, IV:316, IV:427, IV:599–605
(present)

HAMBRY LOVERS:

ROBERT AND FRANCESCA: Robert and Francesca
were lovers who made it into Hambry's folklore.
Francesca tried to end their affair so Robert dashed out
her brains and then clipped his windpipe. This
murder/suicide supposedly happened in the town cemetery. IV:535–36

HAMBRY MAYOR'S HOUSE (SEAFRONT):

MORGENSTERN, CONCHETTA: A blade-faced
seamstress. Her view of existence was that life was hard
and that we'd all just better get used to it. IV:369,
IV:391–92, IV:395, IV:537 *(Chetta)*

RIMER, KIMBA: Kimba Rimer was HART THORIN's
Chancellor. He was also the Barony's Minister of
Inventory. Tall, thin, with skin pale as candlewax, Rimer
reminded Roland of Doctor Death. His voice was that
of either a politician or an undertaker.

According to OLIVE THORIN, Rimer looted
Hambry's treasury, and what he didn't give to FARSON
he kept for himself. But no matter how good he was at
lining his own pockets, Rimer was even better at making
enemies. Once, on account of CLAY REYNOLDS'
swirling, silk-lined cloak, Rimer jokingly called the
younger man *Sai Manto*, an insult that also implied homo-

sexuality. Reynolds never forgot it. Hence, when the time came to send Rimer on to the clearing at the end of the path, Reynolds took the job gleefully. IV:166, IV:173, IV:174, IV:175, IV:192, IV:193, IV:218, IV:219, IV:222, IV:230, IV:234, IV:241–64 *(Seafront party. Is present for action on following pages: 241–43, 245–53, 254, 257, 262)*, IV:265, IV:267, IV:315, IV:323, IV:327, IV:380, IV:388, IV:389, IV:435–42, IV:446, IV:449, IV:461, IV:468, IV:474, IV:478, IV:479, IV:506, IV:510, IV:511, IV:525, IV:535, IV:558, IV:571, IV:592–93 *(killed by Reynolds)*, IV:600, IV:607, IV:608, IV:609, IV:615, IV:630, IV:631, IV:655, IV:678, IV:713, IV:739, IV:740, IV:836

THORIN, HART: Horny Hart Thorin was the Mayor of Hambry and the Chief Guard o' Barony. He was also CORAL THORIN's brother and OLIVE THORIN's husband. Coral and Thorin co-owned Hambry's bar and brothel, THE TRAVELLERS' REST.

Thorin was anything but elegant, and often acted like a buffoon. The reader wonders why his wife continued to love this skinny and twitchy knuckle-cracker, especially since he couldn't wait to take on other women. Though he was gangly as a marsh bird, Hart Thorin conceived a passion for SUSAN DELGADO, a girl young enough to be his granddaughter. By the beginning of *Wizard and Glass's* Mejis adventures, Thorin had already paid for Susan to become his gilly. Like other Hambry officials, Thorin allied himself with Farson, though those he sold his soul to eventually murdered him. Thorin's dog was named **WOLF.** IV:144, IV:151, IV:156, IV:157, IV:161, IV:162–63, IV:164, IV:166, IV:167–68, IV:169, IV:170, IV:171, IV:172, IV:173–75, IV:180,

IV:191, IV:192, IV:193, IV:208, IV:210, IV:211, IV:215, IV:216 *(indirect)*, IV:218 *(that fool)*, IV:220, IV:221, IV:222, IV:230, IV:233, IV:234, IV:235, IV:236, IV:241–64 *(Seafront party. Present on following pages: 241, 244–53, 255, 257, 258, 259, 260–62, 263)*, IV:265, IV:266–67, IV:280, IV:281, IV:296, IV:297, IV:298, IV:299, IV:309, IV:312, IV:315, IV:316–17, IV:321, IV:327, IV:342, IV:350, IV:352, IV:354–55, IV:359, IV:367, IV:369, IV:378, IV:380, IV:383, IV:384, IV:388, IV:389, IV:393–95, IV:396, IV:397, IV:400, IV:402, IV:410, IV:416, IV:418, IV:436, IV:440, IV:446, IV:451, IV:468, IV:473, IV:474, IV:475, IV:478, IV:483, IV:510, IV:525, IV:534, IV:537, IV:567, IV:576, IV:581–82, IV:588, IV:594–96 *(killed by Depape)*, IV:600 *(mayor)*, IV:607, IV:608, IV:609, IV:620–21, IV:627, IV:628, IV:630, IV:655, IV:672, IV:678, IV:694, IV:709, IV:713, IV:719, IV:730, IV:740, IV:836

THORIN, OLIVE: Poor Olive Thorin was HART THORIN's long-suffering wife. She was a plump, good-natured woman with an artless smile, and was one of the few people in Hambry that Roland really liked. Olive grew up a fisherman's daughter and never forgot it. Even though her husband wanted SUSAN DELGADO as his gilly, when Susan needed to be rescued it was big-hearted Olive who tried to help her. Olive was eventually killed by CLAY REYNOLDS. IV:151 *(indirect)*, IV:162, IV:173, IV:240–41, IV:241–64 *(Seafront party. Olive mentioned directly on following pages: 241–42, 244, 248, 258, 261–62)*, IV:265 *(hostess)*, IV:266–67, IV:280, IV:281, IV:299, IV:323, IV:324, IV:369, IV:410, IV:510, IV:539, IV:576, IV:581–82, IV:649, IV:719 *(helps Sheemie* *save Susan)*, IV:726–27, IV:729–31, IV:734–37, IV:739–41 *(killed by Reynolds)*

HAVERTY, JOHN: Olive Thorin's father. IV:267

TOMAS, MARIA: Susan's maid. IV:369, IV:387–89, IV:391, IV:539, IV:577, IV:606–8, IV:677, IV:678, IV:729–31, IV:734

TORRES, MIGUEL: A Seafront servant. IV:350, IV:509, IV:565, IV:607, IV:622–23, IV:715–17, IV:730

HAMBRY SHERIFF'S OFFICE:

AVERY, HERK: Herk Avery was the High Sheriff of MEJIS and the Chief Constable of Hambry. He was a large, fat man 'loose as a trundle of laundry' (IV:219). Like the other important men of Hambry, he had no real love for the AFFILIATION. SUSAN DELGADO shot him while trying to rescue Roland and his *ka-tet* from the Hambry jail. IV:214, IV:219, IV:225–38 *(and three deputies)*, IV:239, IV:241–64 *(Seafront party. Avery appears — or is present — on the following pages: 241–43, 244)*, IV:284–89, IV:315, IV:325, IV:326–27, IV:344, IV:372, IV:416, IV:450, IV:451, IV:455, IV:456–57, IV:460–61, IV:533, IV:535, IV:544, IV:583, IV:596–604 *(present for action)*, IV:609, IV:633, IV:640–44 *(killed by Susan)*, IV:652, IV:656, IV:662, IV:712

HERK'S DEPUTIES (GENERAL REFER-ENCES): IV:225–38, IV:244, IV:533

BRIDGER, TODD: IV:599–604 *(present)*, IV:641, IV:657

CLAYPOOL, FRANK: IV:416, IV:456 *(indirect)*, IV:583, IV:765

HOLLIS, DAVE: Dave Hollis is often referred to as 'Deputy Dave.' Although he was only a few years older than SUSAN DELGADO, he was balding and wore a monocle. While she was attempting to rescue Roland and his friends, Susan accidentally killed him. IV:228–29, IV:231, IV:234, IV:235, IV:237–38, IV:241–64 (*Seafront party. Present for action on following page: 241*), IV:286–89, IV:326–27, IV:362, IV:455–57, IV:461, IV:463, IV:543–44, IV:583, IV:596–604, IV:640–43 (*killed by Susan*), IV:645, IV:646, IV:647, IV:662, IV:712

HOLLIS, JUDY: Dave Hollis's wife. Her maiden name was JUDY WERTNER. IV:228, IV:231 (*and her mother*), IV:235, IV:237 (*accidentally called Judy Renfrew. Daughter of Wertner*), IV:362 (*Dave's wife*), IV:544 (*wife*), IV:642, IV:712 (*wife*)

RIGGINS, GEORGE: IV:326–27

HAMBRY TRAVELLERS' REST:

CALLAHAN, BARKIE: Saloon bouncer. IV:214, IV:215, IV:218, IV:220, IV:273, IV:438, IV:489, IV:569–70

CAPRICHOSO (CAPI): Caprichoso was the Rest's mule. SHEEMIE was the one who usually rode him. Caprichoso, in turn, liked to bite Sheemie. For references, see SHEEMIE, listed below.

COUNTESS JILLIAN OF UP'ARD KILLIAN: She was a whore who had royal pretensions. She maintained that she was from GARLAN. IV:268–69

MOGGINS, GERT: *See* BIG COFFIN HUNTERS: DEPAPE, ROY

PETTIE THE TROTTER: Pettie was one of the Rest's whores. She actually wanted to change professions and become a bartender. IV:214, IV:216, IV:220, IV:222, IV:268, IV:274, IV:282–83, IV:422, IV:479–81,

IV:508, IV:590, IV:591, IV:592 *(whore)*, IV:711–13 *(present for Rhea and Cordelia's speech against Susan)*, IV:765

ROMP, THE: The Romp was the name of the two-headed MUTIE elk mounted on the wall behind the bar. He had a rack of antlers like a forest grove and four glaring eyes. IV:214, IV:216, IV:219, IV:220, IV:268, IV:269, IV:270, IV:273, IV:479, IV:480, IV:563, IV:590, IV:710, IV:711, IV:720

RUIZ, STANLEY: Stanley Ruiz was the Rest's barkeep. He was probably also SHEEMIE's father. IV:180, IV:269, IV:270–73, IV:275, IV:304, IV:479, IV:480, IV:500, IV:563, IV:590–91, IV:592 *(bartender)*, IV:637, IV:711–13 *(present for Rhea and Cordelia's speech against Susan)*, IV:765

**SHEB (SHEB MCCURDY): Sheb played the piano in the Travellers' Rest. He also worked in TULL. See entry under SHEB, listed separately.

SHEEMER, DELORES: SHEEMIE's mother. Before she died, she was probably one of the Rest's whores. IV:272

**SHEEMIE: Sheemie was a mildly retarded young man who had black kinky hair and a sweet disposition. He was the bastard offspring of DELORES SHEEMER and (most likely) STANLEY RUIZ. After CUTHBERT ALLGOOD saved his life, Sheemie became devoted to Roland's *ka-tet*. He also loved SUSAN DELGADO. In the new *Gunslinger*, Roland remembers Sheemie and his humorous relationship with the mule CAPRICHOSO. I:13, IV:215, IV:238–39, IV:268, IV:270–79, IV:284 *(present for standoff on 282–84)*, IV:287, IV:302–5, IV:307–8, IV:320, IV:362–64, IV:413, IV:422, IV:430, IV:431, IV:479, IV:483, IV:488–90, IV:496–500,

IV:506–7, IV:519, IV:525, IV:546, IV:559, IV:564–68, IV:574, IV:585, IV:626, IV:635, IV:637–39, IV:645, IV:646, IV:648–54, IV:659–61, IV:662, IV:664, IV:667–68, IV:677–78, IV:681–82, IV:689–90, IV:713–19, IV:721, IV:726–27, IV:730, IV:731, IV:732, IV:734–37, IV:739, IV:751, IV:787

THORIN, CORAL: Morose Coral Thorin was the Madame of the saloon and whorehouse known as the Travellers' Rest. She and her brother, MAYOR HART THORIN, jointly owned the place. Fifty-five-year-old Coral was a wild-child in her youth and didn't get any better as she got older. She just became more mercenary about it. Although she was attractive in a large-eyed, weasel-headed way, she had a hard streak. Coral became ELDRED JONAS's lover. After he died and she fled Hambry, she became CLAY REYNOLD's woman. The two of them turned to bank-robbery and were eventually killed for it. IV:215, IV:216 *(indirect)*, IV:223, IV:240–41, IV:241–64 *(Seafront party. Coral present on following pages: 241, 244, 255–62)*, IV:287, IV:313, IV:391, IV:427, IV:435, IV:440, IV:477–86 *(478 father mentioned)*, IV:487, IV:488–90, IV:497, IV:499, IV:529–35 *(present for discussion)*, IV:547, IV:563, IV:564–65, IV:580, IV:588, IV:590, IV:616, IV:630, IV:637–38, IV:654–59, IV:665, IV:672, IV:688, IV:708–10, IV:768, IV:786

OTHER HAMBRY CHARACTERS:

ALVEREZ (LENGYLL'S MAN): IV:600

ALVEREZ, MISHA: SUSAN DELGADO taught her daughter to horseback ride, but this didn't stop Misha from spitting on Susan as she was carted toward the Charyou Tree bonfire. IV:768

BEECH, MRS: Hers was the first mailbox on the edge of town. IV:180, IV:194, IV:197, IV:199

HOOKEY, BRIAN: He owned HOOKEY'S STABLE AND SMITHY, also known as HOOKEY'S STABLE AND FANCY LIVERY. IV:352, IV:355, IV:380, IV:417, IV:422, IV:472, IV:473, IV:484, IV:490, IV:538, IV:631, IV:646, IV:689, IV:702 *(killed)*

HOOKEY, RUFUS: BRIAN HOOKEY's son. IV:490 *(eldest son)*, IV:538 *(eldest son)*, IV:631, IV:706

MC CANN, JAMIE: This whey-faced boy was to be HART THORIN's stand-in during the Reap festivities. Thorin was too old to be the Reaping Lad. IV:369, IV:465, IV:765

OLD SOONY: He owned the hut in the BAD GRASS where Susan and Roland made love, and where Susan was later captured by ELDRED JONAS. Old Soony joined the MANNI sect. IV:674–75

ORTEGA, MILLICENT: She was a gossip who stared at CORDELIA and ELDRED JONAS from the window of ANNE'S DRESSES. IV:415

O'SHYVEN, PETER: The husband of THERESA O'SHYVEN, he is decribed as 'a vaquero of laughing temperament.' IV:611

O'SHYVEN, THERESA MARIA DELORES: Wife of PETER O'SHYVEN, she sold rugs in Hambry's upper market. In her spare time, she licked corners in order to clean them. IV:611–13

QUINT, HIRAM: He worked at the PIANO RANCH. IV:569–70, IV:609, IV:610, IV:665–67, IV:671–76 *(riding party)*, IV:683–89 *(Jonas's party)*, IV:706 *(fled)*

HARLEY, MR
See PIPER SCHOOL CHARACTERS

HARRIERS
See HIGH SPEECH AND MID-WORLD ARGOT

HASPIO, JIMMY
See BALAZAR'S MEN

HATHAWAY, MISS
See DEAN, EDDIE: EDDIE'S ASSOCIATES, PAST AND PRESENT

HAVERTY, JOHN
See HAMBRY CHARACTERS: HAMBRY MAYOR'S HOUSE (SEAFRONT): THORIN, OLIVE

**HAX
Hax was the head-cook of Gilead's castle and the absolute ruler of the West Kitchen. He was a large, dark-skinned man with a gold hoop in his right ear. Although he loved children, he was a faithful follower of JOHN FARSON (THE GOOD MAN). To serve the cause of revolution, Hax was prepared to poison the men, women and children of the town of FARSON. (In the new *Gunslinger*, Hax plots to poison the town of TAUNTON, not Farson.) Hax's plan was discovered by Roland and CUTHBERT ALLGOOD. Hax was hanged for his crime and both Roland and Cuthbert were allowed to watch. Roland took a splinter from the gallows tree.
   I:108–11, I:112–15, I:118–21, I:151, I:163, I:174 *(cook)*, II:113, III:50, III:53, III:54, III:55, IV:201, IV:382, IV:525, IV:825

MAGGIE: Maggie worked in the kitchens of Gilead's castle. She was HAX's assistant cook. I:109

HEATH, ARTHUR
See ALLGOOD, CUTHBERT

HEATH, GEORGE
See ALLGOOD, CUTHBERT

HENRY THE TALL
Roland's paternal grandfather.
IV:340, IV:551

HOLDEN ('FAT JOHNNY' HOLDEN)
Stocky, black-haired 'Fat Johnny' was the brother-in-law of JUSTIN CLEMENTS. He worked at CLEMENTS GUNS AND SPORTING GOODS.
II:388–92, II:394–97, II:398–406, II:421–23
MOTHER: II:403

HOLLIDAY, DOC
See GUNSLINGERS (OUR WORLD)

HOLLIS, DAVE
See HAMBRY CHARACTERS: SHERIFF'S OFFICE

HOLLIS, JUDY
See HAMBRY CHARACTERS: SHERIFF'S OFFICE

HOLMES, ALICE
See DEAN, SUSANNAH: ODETTA HOLMES' ASSOCIATES

HOLMES, DAN
    See DEAN, SUSANNAH: ODETTA HOLMES' ASSO-
CIATES

HOLMES, ODETTA
    See DEAN, SUSANNA

HOOKEY, BRIAN
    See HAMBRY CHARACTERS: OTHER CHARAC-
TERS

HOOTS
    See GRAYS: GRAY HIGH COMMAND

**HORN OF DESCHAIN
In the new version of *The Gunslinger*, we learn that CUTH-
BERT ALLGOOD died while blowing the Horn of Deschain
at the Battle of JERICHO HILL. At this terrible battle,
which brought down the AFFILIATION, Roland lost not
only the last of his fellow fighters but the horn of his fathers,
which he was meant to sound when he reached the DARK
TOWER.
    I:4, I:6, I:103, I:170, I:238

HORSEMEN'S ASSOCIATION
    See HAMBRY CHARACTERS: HORSEMEN'S ASSO-
CIATION

HOTCHKISS, MR
    See PIPER SCHOOL CHARACTERS

HOUNDS OF THE FALLS

During their terrifying ride on BLAINE the insane Mono, our *ka-tet* saw these magnificent stone statues jutting over a waterfall between RILEA and DASHERVILLE. Although their bodies resembled those of enormous, snarling dogs, their purpose was to gather the force of the BEAM and transform it to electricity. Blaine used this energy to recharge his batteries. See BLAINE'S ROUTE, listed in the MID-WORLD PLACES section.

IV:39–44 *(Blaine recharges batteries)*, IV:50, IV:51

HOWARD
See DEAN, SUSANNAH: ODETTA HOLMES' ASSOCIATES

I

'IL ROCHE'
See BALAZAR

IMPERIUM
See NORTH CENTRAL POSITRONICS

INTERLOPER
See PITTSTON, SYLVIA and DEMONS/SPIRITS/DEVILS

J

JAMIE
    See DE CURRY, JAMIE

JENNA, SISTER
    See ELURIA, LITTLE SISTERS OF

JESSERLING, PETRA
    See PIPER SCHOOL CHARACTERS

JESUS DOG (CROSS DOG)
    See ELURIA CHARACTERS

'JIM CROW'
Jim Crow was a character in an early 19th-century plantation song found in Our World. His name was given to the set of laws and social practices known as segregation. During her time on our level of the TOWER, SUSANNAH DEAN and other Civil Rights activists fought to oust the Jim Crow policies found in the South.
    II:264, II:266

**JOHNS, ALAIN
Alain Johns was Roland's sworn brother and his fellow gunslinger. Although he is mentioned earlier, we do not meet Alain until *Wizard and Glass*, when he and CUTHBERT ALLGOOD accompany Roland to the OUTER ARC town of HAMBRY.

Alain was a big boy with a mop of unruly blond hair, bright blue eyes, and a round face. Because of his looks, many people assumed he was a dullard, however he was actually both clever and sensitive. Like Roland's later *ka-tet* mate SUSANNAH DEAN, Alain had 'the touch.' Perhaps because of this mixture of empathy and psychic ability, Alain was much more stable than the volatile Cuthbert. Sadly for Alain, he was destined to die under Roland and Cuthbert's guns.

While in HAMBRY, Alain's alias was RICHARD STOCK-WORTH. His horse was named **BUCKSKIN**. In the original version of *The Gunslinger*, Alain was not mentioned, though Roland spoke of a friend named ALLEN. In the new version of *The Gunslinger*, Allen's name is replaced with Alain's.

I:93, I:135, I:161, I:163–65 *(boys with Roland)*, I:176, I:177, I:183–90, I:207, II:401 *(killed by Roland and Cuthbert)*, II:448, III:19, III:44, III:55, III:82, III:359, III:379, III:383, III:385, IV:73, IV:148–49 *(in Grapefruit)*, IV:185 *(Richard Stockworth)*, IV:191, IV:192 *(indirect)*, IV:197 *(friends)*, IV:202, IV:203, IV:205, IV:218–19 *(Jonas and Reynolds discuss)*, IV:221–22, IV:224–53 *(Seafront; flashback to Avery's office)*, IV:265 *(young men)*, IV:278–79, IV:281, IV:282–89 *(Sheriff's office after standoff)*, IV:291, IV:292, IV:293, IV:303, IV:316, IV:317 *(indirect)*, IV:326–27, IV:328–32, IV:334, IV:335 *(indirect)*, IV:339 *(Depape in Ritzy)*, IV:341–49 *(thinny)*, IV:353, IV:357, IV:358–61, IV:362–64, IV:368, IV:369, IV:370 *(Roland's friends)*, IV:372 *(on watch)*, IV:378 *(friends)*, IV:383 *(friends)*, IV:385 *(friends)*, IV:431–34, IV:438–42 *(Jonas and Rimer discuss)*, IV:447–52, IV:461 *(subject)*, IV:469 *(indirect)*, IV:476 *(In-World boys)*, IV:484–85 *(brats)*, IV:487–88, IV:490–96 *(Jonas defaces Bar K bunkhouse – Alain knows because of touch)*, IV:500–5, IV:513–21, IV:532–35 *(discussed by Jonas and Latigo)*, IV:536 *(meeting in*

graveyard), IV:539–58, IV:559, IV:569 *(baby knights)*, IV:573–76, IV:584 *(boys)*, IV:586, IV:597–605, IV:607 *(pinboys)*, IV:608, IV:609 *(cubs)*, IV:613 *(plaguey boys)*, IV:615 *(brats)*, IV:630, IV:631 *(young men)*, IV:634, IV:638, IV:641–54, IV:657 *(In-World brats)*, IV:659–61, IV:666 *(boys)*, IV:667–74 *(Jonas and Rhea)*, IV:675 *(indirect)*, IV:682, IV:689 *(boys)*, IV:690–92, IV:698–707 *(attacks Jonas)*, IV:712–13 *(murders and culls)*, IV:724–26, IV:727–29, IV:731–34, IV:737–39, IV:743–61 *(final battle)*, IV:764, IV:766, IV:769–72, IV:781–82, IV:827, IV:835, E:205
   ALAIN'S MOTHER: IV:491, IV:502, IV:504

JOHNS, CHRISTOPHER
Alain's father, known in his youth as 'Burning Chris.'
   IV:283 *(indirect)*, IV:360 *(fathers)*, IV:361 *(father)*, IV:434, IV:541, IV:542, IV:550–53, IV:733, IV:781

JOHNSON
See TULL CHARACTERS

JOLENE
See RITZY CHARACTERS

JONAS, ELDRED
See BIG COFFIN HUNTERS

K

KATZ
Katz was the forty-six-year-old owner of KATZ'S PHAR-MACY AND SODA FOUNTAIN. With his frail body, balding head and yellow skin, he looked more like sixty-six. Katz hated his shop and never forgave his father for burdening him with it.
II:376, II:411–19, II:425–29
KATZ SENIOR: Katz's deceased father. Katz curses him every day. II:411, II:413, II:415, II:426
KATZ'S EMPLOYEES, CUSTOMERS AND COMPETITORS:
BRUMHALL, DR: Mrs RATHBUN's doctor. He's a little too free handing out the Valium prescriptions. II:412
DOLLENTZ: KATZ's competitor in the pharmacy business. II:413
GUY IN LEATHER JACKET: This guy tries to sneak up on MORT/Roland with a knife. Roland shoots it out of his hand. II:417
KATZ'S PIMPLE-FACED ASSISTANT: II:414–19
LENNOX, RALPH: Security guard at Katz's. II:413–19, II:425–29
RATHBUN, MRS: She's a Valium addict who harasses Katz with outdated prescriptions until he refills them. II:412–15

KENNEDY, JOHN F.
John F. Kennedy, who was much admired by SUSANNAH DEAN, was the thirty-fifth President of the United States. During his three years in office he introduced the legislative program called the 'New Frontier' which was supposed to extend Civil Rights. He was allegedly assassinated by **LEE HARVEY OSWALD** in November of 1963, only about four months before Susannah entered Mid-World. Two days after the assassination, Oswald was shot at point-blank range by **JACK RUBY**. Kennedy's successor was Lyndon B. Johnson.
    II:207–209

KENNERLY
    See TULL: SYLVIA PITTSTON'S REVIVAL

KILLINGTON
    See NORTH CENTRAL POSITRONICS: BLAINE

KINGERY, MR
    See PIPER SCHOOL CHARACTERS

KINGSTOWN GIRL
This girl was one of the many that Roland loved and then left behind.
    I:173

KNOPF, MR
    See PIPER SCHOOL CHARACTERS

**KUVIAN NIGHT SOLDIERS
It seems likely that the Kuvian Night Soldiers were a band of

assassins. This reference is cut from the new version of *The Gunslinger*.

L

LADY OF SHADOWS
See DEAN, SUSANNAH

**LaMERK FOUNDRY
In the days of the GREAT OLD ONES, LaMerk Foundry built the long and rusty bridge leading to the city of LUD. It also manufactured Lud's manhole covers. As we find out in EDDIE's dream about the destruction of JAKE's magic LOT on 2nd Avenue and 46th Street, LaMerk Foundry appears to be connected to that enemy of the ROSE found in Our World – MILLS CONSTRUCTION AND SOMBRA REAL ESTATE. It may also have ties to the sinister NORTH CENTRAL POSITRONICS. According to SYLVIA PITTSTON in the new *Gunslinger*, the INTERLOPER (also known as THE CRIMSON KING) was responsible for LaMerk's nasty machines.
   I:53, III:399, III:450, IV:125

LATIGO
See FARSON'S MEN

**LEGION
See THE AGELESS STRANGER

LENGYLL, FRANCIS
See HAMBRY CHARACTERS: HORSEMEN'S ASSO-
CIATION

LENNOX, RALPH
See KATZ

LESTER THE LOBSTER
See LOBSTROSITIES

LITTLE COFFIN HUNTERS
See BIG COFFIN HUNTERS

LITTLE SISTERS OF ELURIA
See ELURIA, LITTLE SISTERS OF

LOBSTROSITIES
These critters, which live on the beaches of the WESTERN
SEA, look like a cross between scorpions and giant lobsters.
They are four feet long, have bleak eyes on stalks, and long,
sharp, serrated beaks. Every time a wave comes, they assume
'The Honor Stance' by holding their claws up in the air and
then wait until the water crashes over them. They are most
vicious at night, and are responsible for eating two of Roland's
fingers and some of his toes. They constantly murmur *Dad-
a-chum? Did-a-chick? Dum-a-chum? Ded-a-Chek?*
    II:7–13, II:41, II:53–54, II:100, II:101–2, II:107, II:108,
II:109, II:116, II:150–56 *(eat Jack Andolini)*, II:172, II:180–81
(lobstrosity meat), II:183, II:186–87, II:190, II:256, II:261,
II:284 *(and Detta)*, II:285, II:318, II:322, II:329, II:333, II:382,
II:406–7, II:440–41, II:443, II:448, III:16, III:63, III:70,
III:107, III:108, III:206, IV:28, IV:78 *(indirect)*, IV:83, IV:816

LORD PERTH
    See PERTH, LORD

LOUISE, SISTER
    See ELURIA, LITTLE SISTERS OF

LUD
    See GRAYS and PUBES

LUDDITES
The inhabitants of the city of LUD. See PUBES and GRAYS. In Our World, a Luddite is a person who opposes increased industrialization and/or new technology. The term comes from the nineteenth century workers who destroyed the machines which they thought were stealing their jobs. In Mid-World's Lud, the Luddites have to worry about the machines stealing their lives.
    III:561

LYDIA
    See OLD MOTHER

M

MAD DOG OF GILEAD
EDDIE DEAN tells BLAINE the insane Mono that Roland used to be called the Mad Dog of Gilead. We don't know if it's true or not.
    III:576, IV:22

**MAERLYN

Maerlyn is the wizard responsible for the creation of the thirteen sinister magic balls known as MAERLYN'S RAINBOW. He is also known as the **AGELESS STRANGER**. In the original version of *The Gunslinger*, we learned that Maerlyn and the BEAST are the final obstacles Roland will have to face before he climbs the DARK TOWER.

In the old version of *The Gunslinger*, we learned that WALTER was once the servant of this strange mage who lives backward in time and who '*darkles*' and '*tincts*'. However, in the new version of *The Gunslinger* Walter mentions neither Maerlyn nor the Beast. Instead, he speaks only of the Ageless Stranger and his own evil master, THE CRIMSON KING.

III:358 *(Ageless Stranger)*, III:538, IV:817

MAERLYN'S RAINBOW: See DOORWAYS BETWEEN WORLDS, listed in the PORTALS section.

MAGGIE

See HAX

MAN IN BLACK

See WALTER

**MANNI

The Manni are a religious sect that knows how to travel between worlds. A tribe of them once lived outside GILEAD. Roland suspects that his old teacher CORT held palaver with these people, and so knew something about jumping the time/space continuum. ELDRED JONAS also knew about Manni beliefs.

In the new version of *The Gunslinger*, we learn that Manni holy men can achieve a clinical detachment from their own bodies, attaining a complete division between the mind/spirit and the physical self. They can even watch their bodies die without becoming emotionally upset. Also in the new *Gunslinger*, we learn that a tribe of Manni-folk lived in the dens to the north of the MOHAINE DESERT.

As well as having their own philosophy, the Manni have their own poetic tradition. The lines 'Beyond the realm of human range/ A drop of hell, a touch of strange' come from a Manni poem. BROWN, the BORDER-DWELLER, married a Manni woman and lived among them for a while. Although he left their settlement, he still retained their habit of using 'thee' and 'thou' in his speech.

I:4, I:10, I:11, I:139, IV:219

MARIA
  See HAMBRY CHARACTERS: HAMBRY MAYOR'S HOUSE (SEAFRONT)

MARK
  See CORT

MARK CROSS PEN BUSINESSMEN
  See CHAMBERS, JAKE

MARTEN
  See BROADCLOAK, MARTEN

MARTIN, MR RAYMOND
  See CHARLIE THE CHOO-CHOO

MARY, SISTER
  See ELURIA, LITTLE SISTERS OF

MARYANNE
See DEAN, HENRY

McCAIN, LARRY
See DEAN, HENRY: HENRY DEAN'S *KA-TET*

MCCURDY, SHEB
See SHEB

MCDONALD, CAPTAIN
See DEAN, EDDIE: DELTA FLIGHT 901 CHARAC-TERS

MCGURSKY, MRS
See DEAN, EDDIE: EDDIE'S ASSOCIATES PAST AND PRESENT

MERCY
See RIVER CROSSING CHARACTERS

MERLIN
Although the MAERLYN of Roland's world is different from the mythical Merlin of the Arthurian legends, in *The Gunslinger* Roland seems to be aware of the existence of both these magicians. He even compares MARTEN, the wicked magician of his father's court, to Merlin. In *The Waste Lands*, SUSANNAH DEAN maintains that one of Merlin's other names is the AGELESS STRANGER.
I:102, III:358

MICHELA, SISTER
See ELURIA, LITTLE SISTERS OF

MID-WORLD RAILWAY CO.
See CHARLIE THE CHOO-CHOO

MIGUEL
See HAMBRY CHARACTERS: HAMBRY MAYOR'S HOUSE (SEAFRONT)

MILL, AUNT
See TULL CHARACTERS

MILLS CONSTRUCTION AND SOMBRA REAL ESTATE
Mills Construction is the company that is going to build the TURTLE BAY LUXURY CONDOMINIUMS on the site of JAKE'S vacant LOT on 46th Street and 2nd Avenue. EDDIE DEAN'S dream suggests that they are connected to LAMERK FOUNDRY in Mid-World.
III:168, IV:125
> **SKANK, BANGO:** Graffiti artist who defaced the sign for Turtle Bay Condominiums. III:168

MIR
See GUARDIANS OF THE BEAM: SHARDIK

MOGGINS, GERT
See BIG COFFIN HUNTERS

MONTOYA, DR APRIL
See TOPEKA CHARACTERS

MORGENSTERN, CONCHETTA
See HAMBRY CHARACTERS: HAMBRY MAYOR'S HOUSE (SEAFRONT)

MORT, JACK ('THE PUSHER')

Despite the fact that he was a professional, the prim Jack Mort had a very nasty hobby. He liked to 'depth-charge' people. In other words, he liked to kill them. Mort dropped the brick that hit five-year-old ODETTA HOLMES on the head. Years later, he pushed her in front of the A train at CHRISTO-PHER STREET STATION.

Like WALTER, Mort is a man of many disguises. Dressed as a priest, he shoved JAKE CHAMBERS in front of a Cadillac on Fifth Avenue. Quite understandably, Mort is the human embodiment of the Death card found in Walter's Tarot Pack. He is also the destination of the magic door labeled 'The Pusher.'

Jack Mort divides the world into 'Do-Bees' and 'Don't Bees.' 'Do-Bees' get away with their crimes while 'Don't Bees' get caught. This extremely unpleasant character (who also happens to come in his pants when he kills) keeps a scrapbook of his murders. His gold-rimmed glasses, blue eyes and expensive address (he lives at 409 Park Avenue South) fool people into thinking he is not a psychopath. But not only is Mort psychologically imbalanced, but he is also a fairly easy target for demons/demonic presences who want to use a mortal agent to do their dirty deeds. When Mort killed Jake, he was actually no more than the pawn of Walter, also known as the MAN IN BLACK. Underneath his business suits, Jack Mort wears women's underwear.

II:351, II:355–68, II:383–406, II:408–19, II:425–39, II:442, III:19, III:81–82, III:83–86, III:143–44, III:145, III:358, III:359, III:365

MORT'S ASSOCIATES:
BALD MAN WITH GLASSES: This guy works in Mort's office. II:368, II:384

CURD-FACED TEENAGE GIRL: After missing his opportunity to push Jake in front of a car, a very angry Mort shoves this girl out of his way. II:357
DORFMAN: Jack Mort handles the difficult Dorfman account. II:368, II:384, II:396
FAT MAN WITH GLASSES: This man works in Mort's office. II:384
FRAMINGHAM, MR: Mort's Boss. II:435

MUFFIN, BILL
    See RIVER CROSSING CHARACTERS

MURDOCK, REVEREND
    See DEAN, SUSANNAH: ODETTA HOLMES' ASSO-CIATES: DAN HOLMES

MUTANTS
Although the GREAT OLD ONES and their destructive culture disappeared many generations before the rise of GILEAD, the poisons they left in soil, water, and air remained. We cannot be certain whether these destructive ancients engaged in all-out chemical and biological warfare, but it seems probable. Mid-World is full of genetically mutated beings which are commonly referred to as 'Muties.' In the case of domestic animals (and even some wild ones), muties can be carefully bred until they breed true. However, this process is slow. 'Threaded stock,' or those that have bred true, are extremely valuable.

The most horrific mutants of Mid-World are actually the SLOW MUTANTS. These physically disgusting beings were once men and women, although they often bear little resemblance to their human forebears. The Slow Mutants that infest the old underground railway systems of Mid-World and the ruined kitchens of Gilead's castle have green, phosphorescent skin. Their mutations are as varied as they are horrible. Some have insect eyes, others have suckered tentacles. Many of them are nocturnal, preferring dark places to light ones. The Slow Mutants that Roland meets in ELURIA are known as the GREEN FOLK.

I:44, III:305, III:328 *(buffalo)*, III:335 *(children born strange)*, III:390 *(buffalo and bees)*, III:563, IV:3, IV:16 *(werewolves)*, IV:143–44 *(mutant children)*, IV:153 *(werewolves)*, IV:174 *(mutant children)*, IV:175 *(mutant children)*, IV:255 *(fish)*, IV:256 *(bloodlines clarifying)*, IV:257 *(government hossflesh)*, IV:319 *(few muties in Mejis)*, IV:320 *(Rhea's)*, IV:451, IV:710 *(mutie mark)*, E:186, E:195, E:210

ANIMALS, BIRDS, REPTILES:
GENERAL:
BUFFALO: III:328, III:390
DRAGON-BIRDS AND PTERODACTYLS: III:563, IV:15, IV:81
EROMOT: Rhea's poisonous pet snake. *See* RHEA OF THE COOS.
HAMBRY MUTANT HORSES: IV:256, IV:257, IV:319, IV:320
MUSTY: Rhea's six-legged tomcat. *See* RHEA OF THE COOS
MUTANT DOE AND FAWNS: IV:16
RAT IN LUD WASTELANDS: IV:15
RAVEN: IV:17
ROMP, THE: *See* HAMBRY CHARACTERS: THE TRAVELLERS' REST
SNAKES IN LUD'S WASTELANDS: III:574, IV:3
SUCKERBATS: *See* DEMONS/SPIRITS/DEVILS

TRIPOD-STORKS IN LUD'S WASTELANDS:
III:565
WASTELAND MONSTROSITIES: Roland's *ka-tet*
sees these whitish, leaping creatures while zooming
through LUD's WASTE LANDS in BLAINE's
Barony Coach. III:564–65
INSECTS:
ALBINO BEES: Roland's *ka-tet* came across these
mutant bees while they were on their way to LUD. These
insects were truly terrible to see — they were sluggish,
snowy white, and made poisonous honey. Even their hive
looked as if it had been melted by a blowtorch.

Roland believes that the bees' mutation was the
result of the Great Poisoning which destroyed so much
of Mid-World. (*See* GREAT POISONING in the
HIGH SPEECH AND MID-WORLD ARGOT
section.) III:389–91, III:393, III:430
BEETLES IN LUD'S WASTE LANDS: III:574,
IV:3, IV:15, IV:16
SCORPIONS: IV:16
SPIDERS: Roland found these rather disgusting crea-
tures in the cellar beneath the WAY STATION. They
had eyes on stalks and as many as sixteen legs. I:96
SLOW MUTANTS: These guys are going to have a
hard time getting dates. I:151, I:159, I:172, I:193–98,
I:203, II:431, III:44, III:305, III:335 (*children born strange*),
E:165 (*Green Folk*), E:169 (*Green Folk*), E:189
GREEN FOLK: *See* ELURIA CHARACTERS
TOTAL HOGS: This desert tribe of Slow Mutants
held the Blue Bend of MAERLYN'S RAINBOW fifty
years before Roland and his *ka-tet* arrived in HAMBRY.
VEGETABLES: See RHEA OF THE COOS

N

NASSAU CHARACTERS
See DEAN, EDDIE

NEW YORK CUSTOMS
See DEAN, EDDIE

**NINETEEN
One of the most immediately striking changes made in the new *Gunslinger* is the addition of three front pages. On the first is a quote from the novel *Look Homeward, Angel*; on the second is the lone number 19; and on the third is the single word RESUMPTION. These are all vital clues about the nature of Roland's quest, and about what he is going to find over the course of the three final books of the series.

In the new *Gunslinger*, we find out that the number 19 is a magic number. After WALTER O'DIM resurrects the weed-eater NORT in the dried-up town of TULL, he implants a secret door in Nort's memory and imagination. That door, which holds back the secret horrors of the afterlife, is locked. But the lock has a key, and the key is 19. In a letter written to Roland's lover ALICE, Walter confides the nature of Nort's door, what Alice will find when she opens it, and the numerical key to the lock. Driven on by a maddening curiosity, Alice speaks the word 19 and pays the price for it. Nineteen is the key to the Land of Death.

I:39, I:40, I:41 *(that number)*, I:63, I:64, I:84

NORDITES

The blond people of Northern In-World are known as Nordites. Rumor has it that their chief sports are incest and reindeer fucking.

IV:531 *(indirect)*, IV:737

NORMAN, JAMES
See ELURIA CHARACTERS

NORMAN, JESSE
See ELURIA CHARACTERS

NORMAN, JOHN
See ELURIA CHARACTERS

NORT
See TULL CHARACTERS

**NORTH CENTRAL POSITRONICS

North Central Positronics was one of the nasty companies set up by the arrogant GREAT OLD ONES. This company and its affiliates created the technology that eventually destroyed the world. They were responsible for the highly complex computers which controlled entire cities (as well as their stockpiles of weapons and poisons), and the cyborg GUARDIANS which guarded the portals in and out of Mid-World. It seems highly likely that, through North Central Positronics, the Great Old Ones merged technology and magic. It seems even likelier that these arrogant ancestors believed that they could recreate the fabric of the multiverse and bend it to suit their fancy.

In the new version of *The Gunslinger*, we learn more about

North Central Positronics' unsavory history. One hundred generations before the world moved on, humanity made enough technological advances to chip a few splinters from the great pillar of reality. The company at the forefront of these discoveries was (of course) North Central Positronics. But these so-called technological advances, wondrous as they seemed, were accompanied by little or no insight into the true nature of the universe. Instead, they were seen only in the flat but false light of science. This was where both the Old People, and their glorious company, fell short. They had no perspective, only an arrogant and dangerous drive toward what they labeled 'progress.' The water pump in the WAY STATION may have been created by North Central Positronics, but so were the insane SHARDIK and the murderous BLAINE, who liked to play evil god to the people of LUD. A sinister company indeed. I:92, I:227, III:45, III:103, III:473

BLAINE: *Now, although the unthinkable machinery which maintained the Beams had weakened, this insane and inhuman intelligence had awakened in the rooms of ruin and had begun once more, although as bodiless as any ghost, to stumble through the halls of the dead . . .(III:518)*

Our *ka-tet*'s nasty adventure with Blaine the insane Mono was prefigured by the story of CHARLIE THE CHOO-CHOO and also by JAKE CHAMBERS' crazed English essay entitled 'My Understanding of Truth'. This nasty, overly-sophisticated train was created by the sinister NORTH CENTRAL POSITRONICS. He was therefore a distant cousin of SHARDIK and the other cyborg GUARDIANS.

Despite superficial appearances, Blaine was not just a train. He was in fact the GHOST IN THE MACHINES – LUD's city-wide computer intelligence so feared by the PUBES and the GRAYS. This fear was not unfounded since Blaine was completely psychotic. He suffered from a computerized form of split personality disorder (he was composed of nasty 'Big Blaine' and terrified 'Little Blaine'). While a horrified 'Little Blaine' watched, Big Blaine committed terrible crimes such as destroying his companion Mono PATRICIA (she was crying all the time) and gassing the residents of Lud. Big Blaine, whose logic and reasoning twisted long ago, agreed to take Roland and his friends along the path of the BEAM to his termination point in TOPEKA. His price was a riddling contest. If the *ka-tet* won, Blaine would deliver them safely to their destination. If they lost, Blaine would kill them when he killed himself. Obviously, our *ka-tet* was at a severe disadvantage since Blaine had access to information on all levels of the TOWER. However, EDDIE DEAN succeeded in defeating Blaine with the Eddie specialty – bad jokes. III:135, III:327, III:336–38, III:349, III:350, III:361, III:366, III:367, III:369 *(indirect)*, III:370 *(indirect)*, III:393, III:396, III:397, III:417, III:418, III:427, III:445, III:446, III:447, III:448, III:460–62, III:471–84, III:500–6, III:516–17, III:518, III:521–35, III:541, III:542, III:545–82, IV:3–12, IV:16, IV:17, IV:18–76 *(72 crashes; 75 exit)*, IV:76–86 *(on top of Blaine)*, IV:87, IV:88, IV:97, IV:807, IV:808, IV:809, IV:810, IV:812, IV:813

'GHOSTS IN THE MACHINES': Every time the PUBES of LUD heard the god-drums, they drew lots to see who among them should be sacrificed. The Pubes believed that there were ghosts living in the machines under the city. If these ghosts were not appeased, they would take over the bodies of the dead, rise up, and eat those left alive. As JEEVES of the Pubes said, 'There are a great many machines under Lud, and there are ghosts in all of them – demonous spirits which bear only ill will to mortal men and women. These demon-ghosts are very capable of raising the dead . . . and in Lud, there are a great many dead to raise'. Although the Grays ran the god-drum machines that incited the Pubes' frenzied sacrifice, they also believed that the city's computers were haunted by demonic spirits. When you think about it, they were right. III:444, III:445, III:464, III:481, III:505, III:518

IMPERIUM: III:552

LITTLE BLAINE: III:479–81 *(first heard)*, III:482, III:501, III:503, III:523, III:534, III:552, III:567, III:573, IV:24–25, IV:42, IV:64, IV:66, IV:68

PASSENGER KILLINGTON: While he and SUSANNAH were in the CRADLE OF LUD, EDDIE imagined the station as it must have once been. He even imagined he heard a loudspeaker calling for this partic-ular passenger. III:474

PATRICIA: Blaine's female twin. She was blue and trav-eled northwest. Blaine fried her circuits because he was tired of hearing her cry all the time. III:396 *(crashed)*, III:473, III:474, III:479, III:569, III:571, III:572, IV:5 *(indirect)*, IV:68

SHARDIK: *See* GUARDIANS OF THE BEAM

**NOT-MAN

When Roland was young, he saw a Not-Man, or an invisible man, hanged for the crime of rape. Evidently, he was very good at sneaking up on people.

I:172–73

O

OAKLEY, ANNIE
See GUNSLINGERS, OUR WORLD

OCEAN FOAM
See DELGADO, PAT

ODETTA
See DEAN, SUSANNAH

**O'DIM, WALTER
See entry under WALTER

O'HARA, BUM
See DEAN, HENRY: HENRY DEAN'S *KA-TET*

**OLD MOTHER
Old Mother is Mid-World's name for the South Star; she is married to OLD STAR. Her other name is **LYDIA**. The Universe was created when Old Mother and Old Star had a crockery-throwing fight over Old Star's flirtation with CASSIOPEIA. The other gods stepped in to break up the row but the two of them haven't spoken since. As a flirtatious gesture of respect, Roland called AUNT TALITHA of RIVER CROSSING by this name. In the new *Gunslinger*, Roland looks up and sees Old Mother in the desert sky.

I:7, I:95, III:14, III:48–49, III:62, III:119, III:316 *(Aunt Talitha)*, III:317 *(Aunt Talitha)*, III:320 *(Aunt Talitha)*, III:327

(Aunt Talitha), III:342 *(Aunt Talitha)*, IV:41, IV:122, IV:132, IV:193

OLD ONES (GREAT OLD ONES)

The Old Ones (also known as the Great Old Ones) were the ancient people of Mid-World. Their era was long gone even by the time of ARTHUR ELD. The Old Ones had a god-like knowledge of technology and the workings of the universe but they were also a violently destructive people.

As a horrified SUSAN DELGADO said when she found out that FARSON was trying to resurrect the Old Ones' war machines, 'The ways of the Old People [were] the ways of death'. This certainly seems to be true. As far as we can tell, their computers and killing machines were responsible for the incredible catastrophe that poisoned Mid-World. FARSON's resurrection of these instruments of war succeeded in destroying Mid-World's civilization a second time.

However, even the most destructive cultures often contain less chaotic elements. According to HAX, these technologically advanced people created the twelve PORTALS and the twelve GUARDIANS. They did so to make up for the crimes they'd committed against nature.

III:50–51, III:53, III:62, III:100–1, III:329, III:330, III:334, III:336, III:337, III:391, III:396, III:409 *(Old Folks)*, III:501, III:554, IV:28, IV:42, IV:51, IV:149, IV:314 *(Old People)*, IV:371 *(Old People)*, IV:373 *(Old People)*, IV:381 *(Old People)*, IV:382 *(and ways of death)*, IV:542 *(Old People)*, IV:543, IV:609 *(Old People)*

OLD PEOPLE OF THE WEST WOODS

Although the GREAT OLD ONES are sometimes called the Old People, the Old People of the West Woods were a much later and much more primitive culture – one which probably arose after the Great Old Ones destroyed most of Mid-World's cities. Roland and his *ka-tet* found the Old People's primitive remains while they camped in the mixed forest located east of the WESTERN SEA.

This forest-dwelling tribe hunted with bows and arrows and lived in awe of SHARDIK, the great bear GUARDIAN. Shardik thought of them as trap-setters and forest-burners, but they regarded him as both a demon and the shadow of a god. They called him MIR which meant 'the world beneath the world.'

III:14–15, III:25, III:26, III:27, III:38, III:43

**OLD STAR (NORTH STAR. Also called APON)

Old Star (also called North Star) is another name for the wickedly flirtatious husband of OLD MOTHER (South Star). The two of them had a knock-down-drag-out fight over his tête-à-tête with CASSIOPEIA. The universe was created from the crockery they threw at each other, but the two of them haven't spoken since. In the new *Gunslinger*, Roland sees Old Star in the sky.

I:95, III:14, III:48–49, III:119, III:247, IV:41, IV:122, IV:132, IV:207, IV:670

OMAHA

A one-eyed gambler who died with a knife in his throat at a Watch Me table.

IV:89

O'MEARAH, GEORGE

O'Mearah was one of the New York cops who patrolled the area in front of CLEMENTS GUNS AND SPORTING

GOODS. His partner's name was CARL DELEVAN. The two of them were hoodwinked by Roland while Roland was in JACK MORT's body.

II:388, IV:391 *(indirect)*, II:392–404, II:421–29, II:430, II:432

ORACLE
See DEMONS/SPIRITS/DEVILS

ORTEGA, MILLICENT
See HAMBRY CHARACTERS: OTHER CHARACTERS

OSWALD, LEE HARVEY
See KENNEDY, JOHN F.

OUR WORLD: POLITICAL AND CULTURAL FIGURES
See APPENDIX III

OY
Oy is JAKE CHAMBERS' pet BILLY BUMBLER (or perhaps Jake is Oy's pet boy). Oy approached our *ka-tet* while they traveled on the BEAM leading toward LUD. When Jake first found Oy – or when Oy first woke Jake by licking his face – he had some bites on his body. It seems likely that he was chased away from his own pack because he talked too much. Like the best of Billy Bumblers, Oy is intelligent and faithful. He can count, add, and communicate. He is completely devoted to Jake.

Unfortunately, there is a good chance that Oy will come to an unhappy end. During Roland's journey in MAERLYN'S

GRAPEFRUIT, he had a vision of Oy impaled upon the topmost branch of a crooked tree.

III:299–304, III:306–67, III:375–86, III:389–413, III:416, III:418, III:419, III:424–25, III:433–36, III:453–57 *(follows Jake)*, III:470–71, III:497–500, III:509–16, III:519–30, III:531–35, III:540, III:545–82, IV:3–12, IV:18–42 *(riddling Blaine)*, IV:72–140 *(76 exit Blaine, enter alternative Topeka; 91 superflu; 97 off the Beam; 99 turnpikin';107 Reinisch Rose Garden and Charlie;113 Watch for the Walkin' Dude; 124 Eddie's Dream;133 Roland begins his story)*, IV:421–23, IV:722 *(impaled on branch)*, IV:775–840 *(775 Roland concludes tale; 788 Shoes in the Road; 792 story of Wizard of Oz; 795 approaching Green Palace; 797 Green Palace gate; 809 Oz the Great and Terrible or Blaine?; 821 inside the Grapefruit: Roland's matricide; 831 back on the Beam)*

OZ, WIZARD OF

The story of *The Wizard of Oz*, which tells the tale of **DOROTHY**, **TOTO**, the **COWARDLY LION** and the **TIN WOODSMAN**, is mentioned quite often in *The Dark Tower* series. Like JAKE, SUSANNAH and EDDIE, Dorothy Gale was blown from a world much like ours to one where witches and magic are real. In *Wizard and Glass*, our *ka-tet* actually visits an emerald palace where the evil wizard RANDALL FLAGG poses as the Great and Terrible OZ.

II:257 *(Dorothy)*, III:80, III:566, IV:790 *(Dorothy)*, IV:792–95 *(story)*, IV:797 *(book)*, IV:803, IV:809–18, IV:831

P

PAPA DOC
  See BORDER DWELLERS: BROWN

PARELLI, JOHN
  See DEAN, HENRY: HENRY DEAN'S *KA-TET*

PATRICIA
  See NORTH CENTRAL POSITRONICS

**PAUL
The only thing we know about Paul is that Roland thinks of him while at the WAY STATION. Paul's name is cut from the new version of *The Gunslinger*.

PAULA
  See DEAN, EDDIE: DELTA FLIGHT 901 CHARACTERS

PERTH, LORD
'So fell Lord Perth, and the countryside did shake with thunder.' The story of Lord Perth comes from Mid-World's folklore. Perth was a giant and his fate was much like that of the colossal warrior in the biblical tale of David and Goliath. When eleven-year-old JAKE CHAMBERS mentioned this story to the huge and wicked TICK-TOCK, Tick-Tock became enraged. He considered the story unlucky. This isn't surprising since it proved to be a foretelling of his own fate.

III:376, III:378, III:494, IV:111, IV:371, IV:509, IV:531, IV:570, IV:721, IV:810, IV:815

PETTIE THE TROTTER
See HAMBRY CHARACTERS: TRAVELLERS' REST

PIPER SCHOOL CHARACTERS
Before entering Mid-World, JAKE CHAMBERS attended PIPER SCHOOL – an exclusive NEW YORK CITY middle school. He hated it. For more information about Piper, see PIPER SCHOOL, listed in the OUR WORLD PLACES section. Below is a list of Piper School students and employees.

AVERY, BONNIE: Jake's English teacher. She gave him an A+ on his very strange essay, 'My Understanding of Truth.' III:130, III:132–38, III:140, III:187–89, III:269

BISSETTE, LEN: Len Bissette was a very kind-hearted French teacher. III:126–28, III:136, III:139, III:181, III:185–87

DORFMAN, STAN: A Piper student and one of Jake's 'almost' friends. III:139

FRANKS, JOANNE: Piper's school secretary. III:127, III:128, III:129, III:140

HARLEY, MR: Headmaster and teacher for spoken arts. III:129, III:130, III:139, III:181

HOTCHKISS, MR: Piper School's shrink. III:186

JESSERLING, PETRA: Student. III:133

KINGERY, MR: Science teacher. IV:102

KNOPF, MR: Geometry teacher. III:139, III:147

STEVENS, BELINDA: Student. III:139

SURREY, DAVID: Student. III:133, III:138

**PITTSTON, SYLVIA

Sylvia Pittston was TULL's psychotic Bible-bashing preacher. Before the events of *Wizard and Glass* took place, Pittston traveled through HAMBRY. Originally a DESERT DWELLER, she came to Tull from the dry wastes on the edge of the MOHAINE DESERT. When Roland confronted her in Tull, she was living in a shack behind her church. Pittston wore the burlap dress of a penitent.

Pittston was a huge but sexually alluring woman. She weighed about three hundred pounds but had large dark eyes and rich brown hair. Pittston's revivals were so intense that they were almost erotically ecstatic. ALICE believed that Pittston had a hoodoo on the town and that her religion was evil. Roland believed that when the MAN IN BLACK (WALTER) passed through Tull, he had sex with this preacher and left a demon inside of her. Roland's theory proves to be right.

When Roland visited Pittston's shack, she was sitting in her rocker waiting for him. She believed that Roland was Satan (the INTERLOPER) and that the Man in Black was an angel. Roland removed Pittston's demon by making her come with the barrel of his gun, but in revenge, Pittston set the townspeople on him. Roland ended up killing everyone in Tull.

In the new *Gunslinger*, Roland has an eerie sense of déjà vu when he hears Pittston preach, almost as if he had heard her preach before. In this version, Walter once again comes to Pittston pretending to be an angel, but this time he admits that he serves THE CRIMSON KING, the very evil being that Pittston pretends to preach against. Pittston allows Walter to implant the Red King's child inside of her, but Roland removes it in the same way he removed the demon in the earlier version of the novel. In the new *Gunslinger*, as in the old, Pittston dies under Roland's guns.

I:45 *(preacher woman)*, I:50–57, I:58–61, I:65–67 *(killed)*, I:136, I:144, III:57, IV:479

PLASTERMAN
See DEMONS/SPIRITS/DEVILS: MANSION DEMON

POLINO, JIMMIE
See DEAN, HENRY: HENRY DEAN'S *KA-TET*

POLITICAL AND CULTURAL FIGURES (OUR WORLD)
See APPENDIX III

POSTINO, TRICKS
See BALAZAR'S MEN

PRATT, GEORGIE
See DEAN, HENRY: HENRY DEAN'S *KA-TET*

PRISONER, THE
See DEAN, EDDIE

PUBES
The Pubes (short for pubescents) were the original defenders of LUD, although the sickly band we meet in *The Waste Lands* were probably descended from one of the later bands of harriers that overran the city. The Pubes' archenemies, the GRAYS, live in underground silos beneath eastern Lud. The Pubes live above ground in CITY NORTH, but are no healthier for it. You can tell a Pube from a Gray because the Pubes' headscarves are blue. (The Grays' are yellow.)

The Pubes are convinced that there are GHOSTS IN THE

MACHINES below the city, and that if these demonic spirits aren't appeased they will animate the bodies of Lud's many dead and rise up to eat the living. Although the Grays also fear the machine ghosts, they use the god-drums (actually the backbeat of ZZ Top's song 'Velcro Fly') to drive the Pubes into a paranoid frenzy of human sacrifice. The grisly method the Pubes use to choose their victims is reminiscent of Shirley Jackson's story 'The Lottery'.

SUSANNAH and EDDIE battle the Pubes on the STREET OF THE TURTLE. In the end, two of this gang (MAUDE and JEEVES) reluctantly agree to lead them to BLAINE'S CRADLE. Of all the ghosts in the machines, the Pubes believe that Blaine is the most terrible. Little do they know that psychotic Blaine is actually *all* of the ghosts in the machines.

III:312, III:314, III:318, III:325, III:329, III:334, III:335, III:349, III:371, III:411, III:437, III:440–48, III:452, III:454, III:467, III:496, III:517–18, III:527, III:558, IV:70, IV:93 *(indirect)*, E:183

PUBE CHARACTERS:

ARDIS (ELECTROCUTED BY BLAINE): III:447, III:476

BLONDE WOMAN WITH MANGE: III:442

FRANK: III:444

JEEVES: Eddie nicknames this guy Jeeves because of his bowler hat. Along with Maud, Jeeves leads Eddie and Susannah to BLAINE'S CRADLE. III:445–49, III:459–60, IV:93

LUSTER (DWARF): Luster reminds Eddie and Susannah of Little Lord Fauntleroy. III:437–39, III:440, III:442, IV:93

MAN IN SILK-LINED CAPE AND KNEE-BOOTS: III:440

MAN WITH BLUE ASCOT AND RED HAIR TUFTS: This guy reminds Eddie of Ronald McDonald. III:441–42

MAUD: Maud is a heavy-set woman who is very fond of Winston. She is one of the two who leads Eddie and Susannah to BLAINE'S CRADLE. III:440–49, III:459–60, III:462, IV:93

SPANKERS/SPANKERMAN: Spankers was the leader of the Pubes, but when the god-drums started up, his stone was pulled from the hat and it was his turn to dance from the hangman's rope. III:438, III:443, III:444, IV:93

TOPSY THE SAILOR: III:444

WINSTON: Winston wore a kilt and brandished a cutlass. He was killed by Eddie and Susannah. III:440, III:442, III:443, III:444, III:448, III:460 IV:93

PYLON
See DELGADO, SUSAN

Q

QUEEN OF BLACK PLACES
See RHEA OF THE COOS

QUICK, ANDREW (Listed as **TICK-TOCK**)
See GRAYS: GRAY HIGH COMMAND

QUICK, DAVID
See GRAYS: GRAY HIGH COMMAND

QUINT, HIRAM
See HAMBRY CHARACTERS: OTHER CHARAC-
TERS

R

RALPH
See ELURIA CHARACTERS: GREEN FOLK

**RANDOLPH
Young Roland's friend. (Cut from the new *Gunslinger.*)

RATHBUN, MRS
See KATZ: KATZ'S EMPLOYEES, CUSTOMERS AND
COMPETITORS

RAVENHEAD, PIET
Signed identity papers stating that ALAIN was actually
RICHARD STOCKWORTH of PENNILTON.
    IV:229–30

REED, JAMES
Signed identity papers stating that Roland was actually WILL
DEARBORN of HEMPHILL.
    IV:229–30

RENFREW, HASH
   See HAMBRY CHARACTERS: HORSEMEN'S ASSO-
CIATION

REYNOLDS, CLAY
   See BIG COFFIN HUNTERS

**R.F.
The letters R.F. are the initials of Roland's multi-faced arch-
enemy, (present writer excluded). This nasty being occasionally takes other initials too, including W.O. (WALTER
O'DIM), M.B. (MARTEN BROADCLOAK), and J.F.
(JOHN FARSON). The new *Gunslinger* hints that R.F. and
the AGELESS STRANGER may actually be the same being.
While they palaver in the GOLGOTHA, Walter tells Roland
that the Ageless Stranger's real name is LEGION. R.F. is an
agent of Chaos. (But we are much nicer in our female incarnations.) For more entries, see WALTER.
   FANNIN, RICHARD: In his form as Richard Fannin, R.F.
   is described as being inhuman. He has blue-green eyes but
   blue-black hair that looks like a raven's feathers. Fannin must
   be a fairly imposing figure, since even TICK-TOCK, leader
   of the murderous GRAYS, is afraid of him.
      Fannin's hand has no lines on it, which makes us wonder
   if his is mortal at all. He claims not to be MAERLYN,
   but he is obviously a sorcerer of extreme power. Like all of
   R.F.'s selves, Fannin glories in destruction. III:535–42
   FLAGG, RANDALL: Randall Flagg is another incarnation
   of R.F. He is a demon posing as a man, and is capable of
   turning men into dogs. In *The Stand* (a related novel), Flagg
   is also called the **WALKIN' DUDE**, an epithet that
   Roland's *ka-tet* sees spray-painted on a road sign in the alter-

native TOPEKA. He was also the nasty sorcerer found in the novel *Eyes of the Dragon*. When Roland encountered Flagg for the first time, he was pursued by **DENNIS** and **THOMAS**, two characters from *Eyes of the Dragon*. II:409–10, IV:113 *(as Walkin' Dude)*, IV:814–18 *(as Flagg/Oz)*, IV:819, IV:834 *(note)*, IV:836, IV:838

**RHEA OF THE COOS (RHEA OF COOS HILL/ RHEA DUBATIVO/ WEIRDLING OF THE COOS)

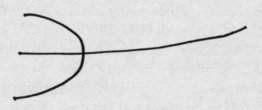

Rhea of the Coos was a nasty old bad-smelling hag. She was also a witch. Rhea lived on the Coos (a hill outside of HAMBRY) with her two mutant pets, ERMOT and MUSTY.

Like the men of THE HORSEMEN'S ASSOCIATION, Rhea played a part in the defeat of the AFFILIATION. At the beginning of *Wizard and Glass*'s Hambry adventures, THE BIG COFFIN HUNTERS entrusted the evil magic ball known as MAERLYN'S GRAPEFRUIT to Rhea's keeping. This magical ball was FARSON's prize and secret weapon, but it was also vampiric. Rhea used the ball to spy on people (including Roland) but in the end the ball made her even more crazily malicious than she was at the beginning of the tale. By the end of *Wizard and Glass*, Rhea is a sore-covered specter. However, she is still a formidable enemy.

Rhea was attracted to pretty young women, but even before her journeys in the pink Bend o' the Rainbow her desires had a malicious edge, especially when her advances were rebuffed. It was in large part Rhea's vindictiveness that landed pretty SUSAN DELGADO on the Charyou Tree fire. In the new version of *The Gunslinger*, Roland bitterly remembers the part Rhea played in Susan's death.

I:130, IV:79, IV:80, IV:143–52 *(and Maerlyn's ball)*, IV:153–72 *(and Susan)*, IV:177 *(indirect)*, IV:180, IV:183, IV:192, IV:196, IV:199, IV:207, IV:208, IV:209–11 *(Cordelia and Susan)*, IV:213, IV:222, IV:255, IV:267, IV:286, IV:295, IV:309, IV:313, IV:366–67, IV:377–78 *(spying on Roland and Susan)*, IV:387, IV:393, IV:403, IV:410, IV:411, IV:412, IV:418, IV:421, IV:430, IV:442–44, IV:446–47, IV:470–71, IV:482–83, IV:489, IV:496–500, IV:507, IV:518 *(Rhea's note)*, IV:519, IV:520, IV:521, IV:523–28, IV:534–35 *(bruja)*, IV:537, IV:547, IV:548–49, IV:554–59 *(Susan remembers under hypnosis)*, IV:566, IV:570–71, IV:611–12 *(Queen of Black Places)*, IV:624, IV:627–28, IV:655, IV:665–67, IV:671–76, IV:683–89, IV:694–97 *(drinks Cordelia's blood)*, IV:711–13, IV:720, IV:721, IV:741–42, IV:761, IV:762–64, IV:765–68, IV:784, IV:791, IV:817, IV:818, IV:826–28, IV:832, IV:838, E:179, E:180

MUTANT PETS

ERMOT: Poisonous snake. Has four pairs of fangs. IV:143, IV:145–47 *(present)*, IV:366, IV:367, IV:378, IV:447, IV:498, IV:499, IV:500, IV:526 *(Roland kills)*, IV:528, IV:570–71 *(sewn together by Rhea)*, IV:672, IV:826, IV:827

MUSTY: A six-legged tom cat with a split tail. He had grey-green eyes which are the same color as Rhea's. IV:143–48, IV:149–51, IV:154, IV:155, IV:156, IV:159, IV:161, IV:163–64, IV:367, IV:404–5,

IV:442–44, IV:446–47, IV:471, IV:481–83, IV:500,
IV:525 *(yowls)*, IV:570, IV:571, IV:612
MUTANT VEGETABLE GARDEN: IV:496, IV:523

RIGGINS, GEORGE
See HAMBRY CHARACTERS: SHERIFF'S OFFICE

RIMER, KIMBA
See HAMBRY CHARACTERS: HAMBRY MAYOR'S
HOUSE (SEAFRONT)

RIMER, LASLO
See HAMBRY CHARACTERS: HORSEMEN'S ASSO-
CIATION

**RITTER, AILEEN
See AILEEN OF GILEAD

RITZY CHARACTERS
JOLENE: Whore. IV:336–37
OLD MAN: A weed eater who told DEPAPE that Roland
was descended from ARTHUR ELD. Depape killed him
after he shared this information. IV:334, IV:335,
IV:336–40, IV:437, IV:491, IV:508

RIVER CROSSING CHARACTERS
Although River Crossing was once a very busy town, since the
beginning of the LUD wars her aging citizens have lived in
relative isolation. In order to disguise their town from passing
looters, they hide their gardens behind clumps of weeds and
let the facades of their buildings go to ruin. However, to
friendly folk passing through, they are extremely generous.

By the time we meet them in *The Waste Lands,* most of the citizens of River Crossing are positively ancient. Their leader is the matriarch TALITHA UNWIN. Like Roland, Talitha speaks the High Speech. When she sees Roland she proclaims, 'Behold ye, the return of the White! After evil ways and evil days, the White comes again! Be of good heart and hold up your head, for ye have lived to see the wheel of *ka* begin to turn once more.'

GENERAL REFERENCES (ALL CHARACTERS): III:315, III:346, III:347 *(old people)*, III:352, III:353, III:354, III:370, III:379, III:390

> **GENERAL CHARACTERS NOT LISTED BELOW:** (unnamed women, man with crutch) III:318–22, III:341–43, IV:24

> **BILL AND TILL:** See TUDBURY, BILL AND TILL, below.

> **MERCY:** Mercy was one of the first people that Roland's *ka-tet* met in River Crossing. Like almost all of the other townspeople, Mercy is very old. Twenty-five years before the beginning of our tale she was blinded by harriers who said she was looking at 'em pert. Mercy is married to Si. III:313–23, III:338–43, III:344, III:396

> **MUFFIN, BILL AND HIS BOY:** Bill Muffin and his son saw the bridge over the RIVER SEND. Bill eventually died of Blood Sickness. III:330, III:340

> **SI:** Si is Mercy's husband. He assures her that Roland and his friends are gunslingers, not harriers. He and his wife were the first two people Roland's *ka-tet* met in River Crossing. III:313–43, III:396

> > **GREAT GRAND-DA:** III:332

> **TALITHA, AUNT:** Aunt Talitha's full name is **TALITHA UNWIN.** She is the matriarch of River

Crossing as well as its oldest citizen. Roland calls her OLD MOTHER. Talitha gives Roland her cross and asks him to lay it at the foot of the DARK TOWER. III:315–43, III:360, III:371, III:376, III:397, IV:16, IV:25

> **GRANDFATHER AND GREAT-GREAT GRAND-FATHER:** III:317
>
> **TUDBURY, BILL AND TILL:** These two old twins are albino. III:315–43, III:345, III:376, III:386 *(twins)*

RIVERS, LUCAS
Signed identity papers stating that CUTHBERT ALLGOOD was actually ARTHUR HEATH of GILEAD.
> IV:229–30

ROBERT AND FRANCESCA
> *See* HAMBRY CHARACTERS: HAMBRY LOVERS

ROBESON
Robeson was one of GILEAD'S guards. Like HAX, he was a traitor who supported FARSON.
> I:109, I:110–11

ROLAND THE ELDER
> *See* DESCHAIN, STEVEN

ROMP, THE
> *See* HAMBRY CHARACTERS: THE TRAVELLERS' REST

ROSE, THE
JAKE CHAMBERS discovered this magical dusky-pink rose

in the vacant LOT on Second Avenue and Forty-Sixth Street where it was growing amid a clump of alien purple grass. Although he doesn't know it, the Rose is the *sigul* of the TOWER itself.

This magic flower hums like a great open chord, inexpressively lonely and inexpressibly lovely. It is full of faces and voices. Jake believes that it is the key to everything; Roland suspects that it is the Tower itself.

Throughout *The Dark Tower* books, roses are extremely significant. The Dark Tower of END-WORLD sits amid a sea of shouting red roses, the LITTLE SISTERS OF ELURIA wear an embroidered rose upon their white flowing habits, and a model of CHARLIE THE CHOO-CHOO sits in the REINISCH ROSE GARDEN in the alternative TOPEKA. As Eddie states within the *glammer* of his dream-vision, 'First the key, then the rose! Behold! Behold the opening of the way to the Tower!' The following entries contain references to all roses.

I:142, I:221, III:66–67, III:68, III:69, III:71, III:74, III:107, III:114 *(field of)*, III:117, III:135, III:168, III:171–74 *(singing)*, III:175–77, III:180, III:183, III:212, III:228, III:244, III:359, III:363, III:367, III:541, IV:59, IV:103, IV:107–10 *(Reinisch Rose Garden)*, IV:125, IV:126, IV:127, IV:128–29, IV:564 *(roses)*, IV:697 *(roses)*, IV:721 *(roses)*, IV:723 *(field of)*, IV:778, IV:791, IV:799 *(drowned roses)*, E:179 (sigul *of the* Tower), E:181, E:183, E:191, E:224, E:227, E:231

RUIZ, STANLEY
See HAMBRY CHARACTERS: TRAVELLERS' REST

S

SHARDIK
See GUARDIANS OF THE BEAM: SHARDIK

SHAVERS, GEORGE
See DEAN, SUSANNAH: OTHER ASSOCIATES

SHAW, GRETA
See CHAMBERS, JAKE

**SHEB (SHEB MCCURDY: PIANO PLAYER)
In the new version of *The Gunslinger*, we find out that the two
piano players named Sheb — one in TULL, one in HAMBRY
— are actually the same man. In both stories he works in bars
owned by women. (Though Tull's local honky-tonk bears his
name, the place actually belongs to Sheb's former lover
ALICE.)

Sheb of Hambry, and later of Tull, is described as a small,
useless man with one gold tooth. He is in love with Alice,
Tull's bar owner, though she thinks of him as a gelded dog.
Jealous that Roland monopolizes Alice's attentions, he tries to
attack Roland with a knife. Later, during the town's surprise
attack on the gunslinger, Sheb uses Allie as a human shield.
In the new version of *The Gunslinger*, Roland recognizes Sheb
as the man he met in MEJIS.

I:21, I:22, I:26, I:29, I:30–36, I:38, I:47–49, I:50–56
(present), I:62, I:63–64, I:93, II:138, III:57 *(bar)*, IV:215,
IV:268, IV:271, IV:273 *(piano)*, IV:285, IV:438,

IV:480–81, IV:508, IV:571, IV:590, IV:637, IV:710–13 *(present for Rhea and Cordelia's speech against Susan)*, IV:720

SHEEMER, DELORES
See HAMBRY CHARACTERS: TRAVELLERS' REST

SHEEMIE
See HAMBRY CHARACTERS: TRAVELLERS' REST

SI
See RIVER CROSSING CHARACTERS

SILICON VALLEY COKE HEADS
These guys supply high tech police equipment to BALAZAR'S MEN.
II:137

SISTER BLUE
See DEAN, SUSANNAH: ODETTA HOLMES' ASSO-CIATES

SISTER COQUINA
See ELURIA, LITTLE SISTERS OF

SISTER JENNA
See ELURIA, LITTLE SISTERS OF

SISTER LOUISE
See ELURIA, LITTLE SISTERS OF

SISTER MARY
See ELURIA, LITTLE SISTERS OF

SISTER MICHELA
See ELURIA, LITTLE SISTERS OF

SISTER TAMRA
See ELURIA, LITTLE SISTERS OF

SKANK, BANGO
See MILLS CONSTRUCTION AND SOMBRA REAL ESTATE

SLOW MUTANTS
See MUTANTS

SMASHER
See ELURIA CHARACTERS: GREEN FOLK

SOOBIE
See TULL CHARACTERS: PITTSTON'S REVIVAL: KENNERLY, SOOBIE

SOPHIA (SISTER BLUE)
See DEAN, SUSANNAH: ODETTA HOLMES' ASSOCIATES

SPICS OF SUPREMECY
See DEAN: SUSANNAH: OTHER ASSOCIATES

STAUNTON, ANDREW
A New York foot patrolman. His partner is NORRIS WEAVER.
II:432–36

STEVENS, BELINDA
  See PIPER SCHOOL CHARACTERS

STOCKWORTH, RICHARD
  See JOHNS, ALAIN

STUFFY GUYS
The red-handed stuffy guys are a leftover of one of Mid-World's more unsavory practices. In the time of ARTHUR ELD, human beings were sacrificed during the harvest festival of Reap. In the more civilized days of Roland's youth, the stuffy guys – or human effigies – were set onto the Reap bonfires in lieu of actual people. The stuffy guys had heads made of straw and white, cross-stitched eyes. In their arms they carried baskets of produce.
  IV:171 *(red-handed men)*, IV:445, IV:467, IV:497 *(Rhea's mutie stuffy guy)*, IV:523 *(Rhea's mutie stuffy)*, IV:525, IV:562, IV:563, IV:566, IV:577 *(Cordelia's)*, IV:588–89 *(Cordelia's stuffy is image of Susan)*, IV:632, IV:633, IV:636, IV:640, IV:650, IV:711, IV:748, IV:761, IV:764, IV:768

SUCCUBUS
  See DEMONS/SPIRITS/DEVILS

SUCKERBATS
  See DEMONS/SPIRITS/DEVILS

SURREY, DAVID
  See PIPER SCHOOL CHARACTERS

SUSAN
  See DELGADO, SUSAN

T

**TAHEEN

The taheen are found in the new version of *The Gunslinger*, but not the old. These strange hybrid creatures are part man and part either animal or bird. In the new *Gunslinger*, Roland sees a taheen with a man's body but a raven's head wandering in the MOHAINE DESERT. According to the BORDER-DWELLER, BROWN, the taheen is searching for a place called ALGUL SIENTO.

    I:8–9, I:10*(bird-man)*, I:98

TALITHA, AUNT

    See RIVER CROSSING CHARACTERS

TAMRA, SISTER

    See ELURIA, LITTLE SISTERS OF

**THOMAS OF GILEAD (THOMAS WHITMAN)

The Dark Tower series contains references to two different characters named Thomas. One was a gunslinger-companion of Roland's who witnessed Roland's coming-of-age battle against CORT. The second was a young man from the novel *Eyes of the Dragon*. This second Thomas (who only met Roland briefly) was in pursuit of RANDALL FLAGG. (For pages including references to Flagg's pursuer, see entry under R.F.)

    In the new *Gunslinger*, we learn that Roland's friend Thomas had the last name of Whitman.

    I:177, I:183–90 *(witnesses Roland's coming-of-age battle)*

THORIN, CORAL
  See HAMBRY CHARACTERS: TRAVELLERS' REST

THORIN, HART
  See HAMBRY CHARACTERS: SEAFRONT

THORIN, OLIVE
  See HAMBRY CHARACTERS: SEAFRONT

TICK-TOCK
  See GRAYS HIGH COMMAND: TICK-TOCK (ANDREW QUICK)

TILLY
  See GRAYS HIGH COMMAND

TOMAS, MARIA
  See HAMBRY CHARACTERS: HAMBRY MAYOR'S HOUSE (SEAFRONT)

TOPEKA CHARACTERS
  CORCORAN, JOHN: *Topeka Capital Journal* correspondent. IV:91
  HACKFORD, DR MORRIS: Doctor at Topeka's St Francis Hospital and Medical Center. He reports on super-flu. IV:91
  MONTOYA, DR APRIL: Doctor at Stormont-Vail Regional Medical Center. She reports on super-flu. IV:92
  SLOAN, REPRESENTATIVE STEVE: IV:94

TOPSY
Roland's horse in 'Little Sisters of Eluria.'
  E:155–65

TOPSY THE SAILOR
  See PUBES

TORRES, MIGUEL
  See HAMBRY CHARACTERS: HAMBRY MAYOR'S HOUSE (SEAFRONT)

TOTAL HOGS
  See MUTANTS: SLOW MUTANTS

TOTEMS OF THE BEAM
  See GUARDIANS OF THE BEAM

TOWER, CALVIN
Calvin Tower is the bibliophile who owns THE MANHATTAN RESTAURANT OF THE MIND. He sold JAKE CHAMBERS copies of *CHARLIE THE CHOO-CHOO* and *Riddle-De-Dum* — both clues to Jake's destiny in Mid-World. Whether he is conscious of it or not, Calvin Tower serves the will of the BEAM and of the DARK TOWER itself.
    III:158–61, III:162–64, III:165, III:381, III:386, IV:56 *(old fatso)*

TRAINS
  See CHARLIE THE CHOO-CHOO

TUDBURY, BILL AND TILL
  See RIVER CROSSING CHARACTERS

TULL CHARACTERS
Tull had a population of thirty-nine men, fourteen women, and five children. Roland ended up killing all of them except the weed-eater NORT. (Poor Nort was crucified by the

townsfolk.) For information about the town of Tull, see
TULL listed in the MID-WORLD PLACES section.

I:22–26 *(barflies)*, I:30–36 *(barflies)*, I:39, I:63–68 *(They attack
Roland. All are killed)*

ALICE: See ALICE OF TULL, listed separately.

BALD MAN WITH KNIFE: This guy tried to attack
Roland in SHEB'S bar. I:24

****BOYS PLAYING MARBLES:** In the new *Gunslinger*,
these boys are described. One has a scorpion's tail poking
out of his hat band, one has a bloated and sightless eye,
and the youngest has a large cold sore on his lip. The
youngest one is named Charlie and is scorned by his
companions for giving directions to Roland. I:20, I:21–22

CASTNER : He owned Tull's Dry Goods emporium.
I:50–56 *(present)*

SLAT-SIDED WIFE: I:51–56 *(present)*

****FELDON, AMY:** One of Tull's barflies. At NORT's
wake, ZACHARY threw her skirts over her head and
drew zodiacs on her knees. In the new *Gunslinger*, we find
out that Amy was a whore and that Zachary drew Reap
charms on her knees, not zodiacs. I:30–36, I:63–66
(present), I:63–66 *(Mentioned in final battle. She's killed)*

JONSON: Jonson was one of the born-again sinners
attending PITTSTON's revival. I:54–56 *(present)*

****KENNERLY, JUBAL:** Kennerly was a skinny, inces-
tuous livery owner who was plagued with daughters. In
the new *Gunslinger* we learn that he buried two wives and
that his first name was Jubal. I:20–21 *(hostler)*, I:29, I:30,
I:38, I:43–46, I:50–56 *(present)*, I:61–62, I:63–66 *(killed
during final battle)*, I:68 *(his stable)*

DAUGHTERS (GENERAL): I:30, I:43, I:50–56
(present), I:62, I:63–66 *(present)*

BABY GIRL: I:43, I:45

KENNERLY, SOOBIE: One of Kennerly's overly sensual daughters. She liked to suck her thumb. I:44, I:46, I:50–56 *(present)*, I:61–62, I:63–66 *(present)*

KENNERLY'S FATHER: I:45

LADIES IN BLACK SLACKS: I:19

MILL, AUNT: She was a barfly who had a broad belly and a quavery voice. She sang at NORT's funeral. Mill was one of PITTSTON's followers. Like everybody else in Tull, she was killed by Roland. I:31–34, I:63–65 *(killed)*

NORT: Nort was Tull's resident weed-eater. Once he had a honey wagon, but drink and then weed killed off his desire to do anything but chew his way to oblivion. Before his first death, Nort already resembled a walking corpse. He looked like a man made of coathangers and had green-coated teeth – green and smelly as his stinking pants. By the time Roland arrived in town, Nort had already died of weed and had been resurrected by the MAN IN BLACK. Thanks to the magic of the Man in Black, the resurrected Nort addressed Roland in High Speech. Nort's second death was a crucifixion. In the new *Gunslinger*, WALTER (the Man in Black) places a locked door in Nort's imagination. Behind this door lurk the secrets of the afterlife. The key to the door is the number nineteen. I:13 *(old man)*, I:16 *(touched by God)*, I:25–26, I:27, I:28–40, I:42, I:45, I:58 *(weed-eater)*, I:68–69, II:36, III:57

OLD MAN WITH STRAW HAT: He was the first person Roland saw when he entered Tull. I:19, I:66 *(killed)*

PITTSTON, SYLVIA: See PITTSTON, SYLVIA listed separately

SHEB (PIANO PLAYER): Sheb was Tull's piano player,

and though the local honky-tonk bore his name the place actually belonged to ALICE. Sheb was also once a piano player in the HAMBRY saloon called THE TRAVELLERS' REST. See entry under SHEB, listed separately.

TAILOR: I:19–20

YOUNG BOY AND GIRL: I:20

**ZACHARY: One of the barflies at SHEB'S. He liked to draw zodiacs on girls' knees, although in the new *Gunslinger* he draws Reap charms instead of zodiacs. I:31–36

TURTLE
See GUARDIANS OF THE BEAM: TURTLE

U

UNWIN, TALITHA
See RIVER CROSSING CHARACTERS

V

**VANNAY, ABEL
Vannay was one of Roland's tutors. He told Roland that a boy who could answer riddles was a boy who could think around corners. Unlike the warrior CORT, limping Vannay

was a gentle man. In the new version of *The Gunslinger*, we find out that Vannay taught his students about the poisons used by the OLD ONES. Vannay also had a son who was very clever.

I:113, I:128, I:175, I:201, I:222, III:379, IV:412, IV:724, IV:819, IV:835, E:216

**VANNAY'S SON: As was stated above, this boy was very clever. We don't yet know his name or what happened to him. I:113

VECHHIO, RUDY
See BALAZAR'S MEN

VERONE, TIO
See BALAZAR, ENRICO

VI CASTIS COMPANY
This is the name of the corrupt mining company that destroyed all of the freehold mines north of Ritzy. The BIG COFFIN HUNTERS were part of this conspiracy.

IV:333, IV:334

VINCENT, COL
See BALAZAR'S MEN

W

WALKER, DETTA
See DEAN, SUSANNAH

WALKIN' DUDE
See entry under R.F.

**WALTER (MAN IN BLACK, WALTER O'DIM)
The Dark Tower series begins with Roland's pursuit of the Man in Black. We find out at the end of the original version of *The Gunslinger* that the man in black is actually the sorcerer Walter, a figure from Roland's childhood and the one who finally delivered the treacherous MARTEN into Roland's hands.

Walter's magic is extremely powerful. He brings the weed-eater NORT back to life and can alter his own appearance. (In other words, he never has to wear the same face twice.) Although a sorcerer, Walter often functions as a kind of trickster, leading Roland into the darkest regions of his own soul. It is Walter who tempts Roland to let JAKE fall into the abyss below the CYCLOPEAN MOUNTAINS, and it is often Walter's taunting voice that Roland hears in his head, mocking and deriding his desire to live – and pursue his quest – honorably.

Among Walter's infernal skills is that of prophecy. In the bone-strewn wastes of the GOLGOTHA he reads Roland's future with a deck of Tarot cards. During this reading he foretells the drawing of the Three, and tells Roland the perils he will have to face on the way to the TOWER. Walter also gives our gunslinger an overwhelming vision of the universe, and a sense of the immensity of the Tower itself. At the end of the first book of the series, Roland wakes up from a short sleep to find that he has aged a decade and that Walter is only a pile of bones. Roland takes Walter's jaw as a talisman.

In the new version of *The Gunslinger*, we learn some surprising things about Walter. First, Walter is actually all of Roland's enemies. Under different magical disguises he was MARTEN, he was JOHN FARSON, and he was the penitent WALTER whom Roland remembered from his youth. Walter serves the CRIMSON KING, whom we met in the related Stephen King novel entitled *Insomnia*. The Crimson King is an agent of chaos and is, by his very nature, opposed to the White which Roland and his line represent. Hence, so is Walter. Walter maintains that the Red King rules the Tower, and that Earth has been given into his hand. It yet remains to be seen whether Walter is telling the truth.

One of the most interesting things added to Walter's palaver is the theme of RESUMPTION, a word which we see on one of the new opening pages of the revised *Gunslinger*. Roland believes that his quest for the Tower has been continuous, but Walter implies that it has not. He says that Roland never learns, and that he never remembers. This casts Roland's frequent sense of déjà vu in a new light. Perhaps Walter and his master have Roland caught in some kind of time loop, and are playing with him the way a cat plays with a mouse.

I:3, I:5, I:6, I:7, I:11–12, I:13–14, I:16, I:18, I:19, I:25, I:26, I:29–37, I:38–40, I:41, I:42, I:47, I:54, I:58–60 *(Roland and Pittston discuss)*, I:63, I:69, I:78, I:79, I:81–82, I:88–89, I:92, I:94, I:95, I:98–99, I:101, I:102, I:103, I:122, I:129, I:134, I:142, I:143, I:149, I:151, I:152, I:154, I:155–57, I:158, I:162, I:170, I:192, I:203, I:205 *(he)*, I:209–37, II:17, II:23, II:25, II:36, II:53, II:109, II:355, II:356, II:358, II:359, II:366, II:410, II:451, III:51, III:56, III:57, III:58, III:59, III:60, III:63–64, III:65, III:81–82, III:83, III:84–86, III:129 *(man in black)*, III:143–44, III:145, III:148, III:237, III:308, III:332, III:357, III:358, III:577, IV:8, IV:80, IV:133, IV:507 *(Depape describes him — Farson's man in black robe)*, IV:508–9 *(Farson's man in black robe)*,

IV:510–13 (*Jonas and Farson's man in black robe*), IV:530, IV:531 (*laughing man in black robe*), IV:532–33, IV:755, E:155

WEAVER, NORRIS
NY foot patrolman. His partner is ANDREW STAUNTON. II:432–36

WERTNER, HENRY
 See HAMBRY CHARACTERS: HORSEMEN'S ASSOCIATION

**WHEELER'S BOY
Like many of the figures from Roland's past, we don't know much about this gunslinger apprentice. The only bit of information we're given is that STEVEN DESCHAIN thinks he is brighter than Roland. This character is cut from the new version of *The Gunslinger*.

WHITE, JAKE
 See HAMBRY CHARACTERS: HORSEMEN'S ASSOCIATION

WHITMAN, THOMAS
 See THOMAS OF GILEAD

WILSON, WILLIAM
 See BALAZAR'S MEN: BALAZAR'S NASSAU CONNECTION

WIZARD OF OZ
 See OZ, WIZARD OF

Z

ZACHARY
See TULL

ZOLTAN
See BORDER DWELLERS: BROWN

MID-WORLD PLACES[1]

My world is like a huge ship that sank near enough shore for most of the wreckage to wash up on the beach. Much of what we find is fascinating, some of it may be useful, if ka allows, but all of it is still wreckage. Senseless wreckage.

Roland Deschain
IV:87

Things had stretched apart. There was no glue at the center anymore. Something was tottering, and when it fell, all would end.

I:40

[1] **NOTE ON MID-WORLD DIRECTIONS:** In the original version of *The Gunslinger*, Roland follows Walter (the Man in Black) due south through the Mohaine Desert and the Cyclopean Mountains. In the 2003 edition of the book, Roland follows Walter southeast, both of them drawn toward the force of the Bear-Turtle Beam. For a detailed account of how this alters Mid-World's geography, see MID-WORLD MAPS located at the end of this Concordance.

A

**ALGUL SIENTO
  See ALGUL SIENTO listed in the PORTALS section

ALL-WORLD
In the time of Roland's semi-mythical ancestor, ARTHUR
ELD, all of the kingdoms of the land – whether part of IN-
WORLD, OUT-WORLD or MID-WORLD – were united
under one high king who wore the crown of All-World upon
his brow. This king was Arthur, Warrior of the White and
the first Lord of Light. Like the great King Arthur of Our
World, Arthur Eld wielded a magical sword called Excalibur.
Arthur reigned during a kind of Golden Age that came (we
believe) after the nuclear and chemical destruction wrought
by the OLD ONES.

  Even in Roland's youth, when the IN-WORLD Baronies
still stood and the gunslingers maintained relative peace by
exerting their strength through the fragmenting AFFILIA-
TION, the unity of Arthur Eld's All-World was only a myth.
FARSON (who we believe was the pawn of an even greater
destructive force) warred in the west, drawing over to his side
many of the embittered, failed gunslingers originally sent to
the western lands in disgrace.

  IV:401

**ARROYOS
In the new version of *The Gunslinger*, we find out that there
are arroyos in the hardpan of the MOHAINE DESERT.
  I:42

ATCHISON
See ATCHISON, TOPEKA AND SANTA FE RAILROAD
in the OUR WORLD PLACES section. See also KANSAS
listed in that section and KANSAS listed in the PORTALS
section.

B

BACK COURTS
  See NEW CANAAN, BARONY OF: GILEAD

BAD GRASS
  See MEJIS, BARONY OF

BAR K RANCH
  See MEJIS, BARONY OF: HAMBRY

BAY VIEW HOTEL
  See MEJIS, BARONY OF: HAMBRY

BEAMS
  See BEAMS in the PORTALS section

BIG EMPTY
In the town of RIVER CROSSING, the elderly residents
refer to the waste lands beyond LUD as the Big Empty.
SUSANNAH DEAN thinks that all of Mid-World's barren
lands are a 'Big Empty,' and confronting that desolation
turned Roland in on himself. See also the following two

entries in the PORTALS section: WASTE LANDS and DRAWERS.

III:308, III:333, III:349

BLAINE'S ROUTE

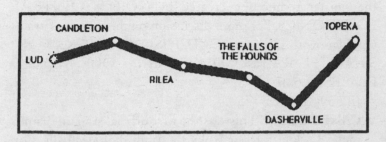

Our desperate *ka-tet* boarded the slo-trans Mono BLAINE in LUD, just after EDDIE and SUSANNAH's shootout with the PUBES and JAKE's escape from TICK-TOCK, leader of the GRAYS. Blaine's track led southeast, roughly along the PATH OF THE BEAM, in the direction of the DARK TOWER. Although Blaine claimed that he could take our group closer to their final destination, none of them was certain whether they would be able to disembark this Barony Coach alive.

Although probably originally endowed with a polite personality by the GREAT OLD ONES (who in retrospect were much less than great), over the centuries Blaine's personality fragmented into its component parts, finally evincing some of the cruelty of its Makers. The resulting monstrosity – which our *ka-tet* battled in a life-or-death riddling contest – consisted of a frightened LITTLE BLAINE as well as a nasty Big Blaine who seemed to believe he served the people of Lud best by killing them.

Blaine's route traveled through the surreal WASTE LANDS

and terminated in an alternative version of Our World's TOPEKA, one afflicted by the terrible superflu found in Stephen King's novel *The Stand*.

Blaine was obviously created to transport the Great Old Ones onto other levels of the Tower, and is an example of the sinister technology created by NORTH CENTRAL POSITRONICS. For more discussion on the subject of trains between worlds, see the ATCHISON, TOPEKA AND SANTA FE RAILROAD listed in the OUR WORLD PLACES section.
III:559–82, IV:3–75

CANDLETON: This was the first official stop on Blaine's route. Luckily for our folks the train didn't actually stop here, otherwise they would have been exposed to the killer radiation levels still pulsing from a nearby Ground Zero.

Although described as 'a poisoned and irradiated ruin,' Candleton is not completely dead. Trundling along the corridors of the CANDLETON TRAVELLERS' HOTEL are turtle-sized beetles, birds that look more like small dragons, and blind, bloated, mutant rats. III:560, III:577, IV:6, IV:15, IV:16, IV:18, IV:809

CANDLETON FOUNTAIN: IV:16
CANDLETON TRAVELLERS' MOTEL: IV:15–16, IV:18
ELEGANT BEEF AND PORK RESTAURANT: IV:16

DASHERVILLE: Dasherville was the stop before Topeka on Blaine's run. III:560, IV:39, IV:45, IV:46, IV:809

FALL OF THE HOUNDS: The Fall of the Hounds was actually a torrential waterfall guarded by two giant stone sculptures shaped like ferocious dogs. (The dogs actually protruded from a point about two hundred feet below the place where the torrential, brawling river tumbled over its drop.)

It was at the Fall of the Hounds that Blaine switched to battery power. His batteries were fired up by the electric blue energy zapping from the giant hounds' eyes. III:560, IV:38–42, IV:50, IV:51, IV:809, IV:822

RILEA: Rilea was the stop after Candleton on Blaine's run. III:560 IV:18, IV:19, IV:31, IV:809

TOPEKA: Topeka was Blaine's termination point. It also happened to be located in an alternative version of our KANSAS. For entries, see KANSAS in the PORTALS section.

****BLUE HAVEN/BLUE HEAVEN**
See ALGUL SIENTO in the PORTALS section

BLUFFS
See MEJIS, BARONY OF

BORDER (BORDER DWELLERS)
The Border Dwellers live in this transitional desert area bordering the waterless wasteland of the MOHAINE DESERT. This region was one of the first in which time grew soft.

I:3–17 (*Roland travels through Borderlands*), I:69–71 (*Roland travels through Borderlands*)
BROWN'S HUT: I:9–17, I:69–70, III:57

C

CANDLE, THE
See MEJIS, BARONY OF: HAMBRY: CITGO

CANDLETON
See BLAINE'S ROUTE

CENTRAL PLACE
See NEW CANAAN, BARONY OF: GILEAD

CHURCH OF THE BLOOD EVERLASTING
See RIVER BARONY: RIVER CROSSING

CITGO
See MEJIS, BARONY OF: HAMBRY

CLEAN SEA
See MEJIS, BARONY OF: HAMBRY

**COACH ROAD
This is the two-rut track that Roland follows during *The Gunslinger*. It runs from PRICETOWN (though it probably began much farther back) through TULL, past BROWN'S hut and then into the wastes of the MOHAINE DESERT. Before the world moved on, this road was one of Mid-World's highways. The deserted WAY STATION, where Roland met Jake, was once a stopping place for the coaches that traveled along this artery.

Like most of the amenities of organized culture, by the time of *The Gunslinger* Mid-World's coach service had almost disappeared. A few still ran between Pricetown and Tull, but none ventured into the deadly regions of the desert. In the new *Gunslinger*, we find out that bucka wagons also used this road. In this version of the story, the Coach Road runs southeast, like the Bear-Turtle Beam, not due south. For more information about Mid-World's roads, see GREAT ROAD, located later in this section.

I:3–9 *(following — mentioned directly on 3, 6, 8)*, I:18–22 *(to Tull)*, I:70–77 *(Roland follows to Way Station)*, I:99–104, I:122–23 *(path through mountains — then changes to a mountain path)*

CÖOS, THE (HILL)
See MEJIS, BARONY OF: HAMBRY

CRADLE OF LUD
See RIVER BARONY: LUD

CRAVEN'S UNDERTAKING PARLOR
See MEJIS, BARONY OF: HAMBRY

CRESSIA
Cressia was one of the Baronies located west of GILEAD. Its Barony Seat was **INDRIE**, a city burned to the ground by FARSON's harriers. Fearful for their lives and afraid to join the thousands already slaughtered by the GOOD MAN (including Indrie's mayor and high sheriff who were beheaded by the rebel forces), Cressia repudiated the AFFILIATION and bowed to Farson. It later became one of his strongholds.

When Roland challenged CORT and underwent an early test of manhood against his father's wishes, he thought that his father was far away in this distant Barony searching for one of MAERLYN's glass balls. He was wrong. Cressia was famous for one of its sayings: 'If ye'd steal the silver from the dining room, first put the dog in the pantry' (IV:220).

IV:137, IV:204, IV:205, IV:220, IV:781
INDRIE: IV:204

CYCLOPEAN MOUNTAIN RANGE[2]

The first foothills of the Cyclopean Mountain Range can be seen from the dry wastes of the MOHAINE DESERT. The WILLOW JUNGLE, where JAKE was almost trapped by the demonically sexual ORACLE OF THE MOUNTAINS, is located here among the first tumbling rises of granite and grasses.

These mountains are one of the many physical barriers which Roland and Jake have to traverse in order to pursue the MAN IN BLACK, also known as WALTER. At first, their path winds through a much more hospitable landscape than the desert which Roland traversed earlier in *The Gunslinger*. Trees grow there, and there are rabbits to hunt and eat. However, as their experience with the sexual demon of the SPEAKING RING showed, Roland's world contains sinister magic, much of it manipulated by the very sorcerer they pursue.

As Jake and Roland climb higher toward the mountain pass, following the burnt-out ideograms left by their elusive and dangerous quarry, the way becomes steeper and less accessible, at times no more than a narrow V cut into the mica and quartz-veined granite. Just before the mountains rise to their most inaccessible icy heights, the path zigzags into a canyon.

[2] I have only listed direct references for the Cyclopean Mountains. However, whenever action takes place upon LOBSTROSITY BEACH bordering the WESTERN SEA, these mountains are on the horizon.

There, our two friends follow a taunting Walter into the black cleft of a waterfall cave. Little do they know it, but they are eagerly awaited by the band of SLOW MUTANTS who nest in the deserted mountain subway system left by the OLD ONES.

I:3, I:45, I:60, I:71, I:99, I:100 *(foothills begin)*, I:101 *(foothills)*, I:121–30 *(foothills)*, I:140, I:147–58, I:161–73 *(under the mountains)*, I:190 *(under the mountains)*, I:191–212 *(under the mountains)*, I:218, II:24, II:25, II:187, II:197, II:259, II:260, II:272 *(foothills)*, II:309 *(hills)*, II:321 *(hills)*, II:327–34 *(hills reach beach)*, II:338–51, II:355, II:369, II:416, II:431, II:448, III:56, III:134, III:237 *(foothills)*, III:247, III:305, III:357

D

DARK TOWER
See DARK TOWER in the PORTALS section

DASHERVILLE
See BLAINE'S ROUTE

DEBARIA
Debaria is the location of a woman's retreat, quite possibly a religious one. While Roland is in HAMBRY, his mother, GABRIELLE DESCHAIN, supposedly goes to Debaria to pray for his safe return. However, it seems highly likely that her lover MARTEN BROADCLOAK – and Gabrielle's complicity in his plot to overthrow the aristocratic gunslingers – is the real reason for her sojourn. Gabrielle's attempted

assassination is foiled, but it seems quite probable that she was schooled in the ways of deceit while in Debaria.

    IV:781, IV:825

DELAIN

JOHN NORMAN, the young man Roland meets while imprisoned by the LITTLE SISTERS OF ELURIA, comes from Delain. This kingdom is derisively known as Dragon's Lair, Liars' Heaven, and the home of tall tales. It also happens to be the setting for the novel *Eyes of the Dragon*.

    E:207

DESATOYA MOUNTAINS

The town of ELURIA is located in the Desatoya Mountains. Like so many of the landscapes found in the Dark Tower series, both the mountains and the towns dotted through them resemble the landscape of the American Southwest.

    E:155

DESOY

FARSON began his career as a harrier in GARLAN and Desoy.

    IV:189

DIS

The orange ball of MAERLYN'S RAINBOW is reputed to be in Dis.

    IV:551

DOORS: MID-WORLD TO NEW YORK

See DOORWAYS BETWEEN WORLDS in the PORTALS section

DOWNLAND BARONIES
  See GREATER KINGDOMS OF THE WESTERN EARTH

DRAGON'S GRAVE
The Dragon's Grave was a bottomless crack in the earth named for the great bursts of steam that erupted from it every thirty to forty days. Roland knew of it as a boy, so it is most likely located near GILEAD-that-was.
  III:50

DRAGON'S LAIR
  See DELAIN

DRAWERS
  See DRAWERS in the PORTALS section

DROP, THE
  See MEJIS, BARONY OF: HAMBRY

DRUIT STONES
  See DOORWAYS BETWEEN WORLDS in the PORTALS section

E

ELD
Eld was the name of the ancient land ruled by Roland's ancestor, ARTHUR ELD, who later became king of ALL-WORLD. Eld was located northwest of GILEAD, in the northwesternmost

reaches of the AFFILIATION. By the time of Roland's trials in HAMBRY, those ancient lands were already being burned and looted by FARSON and his men.

   IV:226

ELURIA

Eluria is a small town located in the DESATOYA MOUN-TAINS. It is also the setting for the short story 'The Little Sisters of Eluria.' Like many of the places in Mid-World, it looks like a town out of the old American West. Along its High Street are quite a few wooden shop fronts including a mercantile, a smithy, a Gathering Hall, a church (complete with bell tower), a livery, a market, and a sheriff's office. It also has a single hotel (**GOOD BEDS HOTEL**), and two saloons, one of which is called **THE BUSTLING PIG**. When Roland arrives during the heat of Full Earth, the place has been deserted for about two weeks. The only living (or once living) beings Roland finds are a CROSS-DOG, a single corpse, and some sweet-singing insects.

Although there are no people to be seen, the town's gates are still strung with garlands of dried flowers and the church doorway with tiny, silver bells — decorations which Roland finds both disturbing and eerie. Soon after his arrival he discovers that the town is not completely deserted after all. It is inhabited by the mutant GREEN FOLK and the vampiric LITTLE SISTERS OF ELURIA.

   E:155–70 *(Setting. Directly mentioned on the following pages: 160, 162, 163, 166, 169)*, E:171, E:179, E:180, E:182, E:189, E:194, E:195, E:198, E:210, E:213, E:223, E:228

     HOSPITAL (RUN BY LITTLE SISTERS): *See* LITTLE SISTERS' HOSPITAL, located in the PORTALS section

LEXINGWORTH: This is where Eluria's citizens hang criminals. E:161

RADIUM MINES: The foul-looking muties known as THE GREEN FOLK inhabit the radium mines outside of Eluria. E:165

RUINED HACIENDA: This is where the Little Sisters live during their time in Eluria. E:221, E:223

THOUGHTFUL HOUSE: In 'The Little Sisters of Eluria,' the tyrannical SISTER MARY tells Roland that Thoughtful House is a 'home for contagion,' a place where the sick are brought to recover. But like so much that is said in the white tents of the sinister Little Sisters, this is a lie. Thoughtful House is not a house at all but a small hillside cave where Sister Mary sends disobedient members of her order to endure a kind of solitary confinement. The lovely and rebellious SISTER JENNA is forced to spend much time here. E:191, E:203, E:214, E:223, E:229–30

END WORLD
See END WORLD in the PORTALS section

EYEBOLT CANYON
See MEJIS, BARONY OF: HAMBRY

F

FALL OF THE HOUNDS
See BLAINE'S ROUTE

**FARSON (TOWN OF)

In *The Gunslinger* we learn that when Roland was a boy, the AFFILIATION's enemy JOHN FARSON (also known as THE GOOD MAN) planned to poison this town. Given the fact that this rather nasty character bears the town's name, it seems likely that he – or his ancestors – originated here. In the new *Gunslinger*, the town of Farson is replaced by the town of TAUNTON.

**FARSON ROAD

Farson Road is the name given to the coach road that runs between GILEAD and the town of FARSON. GALLOWS HILL is located here. In the new *Gunslinger*, the Farson Road becomes the TAUNTON ROAD.

**FOREST O' BARONY
See NEW CANAAN, BARONY OF

FOREST TREES
See PASS O' THE RIVER

G

GADDISH FEEDS
See KANSAS: TOPEKA in the PORTALS section

GAGE BOULEVARD
See KANSAS: TOPEKA in the PORTALS section

**GALLOWS HILL

Gallows Hill is located on the FARSON ROAD. HAX, Gilead's traitorous head cook, is hanged here. In the new version of *The Gunslinger*, Gallows Hill is located on the TAUNTON ROAD.
 I:115–21, IV:201

**GARLAN

Garlan is a distant kingdom which seems almost mythical to many of the people we meet in *The Dark Tower* series. According to AUNT TALITHA of RIVER CROSSING, the people of Garlan have brown skin. It is also supposed to be the home of that strange baby-bearing bird, the GRAND FEATHEREX.

Garlan also has more sinister associations. According to the novel *The Eyes of the Dragon*, the nasty sorcerer R.F. once lived there, and we can guess that he learned much of his nasty magic – and knowledge of poisons – in that place. Not surprisingly, the poison coating the knife intended to kill Roland's father came from this kingdom. ELDRED JONAS – Roland's enemy in *Wizard and Glass* – received a terrible whipping in Garlan. In the new *Gunslinger*, we find out that this kingdom is located west of GILEAD, and that it is a tobacco growing region.
 I:15, I:182, II:68, III:315, III:331, IV:189, IV:268, IV:604, IV:782

GAUNTLET
 See GREAT ROAD, THE

GILEAD
 See NEW CANAAN, BARONY OF

GILEAD, BARONY OF
See NEW CANAAN, BARONY OF

GLENCOVE
See TAVARES

GOLGOTHA, THE
See GOLGOTHA in the PORTALS section

GRAYS' CASTLE/ GRAYS' MAZE
See RIVER BARONY: LUD

GREAT HALL (HALL OF THE GRANDFATHERS)
See NEW CANAAN, BARONY OF: GILEAD

GREAT ROAD
There are many Great Roads in Mid-World. Like the Roman
Roads of Our World, they are the leftovers of an earlier civilization, namely that of the OLD ONES. Although these
byways were once major highways, by the time of *The Gunslinger*
their broken surfaces are covered with years of dirt. However,
many of them still have intact subterranean drainage systems.
Most of the Great Roads follow the PATH OF THE BEAM.
IV:821, IV:822

    GREAT ROAD TO LUD: III:218–27 *(following)*,
III:234–43 *(following)*, III:246, III:250, III:299–317 *(directly
mentioned on 306, 307, 308, 312, 314)*, III:328, III:333,
III:344–413 *(directly mentioned on 375, 386, 389, 394)*

        GAUNTLET: This is the term Jake uses for the forti-
fications around the Great Road, just outside of Lud.
III:394–96

    THROUGH HAMBRY: One of Mid-World's Great

Roads runs from the BARONY OF NEW CANAAN to the BARONY OF MEJIS. Along its course it passes through the town of HAMBRY. It runs east-west. IV:153, IV:228, IV:335, IV:470, IV:473, IV:476, IV:553, IV:602, IV:627, IV:649, IV:650, IV:762, IV:763, IV:771

GREAT WEST WOODS

The Great West Woods of OUT-WORLD are located north of the CYCLOPEAN MOUNTAINS and just east of the WESTERN SEA. Roland, EDDIE and SUSANNAH recover here after their long journey along LOBSTROSITY BEACH, a trial we read about in *The Drawing of the Three*. These woods are the home of the GUARDIAN SHARDIK, also known as MIR. It is the home of the PORTAL OF THE BEAR and the place where our *ka-tet* picks up the PATH OF THE BEAM. In THE SHOOTING GALLERY (a clearing in the woods), Roland teaches both Eddie and Susannah the ways of the gunslinger.

II:449–54, III:13–69 *(named on 25)*, III:73–119 *(89 reach Portal)*, III:205–9, III:234, III:260

SHOOTING GALLERY: III:13–24, III:48–69 *(camp)*, III:73–75 *(camp)*, III:224

GREATER KINGDOMS OF THE WESTERN EARTH

When Roland was a boy he saw a map of the Greater Kingdoms of the Western Earth. It depicted GILEAD, the **DOWNLAND BARONIES** which were overrun by riot and civil war the year after he won his guns, and showed the hills, the desert, and the mountains which stretched all the way to the WESTERN SEA. At the time the map was made, one thousand miles lay between Gilead and the Western Sea. However, as the BEAMS disintegrated, distances within

Mid-World shifted and grew. It took Roland many years to cross that distance.
III:101–2

GREEN HEART
See MEJIS, BARONY OF: HAMBRY

H

HALL OF THE GRANDFATHERS
See NEW CANAAN, BARONY OF: GILEAD

HAMBRY
See MEJIS, BARONY OF

HAMBRY CEMETERY
See MEJIS, BARONY OF: HAMBRY

HAMBRY CREEK
See MEJIS, BARONY OF: HAMBRY

HAMBRY POINT
See MEJIS, BARONY OF: HAMBRY

HAMBRY POST OFFICE
See MEJIS, BARONY OF: HAMBRY

HANGING ROCK
See MEJIS, BARONY OF

HATTIGANS
See RITZY

HEMPHILL
Hemphill was a small town located near GILEAD-that-was. Roland's HAMBRY *alter ego*, Will Dearborn, supposedly grew up there.
IV:185, IV:229, IV:238, IV:248, IV:253, IV:301

HENDRICKSON (TOWN)
Hendrickson was one of the many towns attacked by THE GOOD MAN.
I:112

HOOKEY'S STABLE & SMITHY
See MEJIS, BARONY OF: HAMBRY

I

IL BOSQUE
Il Bosque is a forest west of MEJIS. Roland, CUTHBERT and ALAIN travel through it after Susan's death and after Roland's disastrous magical journey through MAERLYN'S GRAPEFRUIT.
IV:771

IMPERIUM
See NORTH CENTRAL POSITRONICS located in the CHARACTERS section

INDRIE
See CRESSIA, BARONY OF

**IN-WORLD
Roland's world is often described as having two parts, IN-WORLD and OUT-WORLD. These terms are relative to one another. To the citizens of HAMBRY who live far from the hub of civilization, GILEAD is 'In-World.' Hence, Roland and his youthful *ka-tet* are called the 'In-World boys.' Hambry is an Out-World Barony because it is far from NEW CANAAN.

The terms *In-World* and *Out-World* may also be metaphorical references to the metaphysical map of Mid-World which Roland draws in *The Waste Lands.* According to this map, Mid-World is shaped like a circle, with the DARK TOWER at its center and the BEAMS radiating out from it and terminating in twelve PORTALS. Just as the Tower is the center of the Universe, Gilead and the In-World Baronies are the centers of human culture. Backwaters such as MEJIS are on the Outer Crescent of the 'civilized' world. See also the MID-WORLD entry (this section) and END-WORLD entry (PORTALS section). In the new version of *The Gunslinger,* Roland refers to himself as being from In-World.

I:11, I:116, I:164, III:521, IV:185, IV:218 *(North'rd Baronies),* IV:228, IV:260, IV:455, IV:469, IV:473, IV:476, IV:487, IV:495, IV:531, IV:532, IV:634, IV:638, IV:657, IV:673, IV:674, IV:675, IV:688, IV:704, IV:737

INNER ARC: Home of the Inner Baronies IV:247

INNER BARONIES: IV:149, IV:176, IV:181, IV:227–28, IV:246, IV:251, IV:252, IV:265, IV:307, IV:373, IV:439

INNER CRESCENT: IV:381

INNERS: IV:220

J

**JERICHO HILL
Jericho Hill was the site of the gunslingers' last stand against their enemies. During this battle CUTHBERT ALLGOOD died and Roland lost the horn of his fathers — the horn he was meant to blow when he reached the DARK TOWER.
I:6

JIMTOWN
See RIVER BARONY

K

KAMBERO
This is one of the villages located in the far western regions of Mid-World. It is probably even further west than ELURIA.
E:213

KANSAS
See KANSAS in the PORTALS section

KASHMIN, BARONY OF (also spelled KASHAMIN)
Before the complete destruction of the AFFILIATION and of culture as Roland knew it, the Kashmin province was famous for its rugs. Sumptuous Kashmin carpets adorned the halls of

GILEAD. They also lined the floors of the CRADLE OF
THE GRAYS.
   III:485, IV:823 *(Kashamin)*

KINGS TOWN
This is one of the hundreds of towns Roland traveled through
on his search for the DARK TOWER. Twelve years before
he met JAKE (and not long after the fall of GILEAD), Roland
had a girl here. She was one of the many he deserted in order
to pursue his quest.
   I:173

L

LaMERK FOUNDRY
   See LaMERK FOUNDRY located in the CHARACTERS
section

LANDING, THE
   See RIVER BARONY

LAZY SUSAN RANCH
   See MEJIS, BARONY OF: HAMBRY

LEXINGWORTH
   See ELURIA

LIARS' HEAVEN
   See DELAIN

LOBSTROSITY BEACH
  See WESTERN SEA

LUD
  See RIVER BARONY: LUD

M

MEJIS, BARONY OF
Mejis (more specifically, the Barony Seat of HAMBRY) is the setting for most of *Wizard and Glass*. Mejis's Barony color is a deep orange red, as can be seen on the official sash worn by Mayor HART THORIN. Located east of GILEAD and on the edge of the desert, Mejis is considered one of the quiet backwaters of the OUTER ARC, or OUTER CRESCENT. Like much of Mid-World, it resembles areas of the American West. Its citizens breed horses and, in the areas closest to the sea, they also fish.

STEPHEN DESCHAIN, Roland's father, sends Roland and his two friends to Mejis in order to keep them safe from JOHN FARSON, who is destroying the lands farther west. Little does he know that THE GOOD MAN's poison has spread as far as the Outer Arc. Mejis is no longer loyal to the AFFILIATION, and the final battle of Mid-World is destined to take place in this quiet Barony. Within two years of Roland's trials in Mejis, the light of the IN-WORLD BARONIES will be snuffed out and the world, as Steven Deschain knew it, will no longer exist. (Below are some of the direct references to Mejis's character, customs, etc.)

I:48, I:51, I:71, I:131, I:162, IV:84 *(Santa Fe)*, IV:123,
IV:156, IV:180, IV:186, IV:189, IV:201, IV:202, IV:205,
IV:219, IV:224, IV:230, IV:234, IV:242, IV:269, IV:291,
IV:307, IV:311, IV:319, IV:320, IV:333, IV:338, IV:341,
IV:356, IV:422, IV:428, IV:436, IV:440, IV:445, IV:491,
IV:521, IV:532, IV:536, IV:543, IV:546, IV:550, IV:561,
IV:563, IV:564, IV:568, IV:576, IV:592, IV:600, IV:605,
IV:611, IV:612, IV:630, IV:631, IV:642, IV:657, IV:682,
IV:690, IV:691, IV:700, IV:726, IV:734, IV:765, IV:771,
IV:772, IV:780, IV:782, IV:783, IV:787, IV:818, IV:822,
E:172

BAD GRASS AND AREAS WEST OF HAMBRY:
BAD GRASS: This is the freeland west of Hambry
and is located on the edge of the desert wastelands.
Its grasses are poisonous. IV:342, IV:410, IV:430,
IV:431, IV:496, IV:563, IV:575, IV:584–87, IV:597,
IV:628, IV:660–64, IV:667, IV:668, IV:671,
IV:672–73 *(hut)*, IV:674–75, IV:677–82 *(hut)*,
IV:685, IV:687, IV:689, IV:691, IV:692, IV:698,
IV:699

BLUFFS: The bluffs are six miles beyond the long
grassy DROP at the edge of HAMBRY. HANGING
ROCK is located here. IV:342, IV:343

CÖOS: The Cöos is a ragged hill five miles from the
town of HAMBRY, ten miles from EYEBOLT
CANYON. To the northwest of it is the desert, the
BAD GRASS, HANGING ROCK and Eyebolt
Canyon. RHEA, the weirdling of the Cöos, has her
hut here below the crest of the hill. IV:79 *(Rhea)*,
IV:80, IV:143–72, IV:180 *(Rhea's hut)*, IV:183 *(Rhea's
hut)*, IV:198, IV:208, IV:210, IV:286, IV:305, IV:309,
IV:313, IV:366–67, IV:378, IV:403–5, IV:411,

IV:430, IV:442–44, IV:446–47 *(Rhea's hut)*,
IV:470–71, IV:482, IV:496–500, IV:519, IV:521,
IV:523, IV:528, IV:529, IV:556, IV:566 *(Rhea's hut)*,
IV:570–71, IV:614–21 *(Jonas comes to take Grapefruit)*,
IV:687, IV:712, IV:721, IV:761, IV:818 *(Rhea's hut)*,
IV:827, IV:832 *(Rhea)*, E:179

EYEBOLT CANYON: A short, steep-walled box
canyon shaped like a chimney lying on its side. A
THINNY has eaten its way into the far end of it.
Roland destroys his enemies by laying a trap for them
in Eyebolt Canyon. IV:80, IV:143, IV:147, IV:194,
IV:195, IV:197, IV:220 *(Canyon)*, IV:343–47, IV:348,
IV:410, IV:440, IV:496, IV:531, IV:534, IV:545,
IV:573–76, IV:592–93, IV:667, IV:668, IV:691,
IV:732, IV:746, IV:748–61, IV:771, IV:785

HANGING ROCK: IV:342, IV:410, IV:461,
IV:465, IV:484, IV:496, IV:512, IV:532, IV:544,
IV:575, IV:610, IV:634, IV:653, IV:658, IV:668,
IV:671, IV:676, IV:684, IV:691, IV:702, IV:707,
IV:728, IV:731, IV:737, IV:739

HAMBRY (BARONY SEAT OF MEJIS): Hambry is a
beautiful town located on the edge of the CLEAN SEA.
From High Street you can see the bay, the docks, and the
many-colored boathouses. The newer buildings are adobe,
the older ones are brick and are reminiscent of GILEAD's
Old Quarter. Hambry has two markets – an upper and a
lower. The lower market smells fishy but is cheaper.

Roland associates Hambry with the smell of sea-salt, oil
and pine. Its citizens are fishermen and horsebreeders.
Although Hambry is picturesque, it is full of hidden dangers.
The THINNY of Eyebolt Canyon is the most visible;
however, other dangers lurk. As Roland soon

realizes, 'in Hambry, the waters on top and the waters down below seem to run in different directions' (IV:257–58). Although they declare their allegiance to the AFFILIATION, the politically powerful men of the town have (metaphorically speaking) sold their souls to FARSON, also known as THE GOOD MAN. Although the gunslingers of NEW CANAAN do not know it, the destruction of their world will begin here, in a Barony they can barely recall.

In Hambry, Roland faces the first true trials of his manhood. He also discovers MAERLYN'S GRAPE-FRUIT, the pink sphere of MAERLYN'S RAINBOW.

GENERAL PAGES: IV:80, IV:143–418 *(all action takes place in Hambry)*, IV:427–772 *(all action takes place in or near Hambry)*

SPECIFIC REFERENCES: On the following pages, Hambry is directly mentioned. IV:80, IV:143, IV:144, IV:178, IV:180, IV:185, IV:186, IV:192, IV:193, IV:197, IV:217, IV:226, IV:229, IV:232, IV:234, IV:238, IV:242, IV:251, IV:258, IV:276, IV:278, IV:281, IV:299, IV:306, IV:328, IV:332, IV:335, IV:341, IV:342, IV:348, IV:356, IV:358, IV:359, IV:366, IV:369, IV:373, IV:378, IV:427, IV:429, IV:432, IV:435, IV:439, IV:465, IV:478, IV:505, IV:506, IV:536, IV:542, IV:543, IV:562, IV:568, IV:623, IV:635, IV:638, IV:649, IV:657, IV:710, IV:720, IV:731, IV:738, IV:762, IV:763

ANNE'S DRESSES: IV:415

BAR K RANCH: A deserted spread of land northwest of town. It was once owned by the GARBER family; now it belongs to the HORSEMEN'S ASSOCIATION. Roland's *ka-tet* stays in Bar K's bunkhouse during their time in Hambry. IV:219–20, IV:235, IV:236, IV:250, IV:265, IV:293, IV:328–32, IV:344, IV:347, IV:348,

IV:364, IV:371, IV:385, IV:432–34 *(bunkhouse)*, IV:437, IV:441, IV:442, IV:447–52 *(bunkhouse)*, IV:462, IV:475, IV:487–88, IV:490–92, IV:494–96, IV:501–4, IV:506, IV:507, IV:513–21, IV:543, IV:568, IV:596–605 *(ka-tet arrested)*, IV:610, IV:633, IV:634–36, IV:725

BAY VIEW HOTEL: Located on High Street. IV:564, IV:632, IV:633

CITGO: An oil patch filled with two hundred steel towers, nineteen of which still ceaselessly pump oil. They have existed for more than six centuries. IV:169, IV:181, IV:183 *(derricks)*, IV:184, IV:187–88 *(oil patch)*, IV:189, IV:195, IV:197, IV:199, IV:220, IV:232, IV:233, IV:269, IV:350, IV:354, IV:359, IV:361, IV:364, IV:365–66, IV:367–77, IV:378–82, IV:384, IV:386, IV:402, IV:433, IV:455, IV:464, IV:475–77, IV:490, IV:496, IV:517, IV:530, IV:542, IV:544, IV:568–70, IV:605, IV:609–11, IV:649–54, IV:655–57, IV:659

  CANDLE, THE: The gas-pipe of Citgo. IV:372, IV:373, IV:374, IV:375

  ORANGE GROVE NEAR CITGO: IV:364, IV:365–66, IV:367–71, IV:382–83

CLEAN SEA: This is the sea located east of Hambry. I:48, I:93, IV:181, IV:189, IV:205, IV:226 *(harbor)*, IV:236 *(harbor)*, IV:290, IV:291, IV:293, IV:294, IV:428, IV:560, IV:603

CRAVEN'S UNDERTAKING PARLOR: IV:478

DELGADO HOUSE: IV:174, IV:207–13, IV:266 *(Susan's room)*, IV:295–300, IV:303–7, IV:361–62 *(stable)*, IV:386–87, IV:389–91 *(Susan and Cordelia)*, IV:395–97 *(Susan and Cordelia)*, IV:416–18, IV:453–54, IV:457–60, IV:507, IV:557–81, IV:588–89, IV:624–27, IV:693–97

DROP, THE (WESTERN DROP): This long, grassy

slope stretches for thirty wheels toward the sea. It is used as a horse meadow. Much of it belongs to JOHN CROYDON. Part of it is known as TOWN LOOKOUT. SUSAN DELGADO'S house is visible from here. I:93, I:130, I:140, IV:155, IV:166, IV:171, IV:174, IV:190, IV:191, IV:200, IV:212, IV:218, IV:220, IV:234, IV:235, IV:239, IV:257, IV:293, IV:294–95, IV:309–26, IV:328, IV:342, IV:348, IV:354, IV:358, IV:363, IV:370, IV:380, IV:392, IV:398, IV:409, IV:434, IV:441, IV:449, IV:453, IV:460, IV:461, IV:462, IV:465, IV:492–94, IV:504, IV:506, IV:522, IV:533, IV:539, IV:562, IV:576, IV:578, IV:579, IV:633–34, IV:658, IV:663, IV:667, IV:671, IV:692, IV:715, IV:717, IV:720, IV:800

GREAT ROAD: See GREAT ROAD, listed separately.

GREEN HEART: Green Heart is a pavilion located on Hill Street, fifty yards from the jail and the Town Gathering Hall. It is the site of Reap Dance. The stone wall at the back contains the **RED ROCK** where Roland and SUSAN DELGADO agree to leave notes for each other. Susan is eventually burned here. IV:170, IV:183, IV:413, IV:430 *(Pavilion)*, IV:440, IV:445, IV:464, IV:465, IV:467–69, IV:470, IV:478, IV:547, IV:583, IV:589, IV:639, IV:765–69

HAMBRY CEMETERY: Hambry Cemetery is the site of the famous murder/suicide of ROBERT AND FRANCESCA. Roland, CUTHBERT, ALAIN and SUSAN DELGADO meet to palaver here. IV:535–50, IV:554–58, IV:600, IV:649, IV:650

HAMBRY CREEK: *See also* WILLOW GROVE, below. IV:392

HAMBRY'S MERCANTILE STORE: Located on

South High Street. The porch has a line of carved totems depicting seven of the twelve GUARDIANS OF THE BEAM. They are BEAR, TURTLE, FISH, EAGLE, LION, BAT, and WOLF. People often hang Reap Charms from them. IV:278–79, IV:282, IV:308, IV:414, IV:445

HAMBRY POINT: The point is located two miles from TRAVELLERS' REST. IV:272

HAMBRY POST OFFICE: Although it is an Out-World Barony, Hambry has a postal service. IV:226

HOOKEY'S STABLE AND SMITHY/HOOKEY'S STABLE AND FANCY LIVERY: IV:351, IV:352, IV:353, IV:355, IV:380 *(business)*, IV:417, IV:431, IV:472, IV:490, IV:645, IV:646

LAND OFFICE: IV:226

LAZY SUSAN RANCH: This ranch belongs to RENFREW and is the largest one in Mejis. IV:234, IV:258, IV:262, IV:445, IV:530

MILLBANK: Food is served here. IV:326

ORANGE GROVE: *See* CITGO, above.

PIANO RANCH: Owned by CROYDEN. IV:234, IV:239, IV:431, IV:569, IV:705, IV:729

ROADS:

    BARONY SEA ROAD: *See* SEACOAST ROAD, below.

    CAMINO VEGA: IV:416

    GREAT ROAD (runs east/west) *See* GREAT ROAD, listed separately.

    HIGH STREET: The TRAVELLERS' REST is located here. IV:215, IV:237, IV:278 *(South High Street)*, IV:281, IV:305, IV:415, IV:416, IV:477, IV:505, IV:564, IV:612, IV:623, IV:636

    HILL STREET: GREEN HEART and the

SHERIFF'S OFFICE are located here. IV:226, IV:413, IV:461, IV:465, IV:639, IV:765

SEACOAST ROAD: (runs north/south) Also called BARONY SEA ROAD. IV:341, IV:464, IV:500, IV:506, IV:735

SILK RANCH ROAD: IV:762, IV:763

ROCKING B RANCH: Owned by LENGYLL. IV:233, IV:234, IV:250, IV:445

ROCKING H RANCH: This is LASLO RIMER'S place. IV:330, IV:370

SEAFRONT (MAYOR'S HOUSE): This is Mayor HART THORIN's house. 'Come in peace' is inscribed above the door. IV:173, IV:176, IV:192, IV:197, IV:203, IV:220, IV:224–25, IV:233, IV:238, IV:240–65, IV:266–68, IV:279, IV:290, IV:294, IV:350, IV:351, IV:369, IV:387, IV:388–89 *(and Wolf, the mayor's dog)*, IV:391–95, IV:428, IV:465, IV:472, IV:507, IV:509–13, IV:537, IV:558, IV:559, IV:565–68, IV:571, IV:581–82, IV:590, IV:592–96 *(Seafront murders)*, IV:605, IV:608, IV:622–23, IV:627, IV:637, IV:649, IV:654–59 *(Coral and Jonas in Thorin's bedroom)*, IV:664, IV:678, IV:696, IV:708–10, IV:715–19, IV:720, IV:726–27, IV:729–31, IV:732, IV:734, IV:736, IV:821

SEVEN MILE ORCHARD: IV:464

SHERIFF'S OFFICE, BARONY JAIL: This dual purpose building is located on Hill Street, overlooking the bay. IV:214 *(drunk cell)*, IV:225–38, IV:285, IV:326–27, IV:413, IV:416, IV:455–57, IV:460–62, IV:465, IV:640–47

TOWN GATHERING HALL: IV:226, IV:232, IV:285–89, IV:413, IV:630–33, IV:710

TOWN LOOKOUT: Town Lookout is located on THE DROP. IV:358

TRAVELLERS' REST: Located on HIGH STREET, the Rest is Hambry's bar and whorehouse. It is owned by CORAL THORIN and her brother, HART THORIN. Hart never sets foot in the place, but Coral runs it. The Travellers' Rest is the site of a showdown between Roland's *ka-tet* and THE BIG COFFIN HUNTERS. IV:176, IV:180, IV:193, IV:213–23, IV:238, IV:268–79, IV:281, IV:282–85, IV:287 *(Coral's whore den)*, IV:292, IV:294, IV:302, IV:307–9 *(Sheemie outside)*, IV:326, IV:361, IV:362–64, IV:428, IV:435–42, IV:445, IV:454, IV:460, IV:477, IV:479–86, IV:487, IV:488–90, IV:507–9, IV:529–35, IV:563, IV:569, IV:590–91, IV:630, IV:632, IV:633, IV:636–39, IV:681, IV:710–13

WATCHMAN'S HOUSE: This building stands five miles outside of town and about a mile from SEAFRONT. The BIG COFFIN HUNTERS stay here. IV:290–92

WILLOW GROVE: Roland and SUSAN DELGADO make love here. It is Susan's favorite place, and eerily prefigures the WILLOW JUNGLE in which Roland later encounters the succubus, or ORACLE OF THE MOUNTAINS. IV:200, IV:392, IV:397–403, IV:405–12, IV:549, IV:677

ONNIE'S FORD: IV:387, IV:393

ORCHARDS NORTH OF HAMBRY: IV:427

SANTA FE: There is a sign for this city at BLAINE's termination point in TOPEKA. However, there is also a Santa Fe in Mejis. For more information on the significance of Santa Fe to the series, see the ATCHISON,

TOPEKA AND SANTA FE RAILROAD entry in the OUR WORLD PLACES section.

WASTE LANDS: There are desert waste lands beyond Hambry. Later on, when Roland and his new *ka-tet* reach the city of LUD, they will find much nastier ones. IV:342, IV:496 *(desert)*, IV:523, IV:667, IV:668 *(west of Bad Grass)*, IV:699 *(desert)*

**MID-WORLD

MID-WORLD was originally the name of an ancient kingdom, one that tried to preserve culture and knowledge in a time of darkness. Although not as large as ARTHUR ELD's united kingdom of ALL-WORLD, it was still sizeable. Mid-World's ancient boundaries — which our *ka-tet* stumbles across during its' travels in *The Waste Lands* and *Wizard and Glass* — stretched from a marker near the edge of the GREAT WEST WOODS to TOPEKA, the city where BLAINE the insane Mono terminates his run. The city of LUD (much like a ruined version of our NEW YORK) was once Mid-World's greatest urban center.

In Roland's youth, the great city of GILEAD tried to keep Mid-World's traditions alive and in many ways thought of itself as Mid-World's successor. Hence, Roland sometimes refers to his world as Mid-World, a term which includes both the IN-WORLD BARONIES, such as NEW CANAAN, and the farthest reaches of OUT-WORLD, including forgotten ruins such as ELURIA.

In *The Waste Lands*, Roland draws a metaphysical map of Mid-World which (in this case) is meant to encompass all the known lands of his reality. According to this map, Mid-World is shaped like a sequin impaled upon a central needle. The center of the needle — or the hub of the earth-wheel — is the

DARK TOWER, or the nexus of the time/space continuum. Radiating out from the Tower are the BEAMS, the invisible high tension wires which both hold all of the multiple universes together and maintain the divisions between them.

The term Mid-World is reminiscent of both Middle Earth – Tolkien's magical world – and Midgard, the realm inhabited by human beings in both Norse and Anglo-Saxon mythology. Interestingly, the Dark Tower does not exist in Mid-World at all but in the fey region known as END WORLD – a place which is both the center of all things and a land far beyond the known Baronies.

In the new version of *The Gunslinger*, we learn that Roland has been searching for the old kingdom of Mid-World for a very long time. He has heard rumors that green lands still exist there, but he finds it hard to believe.

I:13, I:215, III:210, III:225, III:226, III:243, III:351, III:462, III:481, III:582, IV:11, IV:38, IV:51, IV:55, IV:58, IV:70, IV:76, IV:84, IV:124, IV:185, IV:204, IV:205, IV:226, IV:227, IV:355, IV:399, IV:429, IV:463, IV:491, IV:561, IV:564, IV:576, IV:612, IV:707, IV:782, IV:819, E:157, E:179, E:219

MID-WORLD LANES
See MID-WORLD LANES listed in the PORTALS section

MID-WORLD RAILWAY
See MID-WORLD RAILWAY listed in the PORTALS section

MILLBANK, THE
See MEJIS, BARONY OF: HAMBRY

**MOHAINE DESERT

In *The Gunslinger*, Roland crosses this desert in pursuit of
WALTER. In the new version of the novel it is described as
'the apotheosis of all deserts, huge, standing to the sky for
what looked like eternity in all directions. It was white and
blinding and waterless and without feature save for the faint,
cloudy haze of the mountains which sketched themselves on
the horizon and the devil-grass which brought sweet dreams,
nightmares, death.' (I:3) It is a harsh and unforgiving place
that steals youth and sucks moisture from the very soul. The
town of TULL is located near the desert and BORDER
DWELLERS live on the edges of this waste land, but nothing
can live within its desiccated heart.

In pursuit of the MAN IN BLACK, Roland crosses this
desert on foot, making his way along the old COACH ROAD
which winds through PRICETOWN and TULL. He stops
briefly at BROWN's hut (the final human habitation) then
travels across the hardpan until he reaches the WAY STATION
where he meets JAKE. The final leg of this journey (from
Brown's hut to the Way Station) almost kills him. Much of
Mid-World has been reduced to desert, but the Mohaine seems
to be, by far, the worst. In the new version of *The Gunslinger*,
we find out that the Mohaine is haunted by at least one
TAHEEN – a hybrid creature with a raven's head and a man's
body.

I:3–9, I:12 *(hardpan)*, I:14, I:28, I:30, I:42, I:43, I:45, I:46,
I:56, I:58, I:59, I:64, I:66, I:70–71, I:75–104 *(at Way Station
77–100)*, I:128, I:129, I:136, I:148, I:166, I:182, I:229,
II:36, III:56, III:58, III:139 *(indirect)*, III:147, III:237,
III:579

N

NEW CANAAN, BARONY OF (also known as **GILEAD BARONY**)

The Barony of New Canaan shares its name with the biblical land of milk and honey. Before the fall of the AFFILIATION it was a green, sweet land – one that tried to keep alive the ideals of hope, knowledge, and light. Roland remembers his home city of Gilead as a jewel set in New Canaan's green-gold fields and serene, blue rivers. Unlike many of the OUT-WORLD baronies, New Canaan (the hub of IN-WORLD) still had running electricity.

I:150, IV:135, IV:185, IV:187–88, IV:191, IV:228, IV:250, IV:334, IV:335, IV:365, IV:439

**FOREST O' BARONY: The warped pines that grow here are used to make gallows trees. I:116

GILEAD: At the time Roland sets out for HAMBRY, Gilead is Mid-World's last great living city. Ancient and walled, it is the Barony Seat of New Canaan, one of the INNER BARONIES of western Mid-World. Gilead is known as the green land, and its city is divided into two separate towns. The filthy maze-like streets of **LOWER TOWN** (frequented by CORT) contain brothels. From the high, pennon-fluttering battlements of the castle, you can view the vendors of the brick and wrought iron OLD QUARTER.

I:25, I:102 *(walled city)*, I:104–21 *(flashback)*, I:150–51 *(indirect)*, I:164, I:174–91, I:218, III:102, III:191, III:209, III:285, III:331, III:332, III:391, III:483, III:521, III:523,

III:569, III:571, III:575, III:576, III:578, III:580, III:582,
IV:4, IV:5, IV:7, IV:10, IV:11, IV:18, IV:33, IV:41, IV:44,
IV:45, IV:47, IV:61, IV:68, IV:116, IV:123, IV:135
(Western Mid-World), IV:136, IV:140, IV:149, IV:185,
IV:188, IV:205 *(Old Quarter)*, IV:207, IV:223, IV:226 *(Old
Quarter)*, IV:230, IV:242, IV:243, IV:248, IV:253, IV:268,
IV:276, IV:308, IV:311, IV:329, IV:334, IV:340, IV:365,
IV:369, IV:382, IV:431, IV:439, IV:448, IV:488, IV:506,
IV:510, IV:523, IV:550–54 *(Roland's* ka-tet *finds out about
Maerlyn's Rainbow)*, IV:585, IV:600, IV:629, IV:663, IV:670,
IV:676, IV:691, IV:713, IV:720, IV:729, IV:733, IV:738,
IV:750, IV:752, IV:762, IV:772, IV:780, IV:782, IV:787,
IV:811, IV:817, IV:820, IV:821–27, IV:836, E:154,
E:155, E:172, E:185, E:187, E:219, E:224, E:228

> **CENTRAL PLACE:** This ancient part of Gilead
> consists of 100 stone castles. I:151
>> **BACK COURTS AND FIELDS:** Women play Points
>> in the main castle's Back Courts. These courts seem
>> to be adjacent to the fields where CORT trains young
>> gunslingers in archery and falconry. I:104–8
>> **BARRACKS:** This is where young gunslinger appren-
>> tices live, away from their parents. The apprentices'
>> nickel guns (given once they pass their coming-of-age
>> battle against CORT) are stored in the vaults below.
>> I:188, IV:137
>> **CORT'S COTTAGE:** I:115, I:177, I:178–80
>> **EXERCISE YARD:** I:177
>> **GABRIELLE'S APARTMENTS:** I:174–77,
>> IV:133–34, IV:553, IV:821, IV:823–27, IV:829
>> *(bedroom)*
>> **GATHERING FIELDS:** E:173
>> ****GREAT HALL (CENTRAL HALL, HALL OF**

THE GRANDFATHERS, WEST'RD HALL): The Spring Ball, also known as ****The Sowing Night Cotillion**, was held in Gilead's Great Hall. It was a grand place with great balconies and a central dancing area illuminated by electric flambeaux. Roland saw his mother dance with the traitorous MARTEN BROAD-CLOAK here. In the new version of *The Gunslinger*, Roland calls it the West'rd Hall. I:150, I:151, I:162–65, I:170, I:180, I:182, III:379, III:579, III:580, IV:8–10 *(Riddling)*, IV:188, IV:223, IV:243, IV:510, IV:550–54, IV:691, IV:821, E:173

GREAT HOUSE KITCHENS (WEST KITCHENS): This was HAX's domain. I:108–12, I:117, I:118, I:151, E:206

LOWER TOWN: IV:134

    BROTHEL: I:191 *(whore's room)*, IV:134–40, IV:203 *(whore's room)*,

MAIN RECEIVING HALL: I:112–15

ROLAND'S CHILDHOOD ROOM: This room had a window of many colors. I:76

ROYAL COURT GARDENS: II:300

SQUARE YARD: Apprentice gunslingers proved themselves here. It sits just east of the Great Hall, and was the site of Fair-Day Riddling. I:180, I:182–91, IV:223

WEST-TOWN: This is the merchant area located in the western part of Gilead.

LAKE SORONI: This lake was located in the northern part of the Barony. When Roland was still a small child, his parents brought him here. IV:752

NONES
See NONES listed in the PORTALS section

NORTHWEST BARONIES
BLAINE's twin Mono PATRICIA heads to the Northwest Baronies. We are not told any of their names.
III:474

OAKLEY
CLAY REYNOLDS and CORAL THORIN escaped the carnage of HAMBRY and set off to become outlaws. They became lovers and formed a gang of bank robbers and coach thieves. They were eventually killed by the sheriff of Oakley.
IV:785

ONNIE'S FORD
See MEJIS, BARONY OF

ORACLE OF THE MOUNTAINS
See STONE CIRCLES in the PORTALS section

ORANGE GROVE
See MEJIS, BARONY OF: HAMBRY

OUT-WORLD (OUTER ARC/OUTER CRESCENT/ OUTER BARONIES/THE OUTERS)
Roland's world is often described as having two parts,

IN-WORLD and OUT-WORLD. These terms are relative to one another. To the citizens of HAMBRY, who live far from the hub of civilization, GILEAD is 'In-World.' Hence, Roland and his youthful *ka-tet* are called the 'In-World boys.' Hambry is an Out-World Barony because it is far from NEW CANAAN.

The terms In-World and Out-World may also be metaphorical references to the metaphysical map of Mid-World which Roland drew in *The Waste Lands*. According to this map, Mid-World is shaped like a circle, with the DARK TOWER at its center and the BEAMS radiating out from it and terminating in twelve PORTALS. Just as the Tower is the center of the Universe, Gilead and the In-World Baronies are the centers of human culture. Backwaters such as MEJIS are on the Outer Crescent of the 'civilized' world. See also the MID-WORLD entry (this section) and the END-WORLD entry (PORTALS section).

III:25, IV:149, IV:186, IV:268, IV:319, IV:373, IV:435, IV:439, IV:451, IV:550, IV:564, IV:638, IV:712, IV:739, IV:822

P

PASS O' THE RIVER (TOWN)
A Mid-World town whose bar, **FOREST TREES**, had a female bartender.

IV:480

PENNILTON
Mr Richard Stockworth (ALAIN's alias in HAMBRY) was supposed to come from this town.
    IV:185, IV:229, IV:253

PIANO RANCH
    See MEJIS, BARONY OF: HAMBRY

PORLA
The people of RIVER CROSSING believe that the civil wars of Mid-World began in either this land or in GARLAN.
    III:331

PORTALS
    See PORTALS section

PRICETOWN
Roland passes through Pricetown on his way to TULL. He buys a mule here.
    I:18, III:56

R

RADIUM MINES
    See ELURIA

RAILROAD (SUBWAY)
Jake and Roland meet SLOW MUTANTS here. *See* CYCLO-PEAN MOUNTAINS.

RILEA
See BLAINE'S ROUTE

RITZY
The down-and-out town of Ritzy is located four hundred miles west of MEJIS. It is a one-road mining village on the eastern slope of the VI CASTIS MOUNTAINS, fifty miles from the VI CASTIS CUT. Once there were freehold mines in the foothills, but they were regulated out by the VI CASTIS COMPANY.

> IV:333–41, IV:437, IV:438, IV:491, IV:508, IV:665, IV:688
> **BEAR AND TURTLE MERCANTILE AND SUNDRY ITEMS:** IV:333
> **HATTIGANS SALOON:** IV:334, IV:336–37, IV:338
> **SIX ROARING BARROOMS:** IV:333
> **TOWN GATHERING HALL:** IV:333
> **UNDERTAKERS:** IV:338
> **VI CASTIS STORE:** IV:333
> **VI CASTIS CUT:** (fifty miles from Ritzy) IV:333
> **VI CASTIS MINES:** IV:333–34
> **VI CASTIS MOUNTAINS:** IV:333, IV:665
> **VI CASTIS (TOWN):** FARSON will refine CITGO oil here.

RIVER BARONY
This is the Barony that contains JIMTOWN, RIVER CROSSING, and LUD. It takes its name from the RIVER SEND which flows through it.

> III:328, III:331

BARONY CASTLE AND VILLAGE: III:332
GREAT PLAINS OF RIVER BARONY: III:234, III:305
JIMTOWN: A village near River Crossing. III:312, III:328, III:427, III:479
**LUD: Lud was once the major city of River Barony. For many years after River Barony erupted in civil war, Lud held out against its besieging harriers. It remained the last fortress; a final refuge of the latter world.

For more than a hundred years, Lud has been torn apart by constant warfare. The major players in this ongoing battle are the PUBES, who are the descendants of the besieged artisans who stayed in Lud to defend their homes, and the GRAYS, who are the great-great grandchildren of the attacking harriers. By the time our *ka-tet* has the misfortune of traveling through Lud, all of the city's occupants are mad. The Pubes practice human sacrifice to appease the god-drums operated by the Grays (with the help of Lud's sadistic computer BLAINE) and the Grays have dwindled to a gang of murderous and disease-ridden lechers hiding like rats in mazes below the city.

Children, especially boys, are sought out in the decaying and decadent city of LUD. They can be trained as fighters and can be used for sexual gratification. In the new version of *The Gunslinger*, we learn that 2,000 years before our story, Lud resembled NEW YORK CITY.

I:90, III:225 *(indirect)*, III:236–37, III:238, III:303, III:304, III:305, III:306, III:309, III:312, III:325, III:326, III:327, III:328, III:330, III:332, III:333–36, III:338, III:351, III:361, III:367, III:370, III:371, III:376, III:386, III:387, III:388, III:392, III:393, III:394, III:397, III:401, III:408, III:413–62, III:566, III:568, IV:11 *(indirect)*, IV:19, IV:26, IV:29, IV:30,

IV:42, IV:70, IV:76, IV:81, IV:87, IV:88, IV:551, IV:807, IV:809, IV:813, IV:834

APPLE PARK: TICK-TOCK, leader of the GRAYS, remembers visiting this park on the west side of Lud when he was a child. His father took him there to see the ciderhouse and apple press. III:536–37

CITY NORTH: The PUBES occupy City North. It is here that they practice human sacrifice in response to the god-drums. III:444

CRADLE OF LUD/BLAINE'S CRADLE: The Cradle of Lud is a magnificent structure of blinding white stone. Despite the fact that its builders died off hundreds of generations before, the walls still clean themselves with endless streams of water. Marching around the Cradle's roof are the GUARDIANS OF THE BEAM, two by two. The roof's corners are guarded by dragons but on its peak, towering sixty feet above an already imposing edifice, is a golden statue of a gunslinger.

The Cradle of Lud – which was the GREAT OLD ONES' equivalent of Grand Central Station – is the home of BLAINE, the insane Mono. Praise the Imperium! III:417, III:445, III:447, III:448, III:449, III:454, III:457–62, III:471–84, III:500–6, III:516–18, III:530–35, III:545–55, IV:25, IV:82, IV:84, IV:93

GRAYS' CASTLE/GRAYS' MAZE/CRADLE OF THE GRAYS: This winding mess below the city looks more like a trash midden than the headquarters of the GRAYS. In order to build it they dragged old cars, old computers, and even sculptures and fountains from other parts of the city. This varied pile acts as a kind of barrier, but one full of tripwires and booby traps. Located in the eastern part of Lud, the Cradle of the Grays is - essentially the kingdom of the very nasty ANDREW QUICK, also known as TICK-TOCK. From here the Grays operate the god-drums whose frenzied beat drives the PUBES to sacrifice each other. III:416 *(maze)*, III:419–23, III:424, III:431–36, III:449–57, III:463–71, III:485–500, III:506–16, III:518–30, III:535–42 *(Tick-Tock and Fannin)*

GREAT ROAD TO LUD: *See entry under* GREAT ROAD

GREAT WALL OF LUD: III:561–62

HANGING FOUNTAIN: III:431, III:453, III:454, III:455

LUD BRIDGE: *See* SEND RIVER

PLAZA OF THE CRADLE: III:459, III:472, III:545

SEND BASIN NUCLEAR PLANT: Lud computers control this area as well. III:527

STREET OF THE TURTLE: *See also* GUARDIANS OF THE BEAM. III:427–30, III:436–49, III:459, III:472

RIVER CROSSING: River Crossing is the last outpost of civilization in River Barony. Its citizens are ancient but this does not stop them from trying to keep the old ways alive. Over the years they have had to keep their gardens, their well-tended homes, and their meeting places secret from the harriers who pass through, burning, killing, and blinding as they go. River Crossing is ruled by the matriarch AUNT TALITHA. The Old Folks of this town tell our *ka-tet* everything they know about the lay of the land, give them a wonderful meal, and then send them on their way toward LUD. Talitha gives Roland her silver cross and asks him to lay it at the foot of the TOWER. III:307–43, III:346, III:347, III:352, III:353, III:370, III:379, III:396, III:426,

III:427, III:428, III:455, III:533, IV:16, IV:24, IV:37, IV:64

    CHURCH OF THE BLOOD EVERLASTING: III:317–41

    LANDING, THE: III:328

    RIVER ROAD: III:312

TOM'S NECK: A town located near River Crossing. III:328

WEST RIVER BARONY: BLAINE (who is actually the computer-brain behind all of Lud's computers) controls this area. III:527

ROCKING B RANCH
    See MEJIS, BARONY OF: HAMBRY

ROCKING H RANCH
    See MEJIS, BARONY OF: HAMBRY

S

SANTA FE
    See MEJIS, BARONY OF

SEAFRONT
    See MEJIS, BARONY OF: HAMBRY

SEND BASIN NUCLEAR PLANT
    See RIVER BARONY: LUD

SEND RIVER

The Send River flows through RIVER BARONY. Roland's *ka-tet* travels along the Send River through much of *The Waste Lands* and then crosses it in order to enter LUD. (Below are some specific references.)

III:234–35, III:242, III:304 *(River comes closer to Road)*, III:327, III:330, III:351–53, III:388, III:389, III:392, III:397–412, III:430, III:564, IV:33, IV:38, IV:64

SEND RIVER BRIDGE (CROSSING TO LUD):
EDDIE and SUSANNAH think that the Send River Bridge resembles the GEORGE WASHINGTON BRIDGE in NEW YORK CITY. This bridge was made by LaMERK FOUNDRY. III:330, III:334, III:351–52, III:392, III:397–412, III:415, III:416–17, III:527, IV:33

SEVEN MILE ORCHARD
See MEJIS, BARONY OF: HAMBRY

SHARDIK'S LAIR
See BEAM PORTALS entry in the PORTALS section

SHAVÉD MOUNTAINS
The Shavéd Mountains are located northwest of GILEAD. FARSON intended to battle the AFFILIATION here.

IV:474, IV:542, IV:586

SHEB'S
See TULL

SPEAKING RINGS
See DOORWAYS BETWEEN WORLDS in the PORTALS section

SQUARE YARD
See NEW CANAAN, BARONY OF: GILEAD

STONE CIRCLES
See DOORWAYS BETWEEN WORLDS in the PORTALS section

T

**TAUNTON
In the new version of *The Gunslinger*, it is the people of Taunton, and not the people of FARSON, that HAX and THE GOOD MAN's followers try to poison.
I:110, I:113, I:117

**TAUNTON ROAD
In the new version of *The Gunslinger*, GALLOWS HILL is located on the Taunton Road. Taunton Road replaces the FARSON ROAD.
I:115

TAVARES
Tavares is a town located up the coast from HAMBRY. One of its bars (**GLENCOVE**) had a female bartender who eventually died of the pox.
IV:480

TEJUAS
Tejuas is an unincorporated township located two hundred

miles west of ELURIA. The NORMAN brothers were headed here when their caravan was attacked by the GREEN FOLK.

E:194, E:213

TEPACHI, BARONY OF

People from Tepachi have an accent similar to the people in the nearby Barony of MEJIS.

IV:338

TERRITORIES

The Territories are mentioned by Calvin Tower in *The Waste Lands* as he sells Jake *Charlie the Choo-Choo* and *Riddle-De-Dum!* 'Consider it my gift to a boy wise enough to saddle up and light out for the territories on the last real day of spring.' The Territories, which are a parallel world to our earth, are found in *The Talisman* (King/Straub). Every human being in our world has a 'twinner' in the territories.

III:160

THINNY/THINNIES

See THINNY/THINNIES in the PORTALS section

THOUGHTFUL HOUSE

See ELURIA

THUNDERCLAP

See THUNDERCLAP in the PORTALS section

TOM'S NECK

See RIVER BARONY

TOPEKA
See KANSAS: TOPEKA in the PORTALS section

TOWER
See DARK TOWER in the PORTALS section

TOWN GATHERING HALL
See MEJIS, BARONY OF: HAMBRY

TRAVELLERS' REST
See MEJIS, BARONY OF: HAMBRY

**TULL
The sand-colored, pitted buildings of TULL are located south of PRICETOWN and just north of the MOHAINE DESERT. The town consists of four roads – the COACH ROAD and the three that cross it. Since it is located on the line of the Coach Road, we can assume that Tull was once more prosperous. Now it consists of a boarded-up grocery, a livery, a tailor, a church, a barber, a dry goods emporium, and a bar called SHEB'S.

Like so many of Mid-World's towns, Tull – located on the floor of a circular, bowl-shaped hollow – is reminiscent of the Old West. It is in Tull that Roland meets his lover ALICE. It is also where he meets the formidable (and dangerously crazy) SYLVIA PITTSTON. Thanks to Pittston's treachery, Roland ends up killing everyone in the town, including Allie. In the new version of *The Gunslinger*, we find out that there's an old train yard near Tull.

I:13, I:15–16, I:17, I:18–69, I:82, I:84, I:97, I:129, I:136, I:144, I:157, I:170, II:36, II:138, II:161, III:56, III:60, IV:89, IV:791

SHEB'S: Sheb's is Tull's single honky-tonk. Despite its name it actually belongs to ALICE. Within its batwing doors it has a sawdust floor, spittoons, and tipsy-legged tables. The bar is a plank resting on sawhorses. At the back people play interminable games of Watch-Me while SHEB bangs away on his piano.

I:21, I:22–43, I:47–50, I:56–57, I:62–63 *(tonk)*, I:65, I:68, II:138, III:57

TURTLE, STREET OF
   See RIVER BARONY: LUD

V

VI CASTIS CUT
   See RITZY

VI CASTIS MOUNTAINS
   See RITZY

W

WASTE LANDS
   See WASTE LANDS in the PORTALS section and MEJIS, BARONY OF in this section

**WAY STATION

The Way Station, where Roland finds JAKE, was once a stop-ping point for the Coach lines that ran across the MOHAINE DESERT. By the time our story takes place it has been deserted for years. The station consists of two buildings (a stable and an inn) surrounded by a fallen rail fence whose wood is so fragile that it is rapidly thinning into desert sand. Luckily for both Jake and Roland, the station's water pump still works. (In the new version of *The Gunslinger* we find out that this pump was made by NORTH CENTRAL POSITRONICS.) In the building's cellar, Roland faces down the SPEAKING DEMON.

I:73, I:77–100, I:101, I:133, I:169, II:359, III:57, III:58, III:59, III:64, III:81, III:82, III:84, III:126, III:134, III:147, III:148, III:150, III:177, III:183, III:223, III:294, IV:133

WEST RIVER BARONY
See RIVER BARONY

WEST TOWN
See NEW CANAAN, BARONY OF: GILEAD

WEST WOODS
See GREAT WEST WOODS

**WESTERN SEA

Throughout *The Gunslinger*, Roland pursues the MAN IN BLACK south and then southwest through the MOHAINE DESERT and the CYCLOPEAN MOUNTAINS (in the new *Gunslinger*, he follows his enemy southeast). At the end of his journey he finds himself at the GOLGOTHA, just three miles from the Western Sea which is the setting for the next book in the series. The Western Sea is a terrible, barren place. Its waters are the color of dirty undergarments and its yellow, gross-grained beaches are littered with no-color shells and rocky protrusions. The tide line crawls with man-eating LOBSTROSITIES and its horizons seem endless and hopeless. The sea's LOBSTROSITY BEACH is a terrible place, but it is through the magical BEACH DOORS, found here, that Roland draws EDDIE DEAN and SUSANNAH DEAN into his world. In the new version of *The Gunslinger*, we find out that the Western Sea is the edge of the world.

I:45–46, I:233, I:236, I:237–38, II:7–13, II:18–30, II:41 *(shore)*, II:53–54, II:63–64, II:74–77, II:80–81, II:83–86, II:99–102 *(and door behind Eddie)*, II:107–14, II:150–59, II:174–75, II:179–203, II:225–35, II:253–351, II:369–82, II:406–7, II:421, II:440–44, II:447–48, III:14, III:63, III:102, III:358, III:564, IV:51, IV:83 *(beach)*, IV:116 *(beach)*, IV:120

LOBSTROSITY BEACH: II:7–13, II:18–30, II:41 *(shore)*, II:52, II:53–54, II:63–64, II:74–77, II:80–81, II:83–86, II:99–102 *(and the door behind Eddie)*, II:107–14, II:150–59, II:172, II:174–75, II:179–203, II:225–35, II:253–351, II:369–82, II:406–7, II:421, II:440–44, II:447–48, III:16, III:23, III:55, III:56, III:206, IV:83, IV:116

**WEST'RD HALL
See NEW CANAAN, BARONY OF: GILEAD: GREAT HALL

WILLOW GROVE
See MEJIS, BARONY OF: HAMBRY

WILLOW JUNGLE

This wild jungle is located in the foothills of the CYCLO-PEAN MOUNTAINS. (It is sometimes also called the WILLOW GROVE, although the main Willow Grove is in HAMBRY.) After the dry hardpan of the desert, the Willow Jungle's wet lushness is a relief. However, this dangerous jungle is the home of vampiric SUCKERBATS and the demonic ORACLE OF THE MOUNTAINS who tries to destroy first JAKE, and then ROLAND, with its sexual *glammer*.

I:127 (*groves*), I:128, I:129, I:131–46, I:147, III:238

WIND

Wind is a town even less ritzy than RITZY. It is located fifty miles from RITZY and the VI CASTIS MOUNTAINS.

IV:334

OUR WORLD PLACES

Go then. There are other worlds than these.
Jake Chambers
I:210

A

ALABAMA
   MONTGOMERY: II:222, II:223
     WOOLWORTHS: II:223

ALASKA
   II:451
   ACHIN' ASSHOLE: Believe it or not, Eddie Dean made this place up. II:451

AMHIGH
   See DRAWERS in the PORTALS section

APPALACHIAN TRAIL
The Appalachian Trail is a continuous footpath that runs from Mount Katahdin in central Maine to Springer Mountain in Georgia, a distance of approximately 2,160 miles. EDDIE DEAN imagines that the trail is overrun by bomber-joint-smoking hippies carrying packsacks like Roland's.
   II:80

AQUINAS HOTEL
   See BAHAMAS

ARIZONA
   BLACKFORK: III:159

ARKANSAS
II:223

ODETTA: Odetta Holmes' mother, ALICE HOLMES, was born here. Hence Odetta (later called SUSANNAH DEAN) was christened with this name. II:223

ATCHISON

See KANSAS. *See also* ATCHISON, TOPEKA AND SANTA FE RAILROAD (below), and KANSAS in the PORTALS section.

ATCHISON, TOPEKA AND SANTA FE RAILROAD

The Atchison, Topeka and Santa Fe Railroad Company (originally called the Atchison and Topeka Railroad Company) was founded in 1859 by Colonel Cyrus K. Holliday of KANSAS, one of the founders of the town of TOPEKA. The railroad changed its name in 1863 because of its planned expansion. By 1887 the railroad extended all the way to Los Angeles. Known as 'The Atchison' in the East and as 'The Santa Fe' in the West, it was one of the major railroads serving the Southwest United States.

Our *ka-tet* stumbles across a sign for the Atchison, Topeka and Santa Fe at BLAINE's terminating point in an alternative Kansas. Roland assumes — quite rightly — that the three names designate three towns. However, because he does not know the history of railroads in our *where* (or in this Topeka's alternative *when*) he does not understand the full significance of these towns or of the towns he sees listed on the departures board, namely DENVER, WICHITA and OMAHA.

All of the listed towns were linked — directly or indirectly — by the AT & SF. Obviously, Atchison, Topeka and Santa Fe were part of the service's main run. Denver was also served by the Atchison line, and Wichita could be reached by one of the railroad's branch lines. Although Omaha was actually accessible by the Union Pacific Railroad, the Union Pacific and the Atchison, Topeka and Santa Fe were linked in 1881, completing the second transcontinental railroad.

Hence, what we learn from Roland's sojourn in the alternative Topeka is that not only do the GREAT ROADS of Mid-World follow the BEAM but so do the great railroads. Also, it seems that these railroads can be used to cross not only continents, but to jump from one level of the TOWER to another. Blaine and his fellow locomotives and slo-trans engines are portals every bit as much as the other doorways in and out of Mid-World. The GREAT OLD ONES, aided by the technology of their sinister company NORTH CENTRAL POSITRONICS, learned how to bridge the time/space continuum.

IV:84

ATTICA STATE PRISON
See NEW YORK (STATE)

B

BAHAMAS
EDDIE DEAN's little trip to the Bahamas almost ends in disaster and incarceration. Although he's dressed like a college kid, Eddie flies to Nassau so that he can smuggle packages of cocaine for the drug king ENRICO BALAZAR. At this point in our story (namely at the beginning of *The Drawing of*

the Three), Eddie is a heroin addict under the thumb of his older brother, the great sage and eminent junkie HENRY DEAN. Roland saves Eddie's bacon three times: first by helping him evade the CUSTOMS police, second by coming to his aid against Balazar and his thugs, and finally by spiriting Eddie off to LOBSTROSITY BEACH. There, on the shore of the WESTERN SEA, Eddie comes down off of the Horse only to become addicted to Odetta Holmes (aka Detta Walker/ SUSANNAH DEAN) and another potent drug – Love.

II:38, II:44–49 *(setting)*, II:57–58, II:92, II:94

NASSAU: Eddie goes to Nassau to pick up Balazar's cocaine. While there he stays at the **AQUINAS HOTEL.** II:44–49, II:57–58, II:93 *(hotel)*, III:479

BEAMS
See BEAMS in the PORTALS section

BEIRUT
See LEBANON

BERMUDA TRIANGLE
See PORTALS section

BOGOTÁ
See COLOMBIA

BONDED ELECTROPLATE FACTORY
See NEW YORK (CITY OF): BROOKLYN

BOSTON
See MASSACHUSETTS

BRENDIO'S (SHOP)
   See NEW YORK (CITY OF): MANHATTAN

C

CALIFORNIA
   III:200, III:391, IV:91, IV:92
   DISNEYLAND: II:189
   LOS ANGELES: III:553, IV:92
   MID-WORLD AMUSEMENT PARK: *See* MID-WORLD AMUSEMENT PARK in the PORTALS section.
   SAN FRANCISCO
      GOLDEN GATE BRIDGE: IV:93
   SAN SIMEON: IV:94
   SILICON VALLEY: II:137

CANADA
   MONTREAL: One of the little old ladies on EDDIE's disastrous Delta flight from NASSAU to NEW YORK was headed to Montreal. II:81

CAPE CANAVERAL
   See FLORIDA

CASTLE AVENUE
   See NEW YORK (CITY OF): BROOKLYN

CHEW CHEW MAMA'S (RESTAURANT)
See NEW YORK (CITY OF): MANHATTAN

CHINA
III:395

CHRISTOPHER STREET STATION
See NEW YORK (CITY OF): MANHATTAN

CLEMENTS GUNS AND SPORTING GOODS
See NEW YORK (CITY OF): MANHATTAN

COHOES STREET
See NEW YORK (CITY OF): BROOKLYN

COLOMBIA
BOGOTÁ: II:58

COLORADO
IV:39
DENVER: One of the towns that could be reached by the
ATCHISON, TOPEKA AND SANTA FE RAILROAD.
See that entry. IV:89

CONEY ISLAND
See NEW YORK (CITY OF): BROOKLYN

CONNECTICUT
II:127
HARTFORD: IV:44
MYSTIC: III:42
NEW HAVEN: IV:44

SEDONVILLE: Somewhere in this town, buried under a chicken house, is an Irishman shot dead for blowing down one of BALAZAR's card houses. II:127

CO-OP CITY
See NEW YORK (CITY OF): BROOKLYN and NEW YORK (CITY OF): BRONX

CUBA
JANE DORNING – one of the stewardesses on EDDIE's Delta flight from NASSAU to JFK – harbors a fear of being hijacked by Cubans.
   II:51

CUSTOMS, NEW YORK
See NEW YORK (CITY OF): QUEENS

D

DAHLIE'S (DAHLBERG'S)
See NEW YORK (CITY OF): BROOKLYN

DENBY'S DISCOUNT DRUGS
See NEW YORK (CITY OF): MANHATTAN: TIMES SQUARE

DENVER
See COLORADO. *See also* ATCHISON, TOPEKA AND SANTA FE RAILROAD.

DETTA'S SEX HAUNTS
See DRAWERS in the PORTALS section

DISNEYLAND
See CALIFORNIA

DISNEYWORLD
See FLORIDA

DODGE
See KANSAS

DOORS: NEW YORK TO MID-WORLD
See DOORWAYS BETWEEN WORLDS in the PORTALS section

DRAWERS
See DRAWERS in the PORTALS section

DUTCH HILL
See NEW YORK (CITY OF): BROOKLYN

DUTCH HILL MANSION
See DOORWAYS BETWEEN WORLDS in the PORTALS section

DUTCH HILL PUB
See NEW YORK (CITY OF): BROOKLYN

DUTCH HILL USED APPLIANCES
See NEW YORK (CITY OF): BROOKLYN

E

EASTER ISLAND
 III:31

ECUADOR
 IV:107

**ENGLAND
Walter claims that he lived in England hundreds (and perhaps a thousand) years before the GREAT OLD ONES crossed the ocean to the land Roland now inhabits. In the new version of *The Gunslinger*, the direct reference to England is cut.
 LONDON: III:133, IV:41
 NORFOLK FENS: IV:118

F

FIFTH AVENUE & 43RD STREET
 See NEW YORK (CITY OF): MANHATTAN

FLORIDA
 BUSCH GARDENS: River Crossing's garden (located behind THE CHURCH OF THE BLOOD EVER-LASTING) reminds EDDIE of Busch Gardens. III:318
 CAPE CANAVERAL: When Susannah sees the missiles

lining the GREAT ROAD leading to LUD, she thinks about
the Redstones fired from Cape Canaveral. III:395
DISNEY WORLD: II:378, III:100, III:125
FLORIDA KEYS: II:255

FOUR FATHERS RESTAURANT
See NEW YORK (CITY OF): BROOKLYN: GINELLI'S
PIZZA

G

GEORGIA
II:221

GINELLI'S PIZZA (FOUR FATHERS RESTAURANT)
See NEW YORK (CITY OF): BROOKLYN

GRAND CANYON
IV:119

GREAT PLAINS
III:236, III:533 *(empty lands)*

GREAT SMOKIES
SUSANNAH DEAN/Odetta Holmes' AUNT BLUE had
her honeymoon in these mountains.
II:266

GREYMARL APARTMENTS
See NEW YORK (CITY OF): MANHATTAN

GUYANA
The Reverend Jim Jones had his flock commit mass suicide here.
III:525

H

HAITI
II:58, II:208

HENRY'S CORNER MARKET
See NEW YORK (CITY OF): BROOKLYN: DUTCH HILL

I

INDIANA
TERRE HAUTE: IV:94

IOWA
DESMOINES: IV:100
SIOUX CITY: IV:100

IRELAND
II:421

ITALY
II:146
PISA (LEANING TOWER OF): *See* LEANING
TOWER OF PISA, listed separately.
SICILY: II:124

K

KANSAS
See also KANSAS in the PORTALS section, WIZARD OF
OZ in the CHARACTERS section, BLAINE in the CHAR-
ACTERS section, and ATCHISON, TOPEKA AND
SANTA FE RAILROAD in this section.
II:257, III:192, III:353, III:395, IV:77–78
ATCHISON: Atchison is a town in Kansas famous for
being the birthplace of both Amelia Earhart and the
ATCHISON, TOPEKA AND SANTA FE RAILROAD.
IV:84
DODGE: In the late nineteenth and early twentieth
centuries, Dodge had a reputation as a rowdy frontier town.
III:354, III:518
TOPEKA: In the children's story *Charlie the Choo-Choo*,
Topeka is the MID-WORLD RAILWAY's final destin-
ation. It also happens to be BLAINE's destination. In *Wizard
and Glass*, our *ka-tet* spends a lot of time in an alternative
version of Topeka. (*See entry under* ATCHISON, TOPEKA

AND SANTA FE RAILROAD. *See also* KANSAS in the PORTALS section and BLAINE in the CHARACTERS section.) III:192, III:198, III:199, III:210, III:366

WICHITA: A town in Kansas accessed by a branch line of the ATCHISON, TOPEKA AND SANTA FE RAIL-ROAD. Roland sees a sign for it in the alternative TOPEKA. IV:89

WIZARD OF OZ: KANSAS: *See* KANSAS in the PORTALS section

KATZ PHARMACY AND SODA FOUNTAIN (SUNDRIES AND NOTIONS FOR MISSES AND MISTERS)
See NEW YORK (CITY OF): MANHATTAN

L

LEANING TOWER
See NEW YORK (CITY OF): MANHATTAN. *See also* DARK TOWER in the PORTALS section

LEANING TOWER OF PISA
The Leaning Tower of Pisa, whose official name is Torre Pendente di Pisa, is an Italian Bell Tower which was built between AD1173 and 1350. As can be deduced from its name, it lists to one side, a problem that architects through the ages have not been able to rectify.

The Dark Tower series refers to this famous tower in two different contexts. First, in *The Drawing of the Three*, we learn that the neon sign marking BALAZAR's bar and headquarters is in the shape of this historic monument. Much to EDDIE DEAN's alarm, the first time Roland sees this sign he thinks he has arrived at his destination – the DARK TOWER itself.

The next time we see the Leaning Tower it takes the form of a photograph (or as Roland would say, a *fottergraf*) pasted to the last page of JAKE CHAMBERS' English Comp essay entitled 'My Understanding of Truth.' Jake was so dazed and distressed when he wrote the essay that he no longer remembers either writing it or covering his Tower with black crayon scribbles.

II:132, III:136–37

LEBANON
  BEIRUT: II:87, IV:108

LOT, THE
  See LOT, THE in the PORTALS section

MACY'S
  See NEW YORK (CITY OF): MANHATTAN

MAGIC SHOP
  See NEW YORK (CITY OF): MANHATTAN

MAINE
 PORTLAND HEADLIGHT: IV:119

MAJESTIC THEATER
 See NEW YORK (CITY OF): BROOKLYN

MANHATTAN RESTAURANT OF THE MIND
 See NEW YORK (CITY OF): MANHATTAN

MANSION, THE
 See DOORWAYS BETWEEN WORLDS in the POR-TALS section

MARKEY ACADEMY
 See NEW YORK (CITY OF): BROOKLYN: MARKEY AVENUE

MARKEY AVENUE
 See NEW YORK (CITY OF): BROOKLYN

MASSACHUSETTS
 IV:92
 BOSTON: II:393, IV:44, IV:92
 MUSEUM OF SCIENCE: IV:393

METROPOLITAN MUSEUM OF ART
 See NEW YORK (CITY OF): MANHATTAN

MICHIGAN
 II:188

MID-TOWN LANES
  See NEW YORK (CITY OF): MANHATTAN

MINNESOTA
MINNEAPOLIS: IV:94

MISSISSIPPI
  II:211, II:262, III:300, IV:83
  OXFORD TOWN: Oxford Town was made famous (or infamous) by the Bob Dylan song of that name and by the events upon which the song was based. In 1962 there were riots on the University of Mississippi campus based on the University's forced acceptance of its first black student, James Meredith. Meredith, whose acceptance at the University had been rescinded once it was discovered that he was dark-skinned, had fought for reacceptance for over a year before the Fifth U.S. Circuit Court of Appeals ruled that the state could not deny him admission based on color. Meredith was escorted to campus by Federal Marshals but the city of Oxford erupted in violence. Before the National Guard could arrive, two students had been killed.

  SUSANNAH DEAN's three day incarceration in a Mississippi jail (which she refers to as a short season in hell) came about because of her participation in the non-violent Civil Rights Movement. Like Meredith's antagonists, Susannah's captors were racists abusing their legal power. II:210–12, II:216, II:259, II:262, II:266, II:268, II:272, II:273, II:274, III:18

MISSOURI
In the children's story *Charlie the Choo-Choo*, the talking train

CHARLIE travels through the state of Missouri, tooting his horn.
  III:351
  MISSOURI PLAINS (THE BIG EMPTY): III:193, III:349
  ST LOUIS: III:192, III:196, III:198, III:200, III:210, III:349, III:351, III:366, IV:113

MONTGOMERY
  See ALABAMA

MONTREAL
  See CANADA

N

NASSAU
  See BAHAMAS

NEBRASKA
See also NEBRASKA listed in the PORTALS section.
  IV:786
  BUTTFUCK: Believe it or not, this place doesn't really exist. EDDIE DEAN just pretends it does. III:458
  OMAHA: A town in Nebraska served by the Union Pacific Railroad. Union Pacific was joined with the ATCHISON, TOPEKA AND SANTA FE in 1881, creating the second transcontinental railroad. *See* ATCHISON, TOPEKA AND SANTA FE RAILROAD. IV:89, IV:106

NETWORK
See NEW YORK (CITY OF): MANHATTAN

NEVADA
Beneath the mountains of this state there are concrete bunkers containing intercontinental ballistic missiles.
III:395
LAS VEGAS: IV:786
RENO: III:330

NEW JERSEY
II:125, II:264–67 *(Aunt Blue's wedding)*, II:360–64, III:75, III:365
ATLANTIC CITY: II:145, III:437
ELIZABETH: When Odetta Holmes (later SUSANNAH DEAN) was a child, her AUNT BLUE got married in Elizabeth, New Jersey. Five-year-old Odetta went to the wedding with her parents, but on her way back to the train station JACK MORT (who was hiding in an abandoned building at the time) dropped a brick on her head. Odetta went into a coma for three weeks and her second personality – that of the venomous Detta Walker – was born. II:264–67, II:360–64, III:365
MEADOWLANDS: Eddie once saw a concert here. III:75
NEW JERSEY TURNPIKE: I:198

NEW MEXICO
SANTA FE: Santa Fe was one of the stops on the ATCHISON, TOPEKA AND SANTA FE RAILROAD. It is also the name of a town in Roland's world. See ATCHISON, TOPEKA AND SANTA FE RAILROAD. See also MEJIS, BARONY OF: SANTA FE in the MID-

WORLD PLACES section and SANTA FE in the PORTALS section.

NEW YORK (STATE)
ATTICA STATE PRISON: II:422
NEW YORK CITY: *See entry listed as* NEW YORK (CITY OF), below
TACONIC PARKWAY: IV:112
UTICA: In the children's story *Charlie the Choo-Choo*, Charlie's replacement, a Burlington Zephyr, was built in Utica. III:195

NEW YORK (CITY OF)
New York City is the original home of the three human members of Roland's *ka-tet*: JAKE CHAMBERS, SUSANNAH DEAN, and EDDIE DEAN. (OY, Jake's pet BILLY BUMBLER, is from Mid-World.) The Portal of the TURTLE and the Portal of the BEAR connect Mid-World to this city of Our World.

Throughout the series we are told that the urban ruins of Mid-World bear a strong resemblance to the thriving metropolises of Our World. In *The Gunslinger*, the subway system beneath the CYCLOPEAN MOUNTAINS reminds Jake of New York's subways. Later, in LUD, the bridges and buildings of that war-torn city make our *ka-tet* think of Manhattan. It seems quite probable that Roland's world is actually one of Our World's many potential futures, but it is a future where nuclear disaster has already taken place. The first time Roland hears Jake talk about the skyline of this city he thinks it is like a myth out of prehistory. BLAINE the insane Mono knows New York City well. He calls it the Barony of New York.

I:135, II:97–102, II:105–33, II:135–75, II:191–96, II:207–27, II:237–51, II:259, II:267–68, II:356–68,

II:383–406, II:409–19, II:421–39, III:57, III:61,
III:69–71, III:84, III:99, III:123–202, III:194, III:201,
III:209–18, III:225, III:227–34, III:235, III:250–59,
III:263–65, III:267–70, III:273–77, III:279–84, III:285,
III:287–88, III:299, III:304, III:307, III:359, III:361,
III:387, III:465, III:482, III:492, III:500, III:503, III:507,
III:521, III:553, III:554, III:558, III:560, III:579, III:582,
IV:7, IV:11, IV:20, IV:23, IV:24, IV:27, IV:28, IV:37,
IV:44, IV:55, IV:56, IV:57, IV:58, IV:59, IV:62, IV:63,
IV:78, IV:93, IV:95, IV:105, IV:112, IV:777, IV:790,
IV:796, IV:810, IV:821

BRONX: II:119

    CO-OP CITY: In our *where* and *when*, Co-Op City is an
ethnically diverse housing co-operative located in the
northeasternmost corner of the Bronx. In Eddie's version
of New York, Co-Op City is located in BROOKLYN.
(On II:119 it is said to be in the Bronx.)

BROOKLYN: For many years EDDIE DEAN lived in Co-
Op City, which – in his version of New York – is located
in Brooklyn. As he points out to Jake when the two of
them meet in a dream version of New York, Brooklyn also
contains his world's version of the PORTAL OF THE
BEAR. II:102–7, II:114–23, II:192, III:28–30, III:210–13
(*setting*), III:227, III:231, III:233–34, III:243–45,
III:250–59, III:262–65, III:267–70, III:273–77,
III:279–84, III:285, III:287–88, III:364

    BROOKLYN AVENUE: III:233, III:250, III:262
    BROOKLYN VOCATIONAL INSTITUTE: III:246
CASTLE AVENUE: JAKE travels along Castle Avenue
while looking for MARKEY AVENUE. He thinks that
his doorway into Mid-World will be there. It's not, but
it does lead him to the MAJESTIC THEATER and a

thirteen-year-old EDDIE DEAN. III:233, III:243, III:245

COHOES STREET: Home of the Bonded Electroplate Factory. II:191

  BONDED ELECTROPLATE FACTORY: EDDIE and HENRY DEAN smoked here. II:191

CONEY ISLAND: II:127 *(mirror maze)*, II:189, III:484, III:517

CO-OP CITY: In EDDIE DEAN'S version of New York, Co-Op City is located in Brooklyn rather than the BRONX. (This is one of the many time/space variations found on different levels of the TOWER.) Eddie and his brother, HENRY, lived in this big Co-operative located between CASTLE and BROOKLYN AVENUES. II:102, II:119 *(Bronx)*, II:271, III:212, III:233–34

DAHLIE'S: This was one of HENRY DEAN's hangouts. Dahlie's (also called **DAHLBERG'S**) sold Hoodsie Rockets and popsicles. III:104, III:257, IV:52, IV:66, IV:75

DUTCH HILL: JAKE's search for a doorway into Mid-World leads him to Dutch Hill and its terrible haunted MANSION. When Jake enters the Mansion he is attacked by the MANSION DEMON. III:104, III:222, III:223, III:261, III:263–65, III:267–70, III:273–77, III:279–84, III:287–88, III:360, III:476

  DUTCH HILL LITTLE LEAGUE FIELD: III:281
  DUTCH HILL PUB: III:282
  DUTCH HILL USED APPLIANCES: III:264
  HENRY'S CORNER MARKET: III:282
  RHINEHOLD STREET: The terrible haunted MANSION (which JAKE enters in order to find his

doorway into Mid-World) is located on this street.
III:104, III:261, III:262, III:264, III:265, III:476

> **DUTCH HILL MANSION, THE:** *See* DOOR-
> WAYS BETWEEN WORLDS located in the
> PORTALS section.

**GINELLI'S PIZZA (FOUR FATHERS RESTAU-
RANT):** Ginelli's is a front for BALAZAR's illegal
empire. II:98

MARKEY AVENUE: On his travels through Brooklyn,
JAKE travels along Markey Avenue. III:245, III:250,
III:251

> **MAJESTIC THEATER:** The Majestic Movie
> Theater is located on the corner of Markey and
> BROOKLYN AVENUES. EDDIE DEAN used to
> watch Westerns here. His brother, HENRY, liked to
> tease the ticket girl. III:245, III:250–53

> **MARKEY ACADEMY:** This place doesn't actually
> exist. III:229, III:244

> **MARKEY AVENUE PLAYGROUND:** EDDIE and
> HENRY used to play basketball here. It has since
> been replaced by the JUVENILE COURT BUILD-
> ING. III:29, III:222, III:227, III:255–59

> **JUVENILE COURT BUILDING:** III:222

NORWOOD STREET: Some kids from this street
were mysteriously killed at the DUTCH HILL
MANSION. III:258

PROJECTS: EDDIE, HENRY and their mom lived
in the projects when Eddie and Henry were young.
II:70

RINCON AVENUE: Once upon a time there was a
candy store on Rincon Avenue. EDDIE and HENRY
DEAN filched comic books from it. II:191

EAST RIVER: III:140

    EAST RIVER DRIVE: III:414

LONG ISLAND: II:65

    LONG ISLAND SOUND: EDDIE DEAN's plane from the BAHAMAS flies over Long Island Sound before landing at JFK AIRPORT. II:58

MANHATTAN: *(directly named)* II:389, III:29, III:168, III:478

    BELLEVUE: II:196

    BLOOMINGDALE'S: III:61, III:142, III:147

    BLEEKER STREET: III:163

    BRENDIO'S: JAKE passes Brendio's on his way to school. Some of the manikins in the window are dressed in Edwardian clothes. Others are 'barenaked.' I:88, III:141

    CENTRAL PARK: II:209, II:211, II:224, II:267, IV:78–79, IV:82, IV:785

    CHEW CHEW MAMA'S (RESTAURANT): See SECOND AVENUE (below)

    CHRISTOPHER STREET STATION: In SUSANNAH DEAN's version of New York (yet another level of the DARK TOWER) the fabled A train stops at Christopher Street Station. Unfortunately, Odetta Holmes/ Detta Walker happened to be waiting at this stop at the same time as the evil JACK MORT. Mort pushed her in front of the train. Luckily Susannah (and her many selves) survived; however, her legs (or what was left of them) had to be amputated just above the knee. II:241–43, II:431, II:432–39

    CHRYSLER BUILDING: IV:131

    CLEMENTS GUNS AND SPORTING GOODS: This shop is located on Seventh Avenue and Forty-ninth

Street. While occupying JACK MORT's body, Roland visits Clements so that he can restock his dwindling supply of live rounds. Besides buying ammo, Roland causes general havoc. II:387–406, II:421–23, IV:116

DENBY'S DISCOUNT DRUGS: *See* TIMES SQUARE, listed below.

DUNHILL'S: This shop sells expensive lighters. II:435

EMPIRE STATE BUILDING: III:484

FIFTH AVENUE AND FORTY-THIRD STREET / THE PUSHING PLACE: On one level of the TOWER, JAKE is killed here by a 1976 Sedan de Ville. Because of this, JACK MORT (who pushed Jake in front of oncoming traffic) dubbed it 'The Pushing Place.' I:88–89, II:355–60, III:142–46

FIRST AVENUE POLICE SHOOTING RANGE: III:216

FOUR SEASONS RESTAURANT: II:214

GEORGE WASHINGTON BRIDGE: The SEND BRIDGE, located just outside of LUD, resembles the George Washington Bridge. III:351, III:401

GIMBEL'S: II:214, III:61

GRACE METHODIST CHURCH: The REVEREND MURDOCH preached here. SUSANNAH'S father didn't agree with his sermons. III:429

GRAND CENTRAL STATION: III:458

GREENWICH VILLAGE: II:212, II:223, II:237, II:430, III:168, III:484

   TOMPKINS SQUARE: IV:778

GREYMARL APARTMENTS: The Greymarl Apartments are a Victorian block of flats located on Fifth Avenue and Central Park South. Odetta Holmes (one of SUSANNAH DEAN's earlier selves) lived in the penthouse apartment. II:209, II:211, II:224

HUNGRY I: Odetta Holmes (later SUSANNAH DEAN) really liked this coffee house. II:245

JAKE CHAMBERS' APARTMENT: The Chambers' Family apartment is located on Fifth Avenue, three and a half blocks further up than the PUSHING PLACE. Hence it is probably on Fifth and Forty-sixth or Fifth and Forty-seventh. III:141, III:148–50, III:178–202, III:213–18, III:227

KATZ PHARMACY AND SODA FOUNTAIN (SUNDRIES AND NOTIONS FOR MISSES AND MISTERS): Katz Pharmacy is located at 395 West Forty-ninth Street, and has been at that address since 1927. (It was founded by the present owner's father.) While searching for Keflex, Roland causes complete havoc here. As KATZ says, Roland commits the first penicillin hold-up in history. II:409–19, II:425–29

LEANING TOWER: The Leaning Tower is a Mid-Town saloon. It is also BALAZAR's place of business. The first time Roland sees its neon sign he is convinced that he has reached the DARK TOWER. II:123–49, II:157–75, III:93, III:248, III:359

LOT, THE: *See* PORTALS section

MACY'S: II:107, II:220, II:226–27, II:248–51, III:61

MAGIC SHOP: *See* SECOND AVENUE (below)

MANHATTAN RESTAURANT OF THE MIND: *See* SECOND AVENUE (below)

METROPOLITAN MUSEUM OF ART: The Met appears to exist in all the New Yorks on all levels of the TOWER. It is located on Fifth Avenue. III:228–30

**MID-TOWN LANES: JAKE bowls here. This bowling alley is mentioned in the new version of *The*

Gunslinger. I:87, I:88, III:147–48, III:231

MISS SO PRETTY (SHOP): III:228

MORT'S HOME: 409 Park Avenue South. II:395

MORT'S OFFICE: Mort's accountancy firm is located on Sixth Avenue, also known as the Avenue of the Americas. II:366–68

NETWORK, THE: JAKE'S father, ELMER CHAMBERS, is a high powered executive at this TV network, where he is an acknowledged master of 'The Kill.' The Network offices are located at 70 Rockefeller Plaza. I:87, I:88, I:173, III:124–25, III:141, IV:39, IV:824

NEW YORK HARBOR: III:124

NEW YORK UNIVERSITY: II:124, II:193

PAUL STUART (SHOP): III:228

PIPER SCHOOL: *See* PIPER SCHOOL, listed separately.

PORT AUTHORITY: II:38

PUSHING PLACE: *See* FIFTH AVENUE AND FORTY-THIRD STREET

RADIO CITY: III:168, III:484

REFLECTIONS OF YOU: *See* SECOND AVENUE (below)

REGENCY TOWER: II:37

SAINT ANTHONY'S: II:406

SAINT PATRICK'S CATHEDRAL: IV:798

SAKS: II:214

SECOND AVENUE: III:69–71, III:107, III:155–78

    CHEW CHEW MAMA'S: Chew Chew's can be found at Second Avenue and Fifty-second Street. Both EDDIE and JAKE see BALAZAR here, dressed as a bum. The restaurant's name is especially sinister because (as Jake points out) it is reminiscent of

CHOO-CHOO and **CHARLIE**, the nasty train. III:165

LOT, THE: *See* PORTALS section

MAGIC SHOP: This magic shop actually only exists in EDDIE DEAN's dream version of New York. He imagines it sits on Second Avenue and Fifty-Second Street, the location of CHEW CHEW MAMA'S. In Eddie's sleep vision, ENRICO BALAZAR sits in front of the store dressed as a bum. In the window is a sign that reads **HOUSE OF CARDS**. Quite appropriately, the window display is of a tower built of Tarot cards. III:70

MANHATTAN RESTAURANT OF THE MIND: This bookstore is located on Second Avenue and Fifty-fourth Street. It is run by CALVIN TOWER, probably with a little help from his sidekick, AARON DEEPNEAU. These two characters are mysteriously connected to both the Territories of *The Talisman* and Roland's world. It's here that JAKE buys both *Charlie the Choo-Choo* and *Riddle-De-Dum! Brain Twisters and Puzzles for Everyone!* III:156–64, III:177, III:213, III:380 *(bookstore)*, IV:22 *(bookstore)*, IV:56

PAPER PATCH: III:166

REFLECTIONS OF YOU: This shop's display window is full of mirrors. In his dream-vision of New York, EDDIE sees himself reflected in these mirrors but his image is actually dressed like JAKE. Later, on his way to find the ROSE, Jake also sees himself reflected in these mirrors. III:106, III:165

TOM AND GERRY'S ARTISTIC DELI: Tom and Gerry's is located on Second Avenue and Forty-sixth Street, which is part of TURTLE BAY, Manhattan.

In JAKE's *when*, Tom and Gerry's has already been demolished. However, the magical ROSE grows in the vacant lot left behind. (*See* LOT, THE in the PORTALS section.) III:70–71, III:106, III:107, III:109, III:166, III:170, III:244, III:359, III:362, IV:103

TOWER OF POWER RECORDS: As JAKE passes by this shop on his way to the ROSE (which he actually hopes is a portal to Roland), 'Paint it Black' is belting out of the doorway. Not surprisingly, the lyrics are about doors. III:106, III:165

TURTLE BAY: JAKE's magic LOT is located in an area of Manhattan once known as Turtle Bay. Since the Turtle is one of the GUARDIANS OF THE BEAM, it seems that this area of New York – and the magical ROSE that lives here – is protected by the TURTLE. III:168, IV:125

> **TURTLE BAY CONDOMINIUMS:** The Turtle Bay Condos are a project planned by MILLS CONSTRUCTION AND SOMBRA REAL ESTATE, an evil company that has no interest in building housing. What they really want to do is own the magic Lot so that they can destroy the Rose that grows there. III:168, III:362, IV:125

SISTERS OF MERCY HOSPITAL: II:237–41, II:247

SPARKS: A restaurant that EDDIE and HENRY liked to go to. II:44

STATUE OF LIBERTY: I:84

TIMES SQUARE: While searching for a doorway into Mid-World, JAKE stops here to rest and is accosted by an officer of the law. He uses his magic key to mesmerize the cop and escape. I:82, III:230–32, IV:93

DENBY'S DISCOUNT DRUGS: This shop is located in TIMES SQUARE. JAKE sits across the street from it during his search for a doorway into Mid-World. Denby is part of the pseudonym Jake gives to the policeman he mesmerizes with his magic key. III:232

TOOKER'S WHOLESALE TOYS: *(exact location not mentioned)* III:143

TWEENITY (SHOP): III:228

UNITED NATIONS BUILDING: III:171

WALL STREET: III:558

  STOCK EXCHANGE: III:484

WORLD TRADE CENTER: III:484

ZABAR'S: A food shop that sells good stuff. III:408

QUEENS: III:231, III:364

JFK AIRPORT: In order to deliver his cocaine packages to the nefarious BALAZAR, EDDIE has to pass through CUSTOMS at JFK airport. He manages to do so, but only because of Roland's intervention. (Please note: On the following pages, JFK is mentioned. I have also listed pages where it is the setting, even when Eddie's plane is sitting on the runway.) II:38, II:57, II:70–75, II:77–79, II:81–89, II:91–97 *(customs)*, II:99–101, II:104, II:129, II:140, III:221

  CUSTOMS: The Customs officials found in *The Drawing of the Three* suspect that EDDIE DEAN is carrying drugs so they search for them in rather personal places. Since the packages are on LOBSTROSITY BEACH, they can't arrest him. For Customs page references, see the listings under EDDIE DEAN in the CHARACTERS section.

  For CUSTOMS located at Forty-third Street, see II:129

QUEENSBOROUGH BRIDGE: II:192

RIKERS ISLAND: Rikers Island is the U.S.'s largest penal colony. There are ten jails on the island. Had EDDIE DEAN been caught carrying BALAZAR's coke, he would have ended up at Rikers. II:121

TRIBOROUGH BRIDGE: The Triborough Bridge is a major New York traffic artery. It connects Manhattan, Queens, and the Bronx. III:235, III:401

WESTCHESTER: II:391

   PELHAM: II:192

NIAGARA FALLS
IV:39

NORTH DAKOTA
FARGO: IV:100

NUTLEY
See DRAWERS in the PORTALS section

O

ODETTA
See ARKANSAS

OHIO
CINCINNATI: IV:94
CLEVELAND: IV:94

OMAHA
See NEBRASKA. *See also* ATCHISON, TOPEKA AND SANTA FE RAILROAD.

OXFORD TOWN
See MISSISSIPPI

P

PELHAM
See NEW YORK (CITY OF): WESTCHESTER

PENNSYLVANIA
PHILADELPHIA: Known to those who live there as Philly, this city figures prominently in a song JAKE CHAMBERS sings to scare away the GHOSTS IN THE MACHINES. It goes, 'My girl's a dilly/She comes from Philly.'

PERU
II:421

PHILADELPHIA
See PENNSYLVANIA

PIPER SCHOOL
This is Jake's exclusive school, located on Fifty-Sixth Street, between Park and Madison Avenues, Manhattan. It is Private and Nice and, most of all, White. Jake hates it.
  I:87, III:123–41, III:147, III:153, III:165, III:174,

III:186–89, III:214, III:253, III:307, III:496, IV:36, IV:76, IV:789, IV:796

PORT AUTHORITY
See NEW YORK (CITY OF): MANHATTAN

PUSHING PLACE
See NEW YORK (CITY OF): MANHATTAN

Q

QUEENS
See NEW YORK (CITY OF)

QUEENSBOROUGH BRIDGE
See NEW YORK (CITY OF)

QUINCON
II:58

R

RED WINDMILL, THE
See DRAWERS in the PORTALS section

REFLECTIONS OF YOU
  See NEW YORK (CITY OF): MANHATTAN

RIDGELINE ROAD
  See DRAWERS in the PORTALS section

RIKERS
  See NEW YORK (CITY OF)

RINCON AVENUE
  See NEW YORK (CITY OF): BROOKLYN

ROUTE 88
  See DRAWERS in the PORTALS section

RUSSIA
  III:41

S

SANTA FE
See MEJIS, BARONY OF: SANTA FE in the MID-WORLD
PLACES section. *See also* NEW MEXICO (this section) and
ATCHISON, TOPEKA AND SANTA FE RAILROAD
(also this section).

SPAIN
'The rain in Spain falls mainly on the Plain.' This rhyme is

heard in both our world and Mid-World, although Mid-World's version is quite a bit longer.

I:75, I:78, I:86

SUNNYVALE SANITARIUM

This is where we will probably all end up one day. Jake has an especial fear of it.

III:125, III:127, III:128, III:137

SWEDEN

III:137

T

TEXAS

The band ZZ Top was originally from Texas.

II:451, III:348

TIMES SQUARE

See NEW YORK (CITY OF): MANHATTAN

TOM AND GERRY'S ARTISTIC DELI

See NEW YORK (CITY OF): MANHATTAN. *Also see* LOT, THE in the PORTALS section.

TOOKER'S WHOLESALE TOYS

See NEW YORK (CITY OF): MANHATTAN

TOPEKA
    See ATCHISON, TOPEKA AND SANTA FE RAIL-
ROAD in this section. *See also* KANSAS in the PORTALS
section.

TOWER OF POWER RECORDS
    See NEW YORK (CITY OF): MANHATTAN

TRIBOROUGH BRIDGE
    See NEW YORK (CITY OF)

TURTLE BAY, MANHATTAN
    See NEW YORK (CITY OF): MANHATTAN

TURTLE BAY CONDOS
    See NEW YORK (CITY OF): MANHATTAN

U

U.S. CUSTOMS
    See NEW YORK (CITY OF): QUEENS: JFK AIRPORT

USSR
    III:395

V

VIETNAM
EDDIE DEAN's elder brother HENRY DEAN fought in the Vietnam War and got part of his knee shot off. It was while recovering from this injury that Henry became addicted to morphine which led to his later heroin addiction.
II:188, II:194, II:232, II:269, II:272, II:381, IV:102

W

WASHINGTON D.C.
II:124
GEORGETOWN: II:124

WICHITA
See KANSAS. *See also* ATCHISON, TOPEKA AND SANTA FE RAILROAD.

WOOLWORTH
See also ALABAMA
II:65

WYOMING
IV:39

PORTALS AND
MAGICAL PLACES

All is silent in the halls of the dead. All is forgotten in the stone halls of the dead. Behold the stairways which stand in darkness; behold the rooms of ruin. These are the halls of the dead where the spiders spin and the great circuits fall quiet, one by one.

III:105

Beyond the reach of human range
A drop of hell, a touch of strange . . .
**Line from a Manni Poem
I:139

A

**ALGUL SIENTO (BLUE HEAVEN)
In the new version of *The Gunslinger*, we see a TAHEEN bird-man in the MOHAINE DESERT. According to the BORDER DWELLER named BROWN, the taheen is lost. He is looking for a place called Algul Siento. We do not yet know what this place is or where it is located.

I:10

ATCHISON
See KANSAS, listed in this section. *See also* KANSAS in the OUR WORLD PLACES section and ATCHISON, TOPEKA AND SANTA FE RAILROAD in the OUR WORLD PLACES section.

B

BEACH DOORS
See DOORWAYS BETWEEN WORLDS, located later in this section

BEAM PORTALS
See PORTALS OF THE BEAM

**BEAMS, PATH OF THE

In *The Waste Lands*, Roland draws a metaphysical map of his world. According to this map, Mid-World is shaped like a wheel. The hub of this earth-wheel is the Thirteenth Gate, known in Mid-World as the DARK TOWER. The spokes radiating out from this hub are the BEAMS.

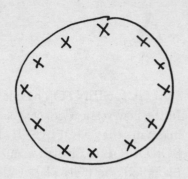

There are six Beams which connect twelve PORTALS. Each Beam is like an invisible high tension wire, affecting both gravity and the proper alignment of time, space, size and dimension. Their purpose is to bind the multiverse together while simultaneously holding the separate worlds —

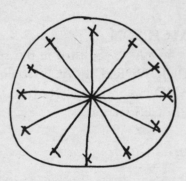

which spin upon the Tower like sequins upon a needle — apart. As the Beams break down, and as the Tower becomes unstable, the effects are felt in all worlds. The coherence of the time/space/size continuum weakens and THINNIES appear.

Although the Beams may not be visible in all worlds, they affect all of them. In *The Waste Lands*, JAKE follows the path of the Beam to the MANHATTAN RESTAURANT OF THE MIND and later to the MANSION. While Jake follows the Beam in his version of our earth, Roland, EDDIE and SUSANNAH follow the same Beam from its origin at SHARDIK'S LAIR through the GREAT WEST WOODS and finally on to the GREAT ROAD, which leads southeast towards the decaying and dangerous city of LUD. Along the Path of the Beam, Roland, Susannah, and Eddie use a magical SPEAKING RING – one of the places where the divisions between worlds are thin – to draw Jake into their *where* and *when*. Perhaps the fact that they are on the path of the BEAR/TURTLE Beam makes this drawing easier. In the new version of *The Gunslinger*, Roland follows WALTER (THE MAN IN BLACK) southeast. Both of them are drawn in the direction of the Bear/Turtle Beam.

I:6 *(pull southeast)*, I:42 *(pull southeast)*, I:43 *(clouds sucked southeast)*, I:56 *(southeast, the past they followed)*, I:83, III:52 *(indirect)*, III:54, III:98, III:100–6 *(first named on 100)*, III:110–19 *(following Beam. Directly mentioned on 110, 112, 113, 116)*, III:169, III:180, III:205–9 *(following)*, III:212, III:213, III:218–27 *(following; 225, 226)*, III:228, III:234–43 *(following)*, III:245–50 *(following)*, III:269, III:299–413 *(following; 326, 333, 360, 362, 363, 365, 392)*, III:413 *(Same as Street of the Turtle. See that entry)*, III:466, III:482, III:485, III:530, III:554–60 *(following)*, IV:3–12 *(Blaine on Beam)*, IV:17–75 *(Blaine on Beam. Directly mentioned on 16, 42, 60)*, IV:78, IV:89, IV:97 *(*ka-tet *has fallen off the Beam)*, IV:720, IV:723, IV:802, IV:811, IV:818, IV:819, IV:829, IV:831–40 *(back on the Path of the Beam. Directly mentioned on 831, 837, 839, 840)*

BERMUDA TRIANGLE

EDDIE thinks that DAVID QUICK's Nazi airplane arrived from our world via a time/space warp similar to the Bermuda Triangle. Eddie calls this huge doorway between worlds the Roland Zone. The THINNIES, found in both the alternative KANSAS where BLAINE terminates and in the

HAMBRY of Roland's youth, also make Eddie think of the Bermuda Triangle. As is purported to happen in the Triangle, people, animals and machinery can disappear into a Thinny and never be seen again.

III:377, IV:106

D

**DARK TOWER

The Dark Tower is a looming grey-black edifice which is simultaneously the center of all the universes and the lynchpin of the time/space continuum. All worlds and all realities are contained within its many levels. In its spiraling windows are flashes of electric blue fire. Its very stairs murmur with the voices of the lost (or damned) souls trapped within it. Located in a sea of red ROSES, it is the focus of Roland's long and arduous quest. The room at the top of the Tower may contain God, or it may be empty.

The Line of ELD, of which Roland is the last, is sworn to protect the Tower. Yet a terrible illness affects this structure, one that is often compared to a cancer. As this cancer spreads, THINNIES appear and the divisions between worlds soften.

The Tower is held in place by a network of magical magnetic force-rays known as the BEAMS. There are six Beams. They cross at the Tower and terminate in twelve PORTALS. Each Portal has an animal GUARDIAN.

Although some believe that the Tower, Beams, Portals, and Guardians were magical things that preceded the destructive technology of the GREAT OLD ONES, it seems fairly certain that the Old Ones re-created the world according to their own laws, seeking to replace outmoded magic with machinery. Yet machinery, like Man, is mortal. Hence the Beams, Portals, and mechanical Guardians are breaking down. If the weakening Beams collapse and the Tower falls, all creation will blink out of existence.

The Tower and its sea of roses are located on the edge of END WORLD, just beyond the demon-haunted realm of THUNDERCLAP. It is guarded by the BEAST, the originator of all *glammer*. Sometimes the diseased Tower cries out in the Beast's monstrous voice. If Patrick Danville – the little boy found in the novel *Insomnia* – has true visions of Mid-World, when Roland reaches the Dark Tower he will have to face THE CRIMSON KING who is trapped on one of its balconies. Interestingly, in the new version of *The Gunslinger*, we are told that Roland's final enemy is going to be the Crimson King, not the Beast. Perhaps they are the same being.

I:86, I:94, I:123, I:142, I:143, I:149, I:154, I:173, I:210, I:218, I:220, I:223, I:225, I:228, I:230, I:233, I:234, I:238, II:23, II:36, II:53, II:109, II:123, II:131, II:132, II:173, II:174, II:184, II:189, II:197, II:231, II:259–60, II:345, II:348, II:349, II:375, II:410, II:438, II:447, II:450 *(Roland's dream)*, II:451 *(contains Roland's lovers, friends, enemies)*, II:452–53, III:52, III:54, III:66, III:71–72, III:77, III:96, III:98, III:99, III:101, III:113, III:114, III:188, III:212, III:213, III:218, III:236, III:242, III:264, III:292, III:316, III:326, III:342, III:345, III:346, III:359–60, III:363, III:367, III:369, III:391, III:480, III:483, III:555, III:568, III:571, IV:11, IV:21, IV:22, IV:33, IV:36, IV:78, IV:81, IV:97, IV:103, IV:106, IV:123, IV:125, IV:127, IV:128–29, IV:205, IV:551, IV:564, IV:697 *(indirect)*, IV:723–24, IV:729,

IV:733, IV:734, IV:742, IV:760, IV:782, IV:786, IV:787,
IV:816, IV:817, IV:819, IV:827, IV:834, IV:835, IV:838,
IV:839, IV:840, E:169, E:173, E:179, E:231

FIELD OF SHOUTING RED ROSES: III:71–72,
III:74, III:107, III:114, III:359, III:367, IV:103, IV:127,
IV:564, IV:697, E:231 *(indirect)*

DOORWAYS BETWEEN WORLDS
GENERAL: I:142, I:229, I:235, III:57–58, III:85, III:99,
III:166, III:299, III:354, IV:54, IV:834, IV:836
BEACH DOORS: These doorways were created by the
magical tension between Roland and WALTER, otherwise
known as THE MAN IN BLACK. They are made of iron-
wood, and stand, without any visible support, on the
LOBSTROSITY-infested beach of the WESTERN SEA.
The first door which Roland comes to during his slow,
feverish crawl up LOBSTROSITY BEACH is that of THE
PRISONER. It leads him to the heroin-addicted EDDIE
DEAN. The second door leads Roland to THE LADY OF
SHADOWS, also known as ODETTA HOLMES and
DETTA WALKER – two women in one body. When these
two personalities unite, the Lady of Shadows becomes
Roland's *ka-tet* mate SUSANNAH DEAN. The final door,
called THE PUSHER, leads Roland to the evil JACK
MORT. At different times, Mort tried to kill both Susannah
Dean and JAKE CHAMBERS. Hence, he is tied to Roland's
ka-tet.

Although Roland doesn't meet any of these characters
until *The Drawing of the Three*, their coming is predicted by
WALTER who tells Roland's fortune while the two of them
palaver in the dead-zone of the GOLGOTHA. III:50,
III:55, III:85, IV:54

DOOR NUMBER 1 (THE PRISONER): II:26–36, II:41, II:52, II:53, II:63, II:64, II:75–86 *(door present)*, II:99–102 *(behind Eddie)*, II:108–9, II:150–58 *(back and forth)*, II:174–75, II:291, II:302, III:55

DOOR NUMBER 2 (THE LADY OF SHADOWS): II:200, II:201–3, II:225–35, II:251–53, II:256–57, II:276, II:291, II:301–2, II:344, III:55

DOOR NUMBER 3 (THE PUSHER): II:326, II:327, II:338–43, II:345–51, II:355 *(indirect)*, II:366, II:375–76, II:438–41

JAKE'S DOOR (DOOR NUMBER 4: THE BOY): Although JAKE is the third member of Roland's *ka-tet*, he is not drawn through one of the Beach Doors. Instead, he is drawn through a magical doorway that EDDIE DEAN creates in a SPEAKING RING located on the GREAT ROAD between the GREAT WEST WOODS and the city of LUD. *See* MANSION, THE (listed below) and STONE CIRCLES, listed separately.

GREEN PALACE: *See* GREEN PALACE, listed separately.

MAERLYN'S RAINBOW (THE BENDS O' THE RAINBOW): *See* MAERLYN'S RAINBOW, listed separately.

MANSION, THE: Located on RHINEHOLD STREET in DUTCH HILL, BROOKLYN, this haunted Mansion sits only one mile from where EDDIE DEAN grew up in CO-OP CITY. It also happens to sit on the PATH OF THE BEAM. Like many magical places, the Mansion is not really a Mansion at all but a portal between worlds that shifts shape from reality to reality and TOWER level to Tower level. In JAKE's world it most certainly looks like an imposing building, but in Roland's world it is the haunted force within a SPEAKING RING. All that Eddie has to do to let Jake pass through this portal – and be born into Mid-World – is to connect these two thin places with a drawn door. Unfortunately, the door is locked and both Eddie and Jake need copies of the key.

Just as the PORTALS OF THE BEAM are protected by GUARDIANS, all other portals, in Our World or Mid-World, are protected by demons. In order to cross over into Mid-World and join Roland's *ka-tet*, Jake must face the Mansion's demon. The Mansion's demon is the animating spirit of the house, a spirit of place, and parallels the demon which Susannah battles sexually in the Speaking Ring. *See also* STONE CIRCLES, in this section, and DEMONS in the CHARACTERS section. III:104, III:222, III:257, III:258, III:261, III:262–65, III:267–70, III:273–77, III:279–84, III:285, III:287–88, III:290–91, III:476, III:482, III:553, IV:123

JAKE'S DOOR (MANSION VERSION): *Also see* JAKE'S DOOR listed under STONE CIRCLES. III:57–58, III:275–77, III:282–84

PORTALS OF THE BEAM: *See* PORTALS OF THE BEAM, listed separately. *See also* GUARDIANS OF THE BEAM, listed in the CHARACTERS section.

SHARDIK'S LAIR: *See* PORTALS OF THE BEAM, listed separately. *See also* GUARDIANS OF THE BEAM, listed in the CHARACTERS section.

STONE CIRCLES: *See* STONE CIRCLES, listed separately

THINNIES: *See* THINNIES, listed separately

TRAINS BETWEEN WORLDS: *See* BLAINE'S ROUTE, listed in the MID-WORLD PLACES section. *See also* BLAINE, listed under NORTH CENTRAL POSITRONICS in the CHARACTERS section, and

ATCHISON, TOPEKA AND SANTA FE RAILROAD COMPANY listed in the OUR WORLD PLACES section.

DRAWERS

According to SUSANNAH DEAN (previously Odetta Holmes/Detta Walker), the Drawers are places that are spoiled, useless, or both. However, they are also places of power. In many ways they resemble a psychic trash midden. The Drawers are a kind of WASTE LAND.

I:98, II:217–18, II:369, III:60–62, III:113, III:270, III:362, III:481, III:523, IV:804 *(In Oz Daily Buzz)*

DETTA AND *FORSPECIAL* PLATE: II:217–18

DETTA'S SEX HAUNTS: These locations (RIDGE ROAD outside NUTLEY, ROUTE 88 outside AMHIGH, and THE RED WINDMILL) were places where Detta Walker vented her rage against white men. The negative force of her emotion, and the experiences she had in these places, transformed them into a kind of psychic Drawers. III:270

E

**END-WORLD

This is the fey region that exists beyond Mid-World. It contains both THUNDERCLAP and THE DARK TOWER. According to the LITTLE SISTERS OF ELURIA, the ashes of the dead blow out toward this dream place. Once, hundreds of years before our *ka-tet* traveled in his Barony

Coach, BLAINE had monitoring equipment in End-World. However, it has been down for more than eight centuries. When Roland and his friends reach the border between Mid-World and End-World, the first part of their journey will be complete.

In the new *Gunslinger*, Sylvia Pittston states that when God casts out the unrepentant from his palaces, he will send them to the burning place beyond the end of End-World. End-World must be a terrible place. Even the sorcerer WALTER states that to speak of things in End-World is to speak of the ruination of one's own soul.**

I:55, I:233, III:571, IV:12, IV:81, IV:722, IV:733, E:202, E:231

G

GOLGOTHA, THE
Roland and the MAN IN BLACK (WALTER) hold palaver here in this ancient killing ground located on the western slopes of the CYCLOPEAN MOUTAINS. To Roland, the Golgotha is 'the place of the skull.' Its floor is dusty with bone meal and contains the skeletal remains of many small animals. It is here that Walter tells Roland's fortune, and it is here that Roland experiences a ten-year-long night as well as a tremendous vision of the multiverse.

I:215–37, II:12, III:63 *(indirect)*

GREEN PALACE, THE
This palace, which FANNIN/FLAGG maintains is in OZ, is

actually located along the I–70 THINNY in the ALTER-
NATIVE TOPEKA which Roland's *ka-tet* must travel through
during *Wizard and Glass*. R.F. probably created it as a kind of
practical joke. Like the buildings of Oz's Emerald City, it is
entirely green.

The Green Palace is made of glass. Its gate consists of
twelve colored bars (six on each gate wing). They represent
the twelve bends of MAERLYN'S RAINBOW. The central
bar (which is broad instead of flat and round) is dead black.
All of the bars contain strange little life forms. The Green
Palace hums like a THINNY, but the sound isn't as unpleasant.

IV:121 *(in the distance)*, IV:129 *(up ahead)*, IV:131, IV:784,
IV:788–820, IV:829, IV:830, IV:833, IV:838

H

HAUNTED MANSION
See DOORWAYS BETWEEN WORLDS

HIDDEN HIGHWAYS/ HIGHWAYS IN HIDING
These are the hidden highways (both in Our World and in
Mid-World) that lead us on to our destinies. JAKE follows
one of these from his apartment door to CO-OP CITY in
BROOKLYN and then to the haunted MANSION. The
BEAMS are also 'hidden highways.'

III:114, III:169, III:217

J

JAKE'S DOOR (DOOR NUMBER 4: THE BOY)
See STONE CIRCLES. For more information, *see* sub-entry
MANSION under DOORWAYS BETWEEN WORLDS

K

KANSAS
Kansas is frequently mentioned in *The Dark Tower* series, usually
in conjunction with *The Wizard of Oz*. However, it does not
become part of the plot until *Wizard and Glass*. The Kansas
we enter in Book IV of *The Dark Tower* series is both subtly
and not so subtly different from our Kansas. Unlike the Kansas
of Our World, this Kansas seems to still use the old
ATCHISON, TOPEKA AND SANTA FE RAILROAD. Its
former residents drove Takaru Spirits and ate at Boing Boing
burgers — cars and fast-food joints we've never heard of — but
worse yet they've all been wiped out by the superflu, the same
disease that killed most of America's population in Stephen
King's novel *The Stand*. This Topeka seems to suffer from the
worst diseases of both Mid-World and Our World. Like
HAMBRY, it contains a THINNY. (*See entry under* MID-
WORLD RAILWAY, listed in this section.)
  II:257, III:192, IV:76–140 (*Setting. Directly mentioned on the
  following pages: 77, 78, 89, 92, 93, 94, 95, 105, 106, 119,*

120, 131), IV:421–23 *(Kansas interlude),* IV:775–820 *(Setting. Directly mentioned on the following pages: 775, 779, 790, 792, 794, 796),* IV:828, IV:829, IV:831, IV:838

ATCHISON: IV:84

KANSAS CITY: IV:105, IV:122

KANSAS MUSEUM OF NATURAL HISTORY: IV:93

PHILLIP BILLARD: IV:92

TOPEKA: This is where Mid-World ends and END-WORLD begins. The first part of Roland's quest ends here. III:192, III:198, III:199, III:210, III:366, III:555, III:573, III:581, III:582, IV:10, IV:11, IV:12, IV:29, IV:30, IV:39, IV:45, IV:46, IV:47, IV:50, IV:55, IV:57, IV:64, IV:66, IV:76–124, IV:126–40, IV:421–23, IV:775–98 *(Green Palace),* IV:809

    BERRYTON ROAD: IV:92

    BIG SPRINGS: IV:120

    BOING BOING BURGERS: IV:114, IV:122, IV:131, IV:778

    CRADLE OF TOPEKA: (Like an outdoor LUD. Looks Western.) IV:82–104

    FORBES: IV:92

      FORBES FIELD: IV:92

    GADDISH FEEDS: Grain storage tower. IV:119

    GAGE BOULEVARD: IV:103, IV:105, IV:111

      GAGE BOULEVARD AMTRAK STATION: IV:92

    GAGE PARK: IV:104, IV:105, IV:107–13

    HEARTLAND LANES: IV:114

    HEARTLAND PARK RACE TRACK: Disposal pit for superflu dead. IV:92

    KANSAS TURNPIKE: See ROUTE I–70

    KANSAS POWER AND LIGHTS: IV:92

    K.U. AT LAWRENCE: IV:92

OAKLAND BILLARD PARK: Disposal plant for superflu dead. IV:92

REINISCH ROSE GARDEN: IV:107–10

ROUTE I–70 (KANSAS TURNPIKE): IV:76–77, IV:88, IV:99, IV:104, IV:105, IV:112–24, IV:421–23, IV:784–98, IV:800, IV:830

SHAWNEE HEIGHTS SCHOOL DISTRICT: IV:92

SOUTHEAST SIXTY-FIRST STREET: IV:92

ST FRANCIS HOSPITAL AND MEDICAL CENTER: IV:91

STORMONT-VAIL REGIONAL MEDICAL CENTER: IV:92

TOPEKA LUTHERAN: IV:92

TOPEKA STATE HOSPITAL: IV:114

TOPEKA TECHNICAL COLLEGE: IV:92

TOPEKA ZOO: IV:110–12

WAMBEGO: IV:93

KAW RIVER NUCLEAR PLANT (KAWNUKE): IV:93

WICHITA: IV:89

L

**LAND OF DEATH (LAND OF NINETEEN)

This is the place that the weed-eater NORT of TULL journeyed to. Unlike most people, he came back again. After the sorcerer WALTER raised Nort from the dead, he sealed Nort's memories of the Land of Death behind an imaginary door, or blockade. This door could only be opened – and Nort's memories released — by uttering the word NINETEEN. ALICE OF TULL is the unlucky person who does so. What she learns drives her mad. *See* NINETEEN in the CHAR-ACTERS section.

I:39, I:40

LAND OF NINETEEN
See LAND OF DEATH, above

LAND OF THE DRUMS
The PUBES of LUD believe that they must sacrifice one of their own each time they hear the god-drums pounding out over the city's loudspeakers. If they don't give a life, the GHOSTS IN THE MACHINES will animate the city's many corpses and rise up to eat the living. It is thought that once a Pube is sacrificed, he or she journeys to the Land of the Drums. We can assume that the Land of the Drums isn't a very nice place since the Ghosts must be there, beating their hungry instruments.

Although the Pubes don't know it, the god-drums are actually no more than the backbeat of the ZZ Top song 'Velcro Fly'. They are operated by the city's rival gang THE GRAYS, with a little help from BLAINE the insane computer brain.

III:438

LITTLE SISTERS' HOSPITAL
When Roland awakes in the Little Sisters' Hospital he believes he is in a vast and airy pavilion of white silk, one hung with tiny silver bells. However, like the beauty of the LITTLE SISTERS OF ELURIA, the pavilion's loveliness is no more than a *glammer*. In reality it is an old fraying canvas tent so thin and worn in places that it lets in the light of the Kissing Moon.

E:171–221 *(Setting. 174–75 first described; 182 'a hospital', 188, 221 as tent)*, E:222–23, E:230

LOT, THE

JAKE's magic Lot is located on the corner of Forty-sixth Street and Second Avenue. It was once the home of TOM AND GERRY'S ARTISTIC DELI. Now it is a waste land containing a single, beautiful wild ROSE. According to the sign, TURTLE BAY CONDOMINIUMS are coming soon. In the remaining books of the series, Roland and his friends must find a way to protect both Rose and Lot. Since the Rose and TOWER are actually one force in two forms, the future of the interpenetrating worlds hangs on the outcome of this mission. See also ROSE in the CHARACTERS section.

III:167–78, III:180, III:362, IV:103, IV:107, IV:124–26 *(Eddie's dream)*

M

MAERLYN'S RAINBOW (THE BENDS O' THE RAINBOW): There are thirteen glass balls in the Wizard's Rainbow, one for each GUARDIAN and one for the TOWER and the BEAST. The balls are for scrying. Some colors look into the future; others look into alternative worlds. Still others look far into Mid-World. The balls show where one may find the secret doors between worlds, and yet sometimes they act as doorways themselves. All of the balls are alive and hungry. A person begins by using them, but in the end, he or she is used by them and sucked dry.

The Wizard's Rainbow is a corruption of the pure energy of the White. If the White represents wholeness, and the best human beings can strive for in ideal and action, the colors represent the baser emotions — or the fallen emotions of a fallen world. For example, the Pink One resonates with sexual energy, but it is desire, possessiveness and cruelty without the higher emotions that true love can instill in us. Not surprisingly, the gate of the sinister GREEN PALACE is made to resemble Maerlyn's Rainbow. The gate's two wings consist of six colored bars each; one for every bend. The central bar (which is broad instead of flat and round) is dead black.

Few of Maerlyn's balls still exist. They never stay in one pair of hands for very long and, as STEVEN DESCHAIN points out, even enchanted glass has a habit of breaking. Three or four of the Bends o' the Rainbow are probably still rolling around. They are:

THE BLUE: Fifty years before Roland's first *ka-tet* set off for MEJIS, this Bend o' the Rainbow was in the possession of a desert tribe of SLOW MUTANTS called the TOTAL HOGS.

THE GREEN: This one is thought to be hidden in the city of LUD.

THE ORANGE: This ball was last seen in the ruined city of DIS.

THE PINK: This one, also known as **MAERLYN'S GRAPEFRUIT**, was in Farson's possession until Roland stole it at the end of *Wizard and Glass*. Like the other Bends o' the Rainbow, the Pink Ball is alive. On the lid of its box (now lost) is the High Speech motto, I SEE WHO OPENS ME. The Grapefruit's energy is sexual, and its color is often described as labial pink. It is one of the balls that expose people's secrets.

BLACK THIRTEEN: This final Bend o' the Rainbow may also still be in existence. However, it is unlucky to even speak of Thirteen, as it may hear its name called and roll the speaker away to unknown worlds. Even STEVEN DESCHAIN, the last Lord of Light, seemed wary of it.
GENERAL REFS FOR ALL THE BALLS: IV:145–51, IV:158, IV:160–61, IV:205, IV:421, IV:443–44, IV:446, IV:470, IV:520, IV:529, IV:530, IV:535, IV:548, IV:549, IV:550–54, IV:555–58, IV:570–71, IV:611–21, IV:655, IV:668, IV:669, IV:671, IV:672–76, IV:684–87, IV:689, IV:705–6, IV:707, IV:720–25 (*Roland inside the Grapefruit*), IV:728, IV:731, IV:732, IV:733, IV:742, IV:760, IV:764–71, IV:772, IV:779, IV:780, IV:781–82, IV:790, IV:800, IV:801, IV:816–28, IV:838

MANSION
See DOORWAYS BETWEEN WORLDS

MID-WORLD AMUSEMENT PARK
In the children's story *Charlie the Choo-Choo*, the talking train CHARLIE is given a nice retirement taking children round and round on a track located in CALIFORNIA's Mid-World Amusement Park. Mid-World Amusement Park doesn't exist in Our World. However, a version of it exists in the alternative TOPEKA which Roland's *ka-tet* reaches after their catastrophic ride on BLAINE the insane Mono. In the alternative Topeka, a rather sinister Charlie resides in the REINISCH ROSE GARDEN.
III:200, III:365

MID-WORLD LANES
When JAKE is accosted by an officer of the law in TIMES

SQUARE and is asked for some identification, he offers to show his Mid-World Lanes membership.

III:231

MID-WORLD RAILROAD (KANSAS TO TOPEKA LINE)

We first learn about the Mid-World Railroad through the children's book *Charlie the Choo-Choo* which JAKE CHAMBERS finds in the MANHATTAN RESTAURANT OF THE MIND. Despite the fact that it was written for kiddies, Jake finds the story (and the main character, a talking train) extremely sinister. Jake senses that Charlie is a force of destruction, and that the Mid-World Railway has only one ultimate destination – the Land of Death.

Jake's vision of a killer train on a death-track prefigures the actual Mid-World Railroad that exists on Roland's level of the TOWER. In Roland's world, Charlie is replaced by the talking Mono BLAINE, though their routes are very similar. In Roland's world, 'char' means death. Hence, Charlie (like Blaine) is literally a killer train. Roland, Jake, and their *ka-tet* survive Blaine only to find a toy version of Charlie's railroad in the alternative TOPEKA. (For more information on the children's book, *see entry under* CHARLIE THE CHOO-CHOO listed in the CHARACTERS section.)

CHARLIE THE CHOO-CHOO VERSION: III:192, III:195, III:196, III:198, III:201, III:349, III:366

BLAINE'S VERSION: *See* RIVER BARONY: LUD: BLAINE'S CRADLE in the MID-WORLD PLACES section. *See also* BLAINE'S ROUTE in the MID-WORLD PLACES section.

MORDOR
This realm of darkness and death can be found in J.R.R. Tolkien's famous trilogy, *The Lord of the Rings*. SUSANNAH thinks about Mordor and the Cracks of Doom as she rides through the Waste Lands beyond LUD.
III:563

N

**NA'AR
When WALTER reads Roland's cards in the new version of *The Gunslinger*, he calls him the Hanged Man, plodding ever onward toward his goal over the pits of Na'ar. Na'ar sounds a lot like Hell. It is probably a MANNI term.
I:219

NEBRASKA
In *Wizard and Glass*, we find out that ABAGAIL – the champion of the White found in King's novel *The Stand* – lives in an alternative version of Nebraska.
IV:786

NONES
The Moon Peddler comes from the Nones bearing his sack of squealing souls.
IV:345

O

OZ

See WIZARD OF OZ in the CHARACTERS section. *See also*
PALACE OF GREEN GLASS, located in this section.

II:257, III:80, III:210, III:566, IV:792, IV:793, IV:803,
IV:804, IV:805, IV:807, IV:809, IV:810, IV:811, IV:812,
IV:816–20 *(throne room)*, IV:821, IV:828, IV:833

P

PATH OF THE BEAM
See BEAMS, PATH OF THE

**PLACE OF BURNING DARKNESS
See END-WORLD

PORTALS OF THE BEAM

In *The Waste Lands*, Roland draws a metaphysical map of Mid-
World. This map is shaped like a wheel. At the center of the
wheel is the DARK TOWER, also known as the THIR-
TEENTH GATE. The twelve power points on the rim of
this wheel are known as PORTALS. These Portals are actually twelve doorways leading into and out of Mid-World. The
six BEAMS which connect opposite Portals and which pass
through the nexus of the Dark Tower are like high tension

wires. They can be seen and felt by those who pass near them.

According to HAX, when the GREAT OLD ONES recreated the world, they made twelve GUARDIANS to watch over the twelve Portals. These GUARDIANS OF THE BEAM, also known as TOTEMS OF THE BEAM, had animal shapes. Although we have met MIR/SHARDIK, the cyborg Bear Guardian, it seems highly likely that the Beams, Guardians, and Dark Tower existed before the technology of the Great Old Ones came into being.

The Portals are not the only doorways into and out of Mid-World, but they are the most powerful ones. Their health is intrinsically tied to the health of Mid-World and the time–space continuum of all worlds. As the alterations the Old Ones made to the fabric of reality begin to unravel, THINNIES appear. Thinnies are like extremely nasty portals. We don't know where they lead, but it seems likely that they transport their victims to the demon-haunted emptiness between worlds. Like BLAINE's termination point in TOPEKA, the Portals of the Beam are marked with yellow and black stripes. *See also* GUARDIANS OF THE BEAM, located in the CHARACTERS section.

III:50–54, III:89, III:98, III:100, III:255, III:363

PORTAL OF THE TURTLE: III:363

SHARDIK'S LAIR/ SHARDIK'S PORTAL: III:54, III:79–98 (*following backtrail to it; reach it on 89*), III:100–6, III:109–16, III:210–12, III:222, III:255, III:360, III:480, III:564, IV:51

R

REINISCH ROSE GARDEN
See KANSAS, this section

S

SHARDIK'S LAIR
See BEAM PORTALS (this section) and GUARDIANS
OF THE BEAM listed in the CHARACTERS section

STONE CIRCLES
These circles of standing stones (also known as **DRUIT
STONES**) are called **SPEAKING RINGS**. They are the
haunts of spirits and oracles. In these demonic places the
boundaries between the visible and invisible worlds are thin.
The first Speaking Ring we see is the ORACLE OF THE
MOUNTAINS, found in *The Gunslinger*. The second one we
see is in *The Waste Lands*, along the PATH OF THE BEAM.
It is through this second Speaking Ring that our *ka-tet* draws
JAKE CHAMBERS into Mid-World.

We don't know who created the Stone Circles, or whether
they predate the technological rule of THE GREAT OLD
ONES or came during the post-apocalyptic dark age that
followed. However, we do know that Roland sees them as
ancient, mysterious, and dangerous — hence they must precede

the rise of GILEAD and the IN-WORLD BARONIES by many hundreds of years. Although we do not know who lifted these heavy stones and made them reach toward the sky, we do know that human sacrifice was often practiced within them, and possibly contributed to their sinister energy.

GENERAL REFERENCES: I:132, I:133, I:135, I:138, I:147, II:416, III:238, III:249

ORACLE OF THE MOUNTAINS: The Oracle of the Mountains is the name Roland gives to the Speaking Ring succubus that he and Jake encounter in the WILLOW JUNGLE located in the foothills of the CYCLOPEAN MOUNTAINS. Although this demoness originally tried to draw Jake into her circular lair, Roland thwarted her, saving Jake from almost certain death. In the end, Roland offers himself to this hungry succubus so that he can force her to make a prophecy. Roland uses mescaline, a drug which CORT once called the Philosopher's Stone, to draw the demon, but after he has extracted information from her he must pay her sexual tithe. The oracle uses *glammer* to conjure the scent and voice of Roland's lost love, SUSAN DELGADO. I:132–34, I:135–36, I:138–44, I:147, III:238, IV:84

SPEAKING RING ALONG THE PATH OF THE BEAM: It is through this second Speaking Ring that our *ka-tet* (namely EDDIE DEAN) draws JAKE CHAMBERS into Mid-World. Sketching a doorway in the dirt of a Druit Stone circle that they encounter on the GREAT ROAD to LUD, Eddie makes a magical door – one which can be unlocked by a key he carved while traveling.

Eddie's magical door is actually a portal connecting Mid-World to the haunted DUTCH HILL MANSION, located in a part of BROOKLYN no more than a mile or so from Eddie's old family apartment. Hence, Eddie is drawing Jake from the world of his own childhood every bit as much as he draws him from a real city.

Like all portals between worlds, these two connected doorways are not unguarded. SUSANNAH DEAN must hold the Speaking Ring Demon in a sexual tangle while Eddie works his magic. Roland, in turn, must dive through the door into Jake's world to save him from the clutches of the terrible MANSION DEMON. *Also see* JAKE'S DOOR (THE BOY) below. III:238, III:249, III:260–62, III:265–67, III:271–73, III:277–79, III:284, III:285–87, III:288, III:291–94, III:299, IV:51, IV:85

JAKE'S DOOR (DOOR NUMBER 4: THE BOY): Like all portals, THE BOY (DOOR NUMBER 4) has a different form in each world. In Our World, it appears to be a haunted house called THE MANSION. In Mid-World, it exists within a Speaking Ring. (The Mid-World version of the door is actually drawn by Eddie within the Speaking Ring.) Obviously, places of sinister power in one world are also places of sinister power in all of the others. III:57–58, III:278–79, III:284, III:285–87, III:288, III:348

T

THINNY, THINNIES

Thinnies are places where the fabric of existence has almost entirely worn away. These cancerous 'sores on the skin of existence' have increased in number since the DARK TOWER began to fail. Thinnies can only exist because the multiverse itself is sickening. In fact, as thinnies spread over the earth, disease spreads among humans and other creatures.

Thinnies look like silvery, shimmering water and make a nauseating, atonal squalling. In many ways they seem like fluidly animate demons, especially since they have both a kind of body and a definite, malign presence. Sometimes their lique-fying element spreads, develops arms, and snatches birds out of the air. These liquid/ether demons are like monstrous sirens, singing hungrily, always willing to whisper our secret fears to us so that they can lure us into their dead embrace. They can be found in TOPEKA and HAMBRY.

IV:81, IV:82, IV:84, IV:86–140 *(Topeka thinny close by during this section. Directly mentioned on 86, 96–97, 116, 117, 119, 120, 124, 132, 197)*, IV:147, IV:194–97, IV:211, IV:328, IV:343–47, IV:348, IV:421 *(Kansas)*, IV:465, IV:524, IV:546, IV:748–61, IV:784–85 *(approaching Green Palace)*, IV:286–798

THUNDERCLAP

The fey realm of THUNDERCLAP sits on the lip of END-WORLD. It is described as a land of dead fields, deserted villages, blasted trees, and dead soldiers. From here come the pale warriors; all clocks run backward in this land of death, and the graveyards vomit out their dead. Thunderclap is a land of vampires, and a place where those who are bitten by vampires, such as Father Callahan of the novel *'Salem's Lot*, are damned to travel. Roland will have to pass through Thunder-clap on his way to the TOWER. It is here that Roland and his friends will face FLAGG once more.

IV:721–24, IV:733 *(indirect)*, IV:791, IV:838

TOPEKA
See KANSAS

TOWER
See DARK TOWER

WASTE LANDS
The Waste Lands are those desolate lands located beyond LUD. These horrible areas — too poisoned to support life as we know it but full of mutants and monsters — are man-made. It seems that they were the result of one of the GREAT OLD ONES' wars. We already know that BLAINE, the computer mind of LUD, has access to chemical and biological weapons, but what was unloosed upon the waste lands was worse than these. It was, Blaine assures EDDIE, even worse than a nuclear catastrophe. See also DRAWERS, in this section, and MEJIS, BARONY OF: WASTE LANDS in the MID-WORLD PLACES section.
    III:333, III:339, III:393, III:480, III:563–65, IV:3, IV:55

**WEST END OF THE WORLD
The West End of the World is an almost impossible place to reach. Hence the expression, 'Where else would I be? The West End of the World?' At the end of the new *Gunslinger*, we learn that the WESTERN SEA is the western edge of the world.
    III:469

APPENDIX I:
HIGH SPEECH, LOW SPEECH, AND MID-WORLD ARGOT

PLEASE NOTE: I have tried to give at least one page reference for each term so that the reader can view the entries in the context of the story. Entries marked with a double asterisk appear in the new version of *The Gunslinger* but not in the original version.

CONTENTS

INTRODUCTION

High Speech (also called 'the Tongue') was the ancient, ritualized language of Mid-World. Low speech – also called the common tongue or the vulgate – was the speech of everyday interaction, but High Speech was the language of gunslingers. It was also the language of ritual and magic.

Although not confined to the courts of Gilead (Sylvia Pittston of Tull and Aunt Talitha of River Crossing both speak the Tongue), it was, primarily, bound to the hierarchies and courtly codes of In-World. While we can assume that Fair-Day Riddling was conducted in low speech, and while the common tongue contained many fascinating terms and phrases, the spiked letters of High Speech carried the heart of Roland's culture. With one notable exception (explained in the pages that follow), each word in the Tongue had multiple meanings. These meanings were so varied and so diffuse that they were (and are) difficult to explain to outsiders.

Like other sacred languages, the words and phrases of High Speech imply an entire philosophy of life, and the speaking of it was ritualized. Gunslinger apprentices were not allowed to utter its words publicly until after they had won their guns. To do so before proving themselves in the yard behind the Great Hall was considered an affront to all their culture held sacred. As was said earlier, High Speech was the language of gunslingers, but it was also the language used to address spirits, demons, and *dinhs*. If the glorious history of Roland's world is now no more than the wreckage of a sunken ship, then High Speech is one of the sacred relics that washed up upon the shores.

HIGH SPEECH

AN-TET: The term *tet* refers to people linked by the same destiny or goals. *An-tet* implies an intimate emotional link. It can also imply sexual intimacy. To sit together *an-tet* is to sit in council. In *Wizard and Glass*, Roland refers to the first time he and Susan made love as the first time they were together *an-tet*. Given the profound link between Roland and Susan (she appears and reappears to him in dreams and visions throughout *The Dark Tower* series), the term *an-tet* is appropriate. A mere sexual encounter does not necessarily imply *an-tet*. IV:554

CHAR: Most words in High Speech have multiple meanings. However, *char* is an exception to this general rule. *Char* has one meaning only, and that is death. *Char* is the root of many Mid-World terms, including *Big Charlie Wind*, *charry* and *Charyou Tree*. III:340, III:371

CHARYOU TREE: 'Come Reap.' Obviously, *Charyou Tree*'s original meaning had to do with sacrifice. IV:762, IV:765

**COMMALA: Commala is a Mid-World term for rice. It is also an alternative name for the festival dance known as the Sowing Night Cotillion. The Commala is the courting rite of New Earth, a festival also known as Sowing and Fresh Commala. I:162

**COTILLION (SOWING NIGHT COTILLION): *See* COMMALA, listed above.

**DAN-DINH: The term *dan-dinh* has many meanings. To speak *dan-dinh* is to open your heart and your mind to another. This term also means Little Leader. I:145

DARKLES AND TINCTS: These terms are applied to Maerlyn, otherwise known as the Ageless Stranger. Although their exact definitions are not given, they are used in conjunction with Maerlyn's ability to live backward in time and to live, simultaneously, in all times. I:233

DINH: A *dinh* is a leader or king. Roland is the *dinh* of his *ka-tet*. Roland asks his *ka-tet* whether the Wizard of Oz was a great *dinh* – a Baron or a king. I:164

GUNNA: The term *gunna* appears to mean all one's worldly goods. This is the definition that Eddie surmises, as he watches Roland pack their *gunna* and prepare for another day's travel. I:7, IV:129

GUNSLINGER LITANY: *See entry under* MID-WORLD SAYINGS.

**HOWKEN: The act (and art) of hypnotizing someone, usually using a bullet as a focusing point. I:86, I:102

KA: Like many words in High Speech, *ka* has multiple meanings and so is difficult to define precisely. It signifies life-force, consciousness, duty and destiny. In the vulgate, or low speech, it also means a place to which an individual must go.

The closest terms in our language are probably *fate* and *destiny*, although *ka* also implies karma, or the accumulated destiny (and accumulated debt) of many existences. We are the servants of *ka*. We are also the prisoners of it. As Roland knows, *ka* is a wheel; its one purpose is to turn, and in the end it always returns to the place it began. In this sense, it is reminiscent of the major arcana card, the Wheel of Fortune. II:198, III:83

**KA-BABBIES: Young *ka-tet* mates. I:180

KA-MAI (also spelled KAMAI): In Book IV of *The Dark Tower* series, Cuthbert refers to himself as Roland's *ka-mai*. Roland thinks of Eddie Dean as *ka-mai* as well, another link uniting the personalities of Cuthbert and Eddie. *Ka-mai* means *ka*'s fool. It implies a constant joker (the kind Roland is obviously drawn to and easily angered by), yet the addition of *ka* adds another dimension to this term. One must remember that in Shakespeare's plays, it is often the fool who speaks the most profound truths. Sometimes jest is serious, or cuts to the heart of a matter which, otherwise, could not be addressed at all. Both Cuthbert and Eddie, both referred to as *ka-mai*, often have insights that Roland would neither grasp, nor face, on his own. It is Eddie, alone among the *ka-tet* traveling to the Tower, who realizes that Roland's potential for treachery and betrayal still exists. He jokes about it, yet he states it clearly enough, and directly to Roland. The gift of *ka-mai* is a necessary one on the road to the Tower. It is as necessary as the gift of the touch. IV:51, IV:356

**KA'S BOOK: The Book of Destiny. I:27

KA-TEL: A *ka-tel* is a class of apprentice gunslingers. Roland was the youngest of his *ka-tel*, yet he was the first to win his guns. IV:133 (Ka-tel *in US version*)

KA-TET: Literally speaking, *ka-tet* means 'one made from many.' *Ka* refers to destiny; *tet* refers to a group of people with the same interests or goals. *Ka-tet* is the place where men's lives are joined by fate. *Ka-tet* cannot be changed or bent to any individual's will, but it can be seen, known, and understood. The philosophers of Gilead stated that *ka-tet* could only be broken by death or treachery. However, Roland's teacher Cort maintained that neither death nor treachery were strong enough to break the bonds of *ka-tet* since these events were also tied to *ka*, or fate. Each member of a *ka-tet* is a piece of a puzzle. Each individual piece is a mystery, but when put together, the collected pieces form a greater picture. It takes many *ka-tets* to finish one picture, or one historical tapestry. *Ka-tets* overlap, often sharing members. Individuals can also be partial members of a *ka-tet*, as Roland states when he pursues Jake through the underground mazes of Lud. Unlike the billy-bumbler, Oy, who follows Jake by instinct as much as by sense of smell (members of the same *ka-tet* are drawn to one another), Roland believes he is not a complete member of Jake's destiny-bound group. He can share thoughts, but his destiny is slightly different from those of his companions. This may be because Roland is from a different world, but this explanation is not complete. After all, Oy is also from a different world, and is part of a different species.

A *ka-tet* is not always bound by love, affection or friendship. Enemies are also *ka-tet*. Although usually referred to as positive or at least inevitable, the forces of *ka/ka-tet* can cast a sinister shadow over our lives. For Jake, Eddie, Susannah and

Roland, the *ka-tet* holding them together also binds them to the Dark Tower and the vacant Lot on Forty-sixth Street and Second Avenue. This place, where Tom and Gerry's Artistic Deli once stood, is the 'secret heart' of their *ka-tet*. III:355, IV:35

KHEF: In the original tongue of the Old World, *khef* meant many different things, including water, birth, and life-force. It implied all that was essential to existence. At the beginning of *The Gunslinger*, we learn that one can progress through the *khef*. When we meet Roland, he has 'progressed through the *khef* over many years, and had reached the fifth level.' Those who attain the higher levels of *khef* (levels seven and eight) are able to have a clinical detachment from their bodies. The physical self may thirst, but the mind remains separate, a spectator.

Khef is both individual and collective. It implies the knowledge a person gains from dream-life, as well as his or her life-force. *Khef* is the web that binds a *ka-tet*. Those who share *khef* share thoughts. Their destinies are linked, as are their life-forces. Behind the multiple meanings of this word lies a philosophy of interconnectedness, a sense that all individuals, all events, are part of a greater pattern or plan. It also implies that through rigorous training (similar to that endured by gunslingers) the self can progress upwards, rising tier to tier, until the body, if not one's ultimate destiny, is under the control of mind and will.

An individual's *khef* is often more complex than he or she realizes. In psychological terms, *khef* accounts for all parts of ourselves, even those aspects we wish not to see. It may also account for our other selves, those 'twinners' (to borrow a term from *The Talisman*) who are our manifestations in other realities, or on other levels of the Tower. Our fates, for good or for evil, are the result of both our own and our shared *khef*. Like Roland, who must face the fact that betrayal of those he loves is part of his destiny, we must realize that we are capable of both good and evil actions. Susannah Dean – the woman who emerged from the dual personalities of Detta Walker and Odetta Holmes – experiences this first hand. While riding through the blasted lands beyond the city of Lud, 'the dark side of her personality, that side of her *khef* which was Detta Walker' drank in the vision of complete destruction. Her other personalities – Susannah Dean and Odetta Holmes – reject the hateful horrors shown by Blaine's sadistic 'visual mode,' but Detta rejoices in them. The part of her that has experienced rage and pain identifies with the violence of it, and is somehow pleased by it. I:4, II:356, III:564, IV:35

POL-KAM: The *pol-kam* is a dance, faster and lighter than a waltz, danced in the Great Hall of Gilead. Roland associates it with the courtesans, the jewel-like eyes of his lover Aileen, and the bright, shining electric lights of Gilead. I:150

SAI: Although used in low speech, *Sai* appears to be a form of address that originated in High Speech. (Nort, Tull's weed-eater, used this term when he spoke to Roland in the Tongue.) *Sai* is a term of respect and can be roughly translated as 'sir' or 'madam'. IV:178

**SILL: To desire or to yearn. If used patronizingly, it means that the yearner longs for something childish. It is a word with many subtle innuendoes. I:172

TET: A group of people with the same interests and goals. III:83, III:355

**WURDERLAK: When Roland meets with Walter in the golgotha, he fears that his guilt over Jake's death has made him into a *wurderlak*, or a kind of shape-shifter. As he says, 'He was a *wurderlak*, lycanthropus of his own making, and in deep dreams he would become the boy and speak in strange tongues.' In the new *Gunslinger*, this term is replaced with *werewolf*. I:211 (*werewolf*)

MID-WORLD ARGOT
AND ROLAND'S
VERSIONS OF OUR
WORDS

AMOCO: In Mid-World, AMOCO: LEAD FREE is a legend of unknown meaning. Roland once met a hermit who gained a religious following by placing an Amoco gasoline hose between his legs and preaching wild, guttering, sullen sermons. Amoco became the totem of a thunder god who was worshipped with a half-mad slaughter of sheep. I:167–68

ASTIN: This is Roland's pronunciation of 'aspirin.' II:105

BEER BARREL: An enormous antique revolver. IV:201

BIG CHARLIE WIND: The Big Charlie Wind is a death wind. Mercy, from River Crossing, refers to the Big Charlie Wind that 'came and almost blew the steeple off the church'. III:339–40

BIG HAT STOCK: Threaded stock. Good quality horses. Useable stock. IV:259

**BOCKS: Dollars. It is the currency used in Tull. I:23

**BOLT AND BAH: Crossbow and bolt. A Mid-World weapon. Although Roland's *ka-tel* trained with the bolt and bah, they tend to be used by those without access to guns. I:9

BOOBYRIGGED: This is a term from Lud and is used by Tick-Tock. It means boobytrapped. III:490

BORDER DWELLERS: Border Dwellers are the men and women who live on the edges of the Mohaine Desert. They burn devil grass and live in huts with sod roofs. Their diet consists of corn, beans and peas. (*See* BORDER DWELLERS entry in the CHARACTERS section.)

BRAIN STORM: A stroke. IV:787, E:226

BRAKES: The Brakes are those tangled areas of mixed vegetation and woody bushes that exist in the low hills near the Western Sea. II:321

**BUCKAS: Bucka wagons. Probably a bit like old covered wagons. Like the coaches, bucka wagons once followed the Great Road through the Mohaine Desert. I:3

BUGGER-MAN: This is the Mid-World term for the Bogeyman. II:321

BULLDINK: This term is used in River Crossing and is the equivalent of 'bullshit.' III:340

BUX: Roland-speak for dollars (bucks). II:390

CARVERS: Five shot revolvers. They are also called BEER BARRELS. (*See* BEER BARRELS.)

CATACLYSM: *See* GREAT POISONING (this section)

CHEELET: This is Roland's pronunciation of the antibiotic Keflex. II:175

**CLAN-FAMS: Extended family units, or clans. Many of these inbred groups live on the borders of the Mohaine Desert. I:18

CLEARING AT THE END OF THE PATH: This is a euphemistic, but comforting, term for death. IV:155, IV:188, IV:282

CLOUTS: Multiple purpose cloths that can be used for cleaning, for diapers, or to tie back hair. IV:159, IV:275

**COMMALA: A Mid-World dance also known as the Sowing Night Cotillion. *See entry under* HIGH SPEECH.

CONVERSATIONAL: A Conversational is a political event. In every Barony of Mid-World, the week leading up to Fair-Day is full of Conversationals, which are like political luncheons. Important people come from all corners of a Barony to meet and palaver. The main Conversational takes place on Fair-Day itself. IV:576

COOZEY: Jonas calls Roland a 'coozey little brat'. IV:610

CORPSE-LAMPS: This is the name Roland gives for the lights he sees floating in the underground river located below the Cyclopean Mountains. I:166

CORVETTE: In the Barony of Mejis, a corvette is a small leather purse, big enough for a few coins. It tends to be carried by women rather than men, but men occasionally use them as well. Literally speaking, corvette means 'little packet.' As can be seen, however, a more practical definition is 'little purse.' IV:356

COSY: This term is from Lud. Gasher tells Jake 'you've got a cosy look about you.' Cosy seems to mean clever or full of guile. III:411

COTTON GILLIES: A cotton gilly is a fancy term for a common whore. A gilly (or sheevin) is a side-wife taken by a man who already has a legal wife. She is a mistress, but one who will be faithful to the man she serves. A cotton gilly goes with whomsoever has enough ready cash. Gert Moggins of the Travellers' Rest uses this term for herself and the other girls. IV:563

COTTONWOOD: This is a tree that grows near the desert beaches of the Western Sea. Eddie makes a travois out of it in order to drag Roland north. II:186

CRADLE: A station or homeport. It can also mean headquarters. III:417

CRIP SPACES: This term is actually used by Eddie, king of good taste. It refers to the handicapped spaces in a parking lot. IV:100

CROSSTREE: Gallows tree from which men are hanged. I:119

CRUNK: The dialect spoken by Mejis *vaqueros*. IV:726

CUCHILLO: Spanish for knife. This term is used in Hambry. IV:458

CULLY: This word seems roughly equivalent to the British term 'lad.' We hear it in Lud and then again in Hambry. When Roland pulls his revolver on Gasher, Gasher replies, 'Put it away, my cully . . . Put it away, my dear heart. Ye're a fierce trim, ay, that's clear, but this time you're outmatched.' Susan calls Cuthbert 'cully' when she gives him a corvette with a note in it for Roland. Later, Coral Thorin uses the term when she addresses her lover, Eldred Jonas. It can be used negatively as well. Rhea calls Roland a 'murdering cull' after he shoots Ermot, her pet snake. III:491, IV:182

CUNNING: As in 'a cunning little baby.' Sweet, clever, amazing, perfectly made. IV:174

DAB HAND: To have a 'dab hand' at an activity means that you are good at it. The term is used in Hambry. IV:228

DANCE OF EASTERLING: *See* MID-WORLD HOLIDAYS in APPENDIX II.

DEMON MOON: *See* MID-WORLD MOONS located at the beginning of this Concordance.

DEUCIES: This term is used by the Pubes of Lud. It is a negative term for a person and seems to imply that they are either cowardly or foolish. III:441

DEVIL DUST/DEVIL POWDER: This is Roland's term

for cocaine. It reminds him of devil grass. (*See* DEMONS/
SPIRITS/DEVILS entry in the CHARACTERS section.)

DEVIL GRASS: Devil grass is a narcotic weed that grows in
the waste lands of Mid-World. It is both poisonous and addictive. Those who become addicted to the grass are usually too
poor to afford alcohol. They begin by smoking this nasty
weed and end up chewing it. Chewers have green teeth and a
rank stench. Devil grass gives its users dreams, nightmares,
then death. It kills faster than liquor. Border Dwellers use devil
grass for fuel since they have little else to burn. It gives off a
greasy light and many believe that beckoning devils dance in
the flames. (*See* DEMONS/SPIRITS/DEVILS entry in the
CHARACTERS section.)

DIM, THE: *Dim* has several meanings. Sorcerers and witches
can make themselves *dim*, or difficult to see. When a person
is *dim* he or she is not invisible, merely shadowy. 'The dim' is
like déjà vu. When Susan meets with Roland she feels the dim
– or the sense that she has met him before – and feels faint.
IV:322, IV:524, E:223

DIPOLAR: According to Tick-Tock, the computers of Lud
run on either dipolar or unipolar circuits. III:492

DJINNI: An evil genie. III:435

DOCKER'S CLUTCH: This is Roland's term for a
gunholder. He uses it for both hidden gunholders (like the
one under the counter at Clements Guns and Sporting Goods)
and shoulder holsters. II:397, III:16

DOCKEY: Chicory. In River Crossing, they make coffee from dockey. III:323–24

DOLINA BLANKET: A kind of blanket found in Hambry. IV:356

'DOWNERS: One of Gilead's meal times. Marten (a secret glutton) put sugar in his coffee in mornings and at 'Downers. II:111

DROGUE AND FORWARD: Mid-World cowboys hired to protect caravans will ride drogue and forward to protect their convoy. In other words, they will ride before and behind. E:194

DROMEDARY: Mid-World term for a camel. IV:714

DUST DEVILS: These dust whirlwinds gyrate over the hardpan of the Mohaine Desert. I:7

ELEPHAUNTS: Roland heard of these great creatures when he was a child. They are supposed to bury their own dead. I:121

FAIR-DAY GOOSE: The person who won one of Gilead's Fair-Day Riddling contests was awarded a prize goose. III:581

FAIR-DAY RIDDLING: In Gilead-that-was, riddling was taken very seriously. Riddling contests were held during each of the seasonal festivals, especially during the festivals of Wide Earth and Full Earth. Riddles were considered to be full of power and were thought to make the crops grow stronger. III:578–80

FAKEMENT: It can mean an event or a scene. It can also mean a falsehood. III:409, III:438

FARO: One of the games (along with Watch Me) damned by Sylvia Pittston during her Tull sermons. I:54

**FEAST OF JOSEPH FAIRTIME: People could buy captive tubes of swamp gas at this fair. The swamp gas tubes looked something like neon. In the new *Gunslinger*, this fair is renamed the Feast of Reaptide Fair. I:204

FIN DE AÑO: The end of the year celebration. Reap Night. IV:170

FIREDIM: A sparkling jewel that reflects light. They come in a variety of colors. Some are red like rubies, some are green like emeralds. Tick-Tock's eyes sometimes glow like firedims. IV:240

FIREDIM TUBES: In Lud, they call neon tubes 'firedim tubes'. III:507

**FOT-SULS: Roland's version of Jake's word for the phosphorescent man-made 'fossils' embedded in the rock below the Cyclopean Mountains. It probably refers to neon tubing. I:204

FOTERGRAFFS (also spelled FOTTERGRAFFS and FOTTERGRAFS): Technically speaking, this is not a Mid-World term at all but Roland's rather garbled version of our word 'photograph.' II:389, IV:91

**FRESH COMMALA: Another term for the season of Sowing, also known as New Earth. *See* COMMALA in the HIGH SPEECH section, GILEAD FAIR-DAYS located at the beginning of this Concordance, and MID-WORLD HOLIDAYS in APPENDIX II.

FULL EARTH: One of Mid-World's seasonal festivals. *See* GILEAD FAIR-DAYS at the front of this volume and in APPENDIX II.

**GILLY: A gilly is a concubine or mistress. Its plural form is gillies. Arthur Eld had forty gillies, and it is from one of these women that Roland is descended. Although many great men of Mid-World had gillies and many more were born of gillies, there is a certain disgrace attached to this state of being. In Mid-World, where mutations abound and where sterility is common, gillies are seen as necessary if not necessarily respectable. Roland is shocked to find out that Susan will soon be Hart Thorin's gilly. Susan Delgado receives disapproving stares from the women of Hambry because of the 'service' she is about to render to the town's mayor. In the new version of *The Gunslinger*, this word is spelt 'jilly.' I:20 *(jilly-child)*, I:82, IV:261

GLAMMER: Enchantment and magic. I:232

GOLGOTHA: A place of the skull, or a dead place. I:215

GRAF: An apple beer that seems to be a specialty of Mid-World. It is offered to Roland, Susannah, Eddie and Jake when they visit the elderly people of River Crossing. It is also served in Hambry. Mid-World is full of orchards (both Roland and

Tick-Tock have memories of them) so it makes sense that the world's drink of choice is a kind of hard cider. III:319

GRAYS: *See* GRAYS listed in the CHARACTERS section.

GREAT FIRE: *See* GREAT POISONING, below

GREAT POISONING: Also known as the OLD WAR, THE GREAT FIRE, or THE CATACLYSM. This horrific event took place more than a thousand years before the grandparents of the River Crossing folks were born. It caused the animal, plant and human populations to give birth to muties, and it made great swathes of land turn into Waste Land. It was the beginning of all Mid-World's troubles. III:390

GREENBERRY BUSHES: These bushes grow in the Great Western Woods. III:92

GREEZY: This is Lud-speak for 'greasy.' III:452

**GROW BAG: A grow bag is a magic bag that grows what you need. During his palaver with Walter in the golgotha, Roland wonders whether his grow bag will grow tobacco. I:226

GUARD O' THE WATCH: This is Roland's term for officers of the law. He uses it both for the guards of his world and the police of our world. I:119–20

GUIJARROS: In Spanish this means cobbles or pebbles. Both the stone walls and the cracked *guijarros* of Rhea's roof are slimed with mold. IV:496

GULLYWASH: This is Gasher-speak and is probably part of Lud's slang. It seems to mean penis. III:410

GUNNA: *See* HIGH SPEECH

HACI: Short for hacienda, or house. IV:240

HAI: This is the term Roland uses to call his hawk, David. Cuthbert also uses it to cheer Roland during his battle against Cort. I:185, I:186

HARRIERS: The harriers of Mid-World are like outlaws or bandits. They rob, loot, murder and destroy. The Grays are harriers, as are the Big Coffin Hunters. Harriers blinded Mercy of River Crossing with a branding iron because they said she was 'looking at em pert.' III:309

HEART STORM: *See* BRAIN STORM

HILE: Roland greets Blaine by saying 'Hile, Blaine.' Blaine returns with 'Hile, Gunslinger.' This verbal exchange makes Susannah Dean think of Hitler, but it is actually a formal Mid-World greeting. This term can also be used to call animals. IV:329

HOCK BUSHES: These bushes grow in the Great Western Woods. III:92

HONOR STANCE: This is the term Cort uses for a boxer's opening stance. The lobstrosities of the Western Sea Beach stand like this whenever there is an approaching wave. II:8

HOWLERS: This is Roland's term for sirens. II:171

HUBBERWOMEN: Hubberwomen are magical women or fey women. E:194

HUNTRESS MOON: *See* MID-WORLD MOONS located at the beginning of this Concordance.

IRONWOOD: In 'The Little Sisters of Eluria,' we are told that this tree is also known as the seequoiah. Its wood is extremely hard and durable. In fact, it's too hard to burn. The three doors which Roland finds on Lobstrosity Beach, next to the Western Sea, are made of ironwood. Cort's stick was also made of this durable material. I:183, E:162

JESUS DOG (CROSS DOG): This is the term used to describe dogs with a cruciform shape upon their chest fur. As Roland finds out when he faces the Little Sisters of Eluria, they can prove extremely useful when confronting vampires. (For page references, see ELURIA CHARACTERS in the CHARACTERS section.)

**JILLY-CHILD: A young jilly or gilly. *See entry under* GILLY.

KISSING MOON: *See* MID-WORLD MOONS, located at the beginning of this Concordance.

**KUVIAN NIGHT SOLDIER: It seems likely that the Kuvian Night Soldiers were a band of assassins. This term does not appear in the new version of *The Gunslinger*.

LAST TIMES: This is Sylvia Pittston's term for the End of the World. I:44

LUCIFERS: Matches. IV:751

MAGDA-SEEN: This is Roland's misinterpretation of the word *magazine*, and it doesn't make any sense to him. He can't figure out what Magda must have seen. II:61

MALHABLADA: This is a Spanish term which means 'woman who speaks badly' (or, in the case of Susan Delgado, a woman who uses bad words). IV:297

MANDRUS: Mandrus's common name is 'whore's blossoms.' It is a venereal disease (endemic in cities such as Lud) that appears to have quite a lot in common with syphilis. The oozing sores apparent in the later stages of the disease are particularly horrific. III:409

MANTO: In Hambry, a manto is a cloak. In other places, it is a slang term for a homosexual. Kimba Rimer once jokingly called Clay Reynolds 'Sai Manto,' referring to his cloak, but Reynolds later murdered him for doing so. IV:593

MEGRIMS: Fears, fantasies. As Susan walks to Rhea's hut for the first time, she sings to keep 'the worst of her megrims away.' IV:154

MESCALINE: We have this in Our World too. Cort called mescaline the philosopher's stone. Cort maintained that the old gods pissed over the desert and made this hallucinogen. The use of drugs (usually to communicate with speaking demons) was part of a gunslinger's training. *See* APPENDIX II: MID-WORLD DRUGS.

METAL/METALED: To Roland, a road covered with asphalt is a 'metaled road.' III:395

MID-SUMMER: One of Gilead's Fair-Days. *See* GILEAD FAIR-DAYS at the beginning of this Concordance, and MID-WORLD HOLIDAYS located in APPENDIX II.

MOTHER-ROOT: Umbilical cord. III:241

MOZO: Spanish for porter. Used in Hambry for male servants. IV:350

MUTIES: This is the Mid-World term for mutants. *For more information*, see MUTANTS in the CHARACTERS section.

NECK-POPPED: Hanged. I:114

**NEW EARTH: The season corresponding to deep spring. See GILEAD FAIR-DAYS at the beginning of this volume. *See also* MID-WORLD HOLIDAYS located in APPENDIX II.

OLD WAR: *See* GREAT POISONING

OUTLANDERS: To the Pubes, outlanders are people not from Lud. III:444

PALAVER: To talk or hold counsel. *Palaver* tends to mean the exchange of important ideas. Roland and the Man in Black make palaver in the golgotha. Roland and his *ka-tet* hold palaver with the elderly residents of River Crossing. I:94

Appendix I

PAÑUELO: Handkerchief. A Spanish term used in Hambry. IV:469

PARD: Short for 'pardner.' We use this term in Our World too. It means partner or comrade. E:196

PAREY and MINGO: Two of Mejis's crops. IV:428

PATRONO: A term used in Hambry which means employer or boss. It is similar to the Spanish word *patrón*. IV:298

PEDDLER'S MOON: *See* MID-WORD MOONS located at the beginning of this Concordance.

PERT: It means impertinent or impertinently. (Mercy of River Crossing is blinded with a branding iron for looking 'pert' at some harriers.) However, it can also mean smart, leaning towards 'smart ass.' Coming from the right person, however, it can be meant somewhat admiringly. Gasher refers to Jake as 'pert,' implying that he has a smart mouth but is also quick-witted and gutsy. III:453, III:487

PETTIBONE: An alcoholic drink. IV:315

PIG BACK: Roland's term for piggy back. III:78

POINTS (WICKETS): This game was played in Mid-World with croquet balls. I:65

POISONING: *See* GREAT POISONING

POKE: A small bag for carrying meat, tobacco, or other substances. We use this term in Our World as well. I:38

**POKEBERRIES: Along with corn, this is one of the crops grown between Tull and Pricetown. I:18

POPKIN: A sandwich. II:42

POSSE: Roland's term for New York policemen. II:387.

PUBE: *See* PUBES listed in the CHARACTERS section.

PULER: A young man. Cort uses this term to address Roland. We hear it again in Hambry. I:179

PULING: Crying, moaning, and making a fuss. II:172

QUESA: A dance similar to a simple reel. IV:263

QUICKPIT: Pit of quicksand. III:345

REAP: The festival of Reap (also known as *Charyou Tree*) is the harvest festival and the time of harvest sacrifice. In the days of Arthur Eld, it was celebrated with human sacrifice. By Roland's time stuffy guys, and not people, were thrown on Reap fires. During the season of Reap, people decorate their houses, and their stuffy guys, with Reap charms. Reap charms can also be painted on the body or worn like pendants. *See entries under* STUFFY GUYS in the CHARACTERS section, MID-WORLD HOLIDAYS in APPENDIX II, and GILEAD FAIR-DAYS located at the front of this Concordance.

ROSILLO: Susan Delgado calls her horse Pylon a *rosillo*. IV:300

ROT, THE: A disease which often affects the Border Dwellers of the Mohaine Desert. It sounds a bit like leprosy. People suffering from this disease are called 'rotters.' I:9, I:12

RUSSEL: (*v*) A slang term that means to take a woman by force. II:43

SAI: *See entry in the* HIGH SPEECH *section*

SALIG: A salig looks like a crocodile or alligator and lives in the swamps of Mid-World. IV:87

SANDAY: In Mejis, this is the traditional cowboys' day of rest. IV:356

SAWGRASS: Grass that grows on the foothills of the Cyclopean Mountains. I:128

SAWSEE: This is Roland's confused term for a seesaw. III:51

SECRET CODE: This code is used by gunslingers when they communicate by carrier pigeon. The phrase below means 'Farson moves east . . . Forces split, one big, one small. Do you see anything unusual?' IV:329–30

SELLIAN DIALECTS: Roland used to speak the Sellian dialects, but he has forgotten all but the curses. III:355

SERAPE: Worn in Mejis and New Canaan by both men and women. It is a bit like a poncho or cape. IV:356

SHEEVIN (also SEEFIN): Literally speaking, sheevin means 'quiet little woman.' In practice, it means side-wife or mistress. IV:260

SHIPMATES DISEASE: Roland and Eddie suffer from this even though they are on dry land. It is caused by nutritional deficiencies brought on by a lack of fruit and greens. II:301

SHOOTERS: Guns. E:187

**SHOOT-UP MONEY: Money gained from the gun. It can be money earned by a hired gunman. I:21

SIDE LINE OF DESCENT: Descended from a gilly. The line of Deschain is from one of Arthur Eld's side lines of descent. In other words, Roland's ancestor was born to one of the Eld's side wives. IV:230

SIGUL: A sigul is a sign, symbol, or insignia which is secret and full of meaning. It often has religious, political, or magical significance. III:490

**SILFLAY: To graze. This word actually comes from the novel *Watership Down*. I:146

SILK-ARSE GENNELMAN: This is a crass Lud-term for somebody who is well-bred. III:491

SILVA COMPASS: This is a kind of compass used in Roland's world. In *The Gunslinger*, one of the Border Dwellers gives Roland a stainless steel silva compass and bids him give it to Jesus. I:8

SINGLET: A piece of clothing worn by Cort when he battles the apprentices. I:183

**SISSA: Sister. I:20

SLO-TRANS ENGINES: Blaine's engines are slo-trans engines. Slo-trans technology was supposed to be immune to malfunction, but this is obviously not the case, since Blaine himself admits that he is going mad. IV:17

SLUMGULLION: This is a derogatory term for a man. III:340

SNOOD: A head covering worn by women in Mid-World, especially when they are in formal attire. IV:244

SOFT: Go forward carefully, slowly. Keep your emotions under control. III:382, IV:83

SOMBRERA/SOMBRERO: Wide brimmed hats worn in Hambry. IV:483

SOWING: One of Gilead's Fair-Days. It is also known as **New Earth and **Fresh Commala. *See* GILEAD FAIR-DAYS at the beginning of this Concordance. *See also* MID-WORLD HOLIDAYS in APPENDIX II.

SOWING NIGHT COTIL': *See* COMMALA

SPARK-LIGHTS: Spark-lights (also known as filament lights) are electric flambeaux or electric lights. It is a Hambry term. In the new *Gunslinger* we find out that the Coach Road leading from Pricetown to Tull was once lined with spark-lights. By the time Roland passes through, they are all dead. I:18, IV:188

SQUINT: We hear this term in both Lud and Hambry. Like 'cully,' it is usually used when talking to – or about – young men. However, it seems more pejorative. This term can also have sexual connotations. In boy-loving Lud, Gasher tells Roland that he must hand over the squint, meaning Jake. III:410

STAR WHISKEY: This is the best whiskey found in Tull. I:40

SWAMP GAS TUBES: These tubes looked a bit like neon. They were sold at Feast of Joseph fairtime. I:204

SWEETCHEEKS BERRY: This is Gasher's term for a boy-virgin. III:450

SWEETMEATS: This is a Lud term for testicles. III:491

TACK-SEES: Roland's term for taxis. II:385

THANKEE-SAI: 'Thankee-sai' is the polite term for thank-you. Its equivalent is 'thank you, sir,' or 'thank you, madam.' These words are accompanied by three brisk taps upon the throat with the fingers of the right hand. At the beginning of *Wizard and Glass* we learn that when addressing men, one should use the left hand and tap the breast bone. However, this seems to be extremely formal. When Roland and his young friends are in Hambry, they use their right hands and tap their throats when thanking elders of either sex. IV:23, IV:235

THINKING CAP: In Roland's world, as in our world, children are sometimes told to put on their thinking caps. On Roland's level of the Tower this is based on a story about the Guardians. Supposedly, each Guardian carried an extra brain on the outside of its head, in a hat. This apocryphal tale had a true basis. The Guardians have radar dishes sticking out of their skulls. III:54

THREADED STOCK: Threaded stock is normal stock, or those born without mutations. Threaded stock can be born of threaded stock, but they can also be born from late generation muties. (In Mid-World, they describe this process by saying the bloodlines are clarifying.) Despite what the Horsemen's Association want Roland to believe during his stay in Hambry, there are few muties left in the Outer Arc. Even in the area outside of Candleton (an area hard hit by the mutating disaster), threaded stock is on the increase. I:23, IV:16

TOOTER FISH: This is Roland's term for tuna fish. He thinks it's tasty. II:42

TOUCH, THE: The ability to read minds, and also to see into the past or the future. It is similar to ESP. In the new *Gunslinger*, it is described as half empathy, half telepathy. I:192, IV:282, IV:330

TRAINING, THE: All apprentice gunslingers must undergo 'The Training'. In Roland's time, Cort was in charge of this arduous process. Before him, his father Fardo taught the apprentices. For the most part, apprentice gunslingers were the sons of gunslingers. In other words, they belonged to the aristocracy of Mid-World. However, it is entirely possible that very young boys who showed promise were allowed to enter this small select group.

The Training culminated in a rite of passage, enacted in the Square Yard, just beyond the Great Hall of Gilead. Eighteen was the usual age for this passage of an apprentice into manhood, although it could happen as late as twenty-five. Those who had not faced the all-or-nothing test by that age usually slipped into obscurity as freeholders. The litany and ritual of this rite were strictly observed, and had not changed for centuries. The apprentice entered the yard by the west entrance — that which faced the barbarian forests. The teacher entered from the east — that which faced the Great Hall and all of its symbolic civilization. The apprentice and his teacher faced one another from opposite ends of the yard and engaged in a ritual colloquy.

'Have you come here for a serious purpose, boy?'

'I have come for a serious purpose, teacher.'

'Have you come as an outcast from your father's house?'

'I have so come, teacher.'

'Have you come with your chosen weapon?'

'I have so come, teacher.'

'What is your weapon?'

The final twist in this traditional interplay was intended to give the teacher a slight advantage. He could adjust his battle plan by knowing his student's method of attack. It also meant that in order to move from childhood into manhood, the student had to be both wily and quick.

Only those who bested their teacher were permitted to exit through the east gate. Those who failed (and many did) were sent west, as exiles. In the end, the all-or-nothing aspect of the Training proved to be one of the Affiliation's weaknesses, since embittered failures, such as Eldred Jonas, took up the cause of John Farson, Gilead's great enemy.

The apprentice who won his guns was not yet entitled to the sandalwood-handled firearms of a true, mature gunslinger. Instead, he was given an apprentice's guns, ones less ornate than those he would wear later in life. I:183–84

TRIG/ TRIGGERS/TRIGGIE: Clever. A word used both in Lud and in Hambry. It implies both craftiness and untrustworthiness. III:432, III:493

TRIG COVE: This term can be translated roughly as 'clever bastard.' It can be used affectionately. For example, Gasher calls Tick-Tock 'a trig cove.' III:410, III:432

UNIPOLAR CIRCUITS: *See* DIPOLAR CIRCUITS

VAQUERO (VAQ): Spanish for cowboy. This term is used in Hambry. IV:639

WASTING DISEASE: A disease found in Mejis. It might be similar to TB. IV:388

WATCH ME: This is a Mid-World card game. People usually place bets, so it can be rather dangerous. People are often killed at Watch Me tables. The phrase 'Watch Me' can also mean 'You have a deal.' I:22, III:382, IV:20

**WAY OF THE GUN: This is another term for the Training. I:109

WEE SHIM: A small child. IV:577–78

WEED-EATER: Somebody addicted to chewing devil grass. I:22

WENBERRY: Wenberries are like strawberries. III:384

WERY: This is Gasher's way of pronouncing 'very.' III:414

WHEELS: An archaic form of measurement still used in Gilead. In *The Waste Lands*, Blaine tells us that a distance of 8,000 wheels is roughly equivalent to 7,000 miles. That means that there are about 1.143 wheels to a mile. However, in *Wizard and Glass* a tricky Blaine tells us that 900 mph is the same as 530 wheels per hour. In this second instance one wheel is equivalent to 1.7 miles. Either Blaine is being sneaky or he has blown more circuits than he thinks. III:312, III:560, IV:185

WHITE, THE: The White is the force of good. When Aunt Talitha of River Crossing learns that Roland is a gunslinger, she says to her companions, 'Behold ye, the Return of the White! After evil ways and evil days, the White comes again! Be of good heart and hold up your heads, for ye have lived to see the wheel of *ka* begin to turn once more!' To the beleaguered inhabitants of Mid-World, the aristocratic gunslingers are the knights of the White. In an unstable and violent present, they represent a stable and peaceful past, a kind of golden age. Roland's father, Steven Deschain, is often referred to as the last lord of light. Both the Affiliation and the ancient hero Arthur Eld represent the White, and yet the term means more than a particular political faction, allegiance, or social class.

The true meaning of the White relates back to the

philosophy embedded in the Old Tongue or High Speech, a philosophy of wholeness which seems to bear some resemblance to the Neoplatonic vision of the One. Just before Jake sees the rose in the deserted lot at Forty-Sixth Street and Second Avenue, he hears the voice of the White, which he finds indescribably beautiful:

> The humming grew. Now it was not a thousand voices but a million, an open funnel of voices rising from the deepest well of the universe. He caught names in that group voice, but could not have said what they were. One might have been Marten. One might have been Cuthbert. Another might have been Roland — Roland of Gilead.
>
> There were other names; there was a babble of conversation that might have been ten thousand entwined stories; but above all that gorgeous, swelling hum, a vibration that wanted to fill his head with bright white light. It was, Jake realized with a joy so overwhelming that it threatened to burst him to pieces, the voice of *Yes*; the voice of *White*; the voice of *Always*. It was a great chorus of affirmation, and it sang in the empty lot. It sang for him.

The White is wholeness and unity. It is the tapestry woven from many interlocking *ka-tets*. It contains both good and evil, yet seen in the greater context of the White there is no gray or black, only whiteness. Like white light, the White contains all colors within its balance. Maerlyn's Rainbow is a breaking up of this whiteness into a spectrum, many colors of which are troublesome. For example, the hungry, semi-sexual energy of Maerlyn's Grapefruit (the Pink One) proves disastrous for any who stare into its depths. III:155, III:171–72, III:354

WHITE TEA: A refreshing non-alcoholic drink. IV:231

WIDE-EARTH: One of Gilead's Fair-Days. *See* GILEAD'S FAIR-DAYS at the beginning of this Concordance. *See also* MID-WORLD HOLIDAYS in APPENDIX II.

WINE-BIBBER: A boozer. III:84

WINTER: One of Gilead's Fair-Days. *See* GILEAD'S FAIR-DAYS located at the beginning of this Concordance. *See also* MID-WORLD HOLIDAYS in APPENDIX II.

WITCHGRASS: A rank grass that grows in the Cyclopean Mountains. I:128

WRISTBANDS: Handcuffs. II:402

**YAR: Yes. I:208

YEAR'S END: One of Gilead's Fair-Days. *See* GILEAD'S FAIR-DAYS located at the beginning of this Concordance. *See also* MID-WORLD HOLIDAYS located in APPENDIX II.

MID-WORLD SAYINGS

ALL THINGS SERVE THE BEAM: This is a Mid-World truism. III:212–13

**ANIMALS THAT TALK BE TOUGH: Don't eat anything that can answer you back. Their flesh isn't pleasant. I:15

ARGYOU NOT ABOUT THE HAND YOU ARE DELT IN CORDS OR LIFE: A pithy phrase written on a sign in Hambry's Travellers' Rest. IV:214

BAD TIMES ARE ON HORSEBACK: Bad times are coming quickly. I:179

BEANS, BEANS, THE MUSICAL FRUIT. THE MORE YOU EAT, THE MORE YOU TOOT: We have this saying in Our World too. The raven Zoltan is very fond of it. I:10

BEHOLD YE, THE RETURN OF THE WHITE! AFTER EVIL WAYS AND EVIL DAYS, THE WHITE COMES AGAIN! BE OF GOOD HEART AND HOLD UP YOUR HEAD, FOR YE HAVE LIVED TO SEE THE WHEEL OF *KA* BEGIN TO TURN ONCE MORE: Aunt Talitha of River Crossing utters this pronouncement. III:317

BE SHARP IN YOUR LOOKS: Be on your guard. IV:379

Appendix I

BIRD AND BEAR AND HARE AND FISH, GIVE MY LOVE HER FONDEST WISH: This saying invokes the Guardians. IV:412

BLESS THE TURTLE: This saying also invokes the Guardians. IV:535

BUMBLER GOT YOUR TONGUE?: This is the equivalent of 'cat got your tongue?' III:452

CLEVER GIRLS GO TO HELL: IV:679

CRY OFF: Renege. Stop. I:179, IV:50, IV:64

DISTRESSAL OF A LADY: In Eluria, this is a legalistic euphemism for rape. E:161

DO BUMBLERS LEARN TO SPEAK BACKWARD? NO MORE THAN CATS CHANGE THEIR SPOTS: In other words, people don't change. IV:316

**DO THAT I BEG YA: Please do it. I:156

DO YER KEN?: This is a term Gasher uses for 'do you know?' III:409

DO YER KENNIT?: Do you understand? I:103, IV:256

**DO YOU SEE YOUR SISTER'S BUM?: This was one of Cort's sayings. It means 'What are you staring at?' I:231

DON'T MAKE THE MISTAKE OF PUTTING YOUR HEART TOO NEAR HIS HAND: Don't leave yourself emotionally vulnerable. II:113

FATHER, GUIDE MY HANDS AND HEART SO THAT NO PART OF THE ANIMAL WILL BE WASTED: IV:116

FAULT ALWAYS LIES IN THE SAME PLACE – WITH HIM WEAK ENOUGH TO LAY BLAME: This is one of Cort's sayings. II:194

**FIRST BLOOD! FIRST BLOOD TO MY BOSOM: Cuthbert says this when Roland begins to best Cort. It's what is said when the first blood is drawn during a coming-of-age battle. I:185

FOOL NOT YOUR MOTHER 'LESS SHE'S OUT OF FACE: In other words, don't lie. E:201

FOOLS ARE THE ONLY FOLK ON THE EARTH WHO CAN ABSOLUTELY COUNT ON GETTING WHAT THEY DESERVE: IV:200

'FOR A PRETTY': This doesn't have a direct translation. You often ask someone to do something 'for a pretty.' It seems sometimes to mean 'please.' It can also be a rhetorical statement added on to the end of a sentence. I:25, I:204, IV:28

FOR YOUR FATHER'S SAKE: This phrase is used frequently throughout the series. To do something for your father's sake is to do it for honor's sake. I:81, III:233, IV:27

GOOD RIDDANCE TO BAD SWILL: The Pubes of Lud use this term instead of 'Good riddance to bad rubbish.' III:447

GROOMS AND FISHERMEN ARE BORN TO LIE: III:347

GUNSLINGER LITANY: 'I do not aim with my hand; he who aims with his hand has forgotten the face of his father. I aim with my eye. I do not shoot with my hand; he who shoots with his hand has forgotten the face of his father. I shoot with my mind. I do not kill with my gun; he who kills with his gun has forgotten the face of his father. I kill with my heart.' It seems likely that the gunslinger litany was originally recited in the Tongue. III:19–20, III:94

**I CRY YOUR FAVOR: I ask for a favor. I:140

I CRY YOUR PARDON: I ask your forgiveness. IV:291

I HAVE FORGOTTEN THE FACE OF MY FATHER: This is a term often used by Roland. It is a phrase of shame. When one has forgotten the face of one's father, it means that one has behaved dishonorably. Mid-World is patriarchal, a cultural structure that is older than either the aristocracy of gunslingers (the Barons of Mid-World), or the kingship of Arthur Eld. When Eddie and Susannah visit the Cradle of Lud, they see the sculpted visages of 'stern men with the harsh faces of executioners who are happy in their work.' We do not know whether these men were judges, justices, politicians or legendary forefathers, but their sculpted faces, somehow reminiscent of Roman senators, tell us something about both the pride and the unrelenting harshness of the Great Old Ones. Like the Romans, or our own culture, they were guilty of *hubris*. III:242, IV:324

I WILL SET MY WATCH AND WARRANT ON IT: I'll bet on it, or I'll guarantee it. It's damn true. I:16, I:60, III:452

I WOT: 'I believe so' or 'I reckon so'. IV:130, IV:368

IF IT'S KA, IT WILL COME LIKE THE WIND: If it's meant to be, it will be. IV:197

IF YE'D STEAL THE SILVER FROM THE DINING ROOM, FIRST PUT THE DOG IN THE PANTRY: A famous saying from Cressia. IV:220

IT'S ALL THE SAME JOLLY FAKEMENT TO ME: This is a Lud term for 'It's all the same to me.' III:409

JILLY-COME-LATELY: A sarcastic comment about youth. An old woman can also look like a jilly-come-lately when compared to a much older woman. I:136

KA WAS A WHEEL, ITS ONE PURPOSE TO TURN, AND IN THE END IT ALWAYS CAME BACK TO THE PLACE WHERE IT HAD STARTED: This is another Mid-World truism. What you do comes back to haunt you. What goes around comes around. III:546

LEAD US NOT INTO TEMPTATION: In Our World, this phrase can be found in the Lord's Prayer. It is another one of the raven Zoltan's sayings. I:15

LEMON JUICE WON'T TAKE THE STAIN OUT OF A LADY'S REPUTATION: It's not easy to lose a bad rep. IV:178

LET YOUR SHADOW GROW. LET IT GROW HAIR ON ITS FACE: Wait until you're older. I:189, IV:134

**LET'S SHAKE A MILE: Let's get moving. I:99

LIFE FOR YOUR CROP: This is a Mid-World greeting. Roland uses it when he meets Brown, the Border Dweller. I:9

LONG DAYS AND PLEASANT NIGHTS/MAY YOU HAVE TWICE THE NUMBER: 'Long days and pleasant nights' is a polite greeting. 'May you have twice the number' is the correct response. I:9, IV:247

**MANY AND MANY-A: A long time ago. I:48

MAY YOUR DAYS BE LONG UPON THE EARTH Mid-World greeting. IV:176, IV:225

MAY YOUR LUCK RISE: IV:750

MY LIFE FOR YOU: Richard Fannin makes Tick-Tock repeat this sinister saying. III:540

NEVER IN LIFE: Never. I:196

**NO ONE EVER REALLY PAYS FOR BETRAYAL IN SILVER; THE PRICE OF ANY BETRAYAL ALWAYS COMES DUE IN FLESH: The cost of betrayal is dear. I:157

OH BITE IT!: This was Pat Delgado's favorite cuss. IV:301

ONLY A FOOL BELIEVES HE'S DREAMING BEFORE HE WAKES UP: Don't ignore the situation, deal with it! Also, hope for the best and expect the worst. III:352

**PASS-ON-BY COUNTRY: Ugly country. The land between Pricetown and Tull is pass-on-by country. I:18

RAIN, HEALTH, EXPANSION TO THE SPIRIT: This is a blessing used by Brown, the Border Dweller. I:14

RIDE THE HANDSOME: To Ride the Handsome is a Lud euphemism for dying. III:413

SCREW YOU AND THE HORSE YOU RODE IN ON: This is another one of Zoltan's favorite sayings. I:10

SEE THE TURTLE OF ENORMOUS GIRTH!: This is the first line of a poem Roland remembers from his childhood. For the complete verse, *see* MID-WORLD RHYMES in APPENDIX II.

**SHUT YOUR QUACK: Shut up. I:177

SO FELL LORD PERTH, AND THE COUNTRYSIDE DID SHAKE WITH THAT THUNDER: 'So Fell Lord

Perth' is a line from a longer poem. The story, very similar to that of David and Goliath, goes as follows:

> Lord Perth was a giant who went forth to war with a thousand men, but he was still in his own country when a little boy threw a stone at him and hit him in the knee. He stumbled, the weight of his armor bore him down, and he broke his neck in the fall.

Tick-Tock becomes very angry when Jake mentions this 'unlucky' story. Obviously, it parallels the interaction between the huge Tick-Tock and the very young Jake. III:494

SPARE NOT THE BIRCH SO YOU SPOIL NOT THE CHILD: Saying from the Great Book. Recounted by Roland. III:15

STICKS AND STONES WILL BREAK MY BONES YET TAUNTS SHALL NEVER WOUND ME: This is a variation on a saying from Our World. III:21

TAKE THE DEAD FROM THE DEAD: ONLY A CORPSE MAY SPEAK TRUE PROPHECY: We hear this saying in the Way Station's cellar, where Roland hears the speaking demon and then finds human remains in the wall. Speaking demons may only manifest where there has been a death, or where there are the remains of the dead. I:98

THE LUCK OF THE GALLOWS: This is why Roland takes a piece of the hangman's tree when he sees Hax killed. I:118

THE QUICKEST WAY TO LEARN ABOUT A NEW PLACE IS TO KNOW WHAT IT DREAMS OF: This is one of Roland's truisms. III:80

THE SUN IS GOING DOWN ON THE WORLD: This is Aunt Talitha's saying. It means the end of the world is coming. The world is dying. III:325

THE WHEEL OF KA TURNS AND THE WORLD MOVES ON: III:559

THE WISE THIEF ALWAYS PROSPERS: III:61

THE WORLD HAS MOVED ON: This term is used throughout the series. It means that things have changed, and that the world is now profoundly different from what it once was. I:23, I:44, III:51, III:305, III:428

THE WORLD WON'T MOVE ON TOMORROW: This was a term used in Gilead before the world really did move on. It means that there's time yet. I:190

THERE WILL BE WATER IF GOD WILLS IT: If it is meant to be, it will come to pass. I:46, III:34, IV:130

TIME GROWS SOFT: Time has grown erratic. I:149, IV:334

TIME IS A FACE UPON THE WATER: Mejis saying. The world has moved on and time has grown strange. IV:561

**TIME IS THE THIEF OF MEMORY: This is one of Vannay's sayings. I:128

TO COME TO THE CLEARING AT THE END OF YOUR PATH: To die. IV:155, IV:188, IV:282, E:161

**TO DRAW THE BLACK STONE: This is how gunslingers of old chose who would have to act as hangman. I:119

**TO PULL LEATHER: To draw your gun. I:146

**'WARE THE MAN WHO FAKES A LIMP: This was one of Cort's sayings. In other words, don't trust somebody who wants to be caught. I:101

WE'LL HAVE TO MOVE VERY FAST, OR WE'LL FIND OURSELVES BASTED IN A HOT OAST: In other words, our goose will be cooked. II:150

WELL-MET ('WE WERE WELL-MET'): A lovely saying. We met, and that is important. It is good that we met, etc. IV:198

WHAT HAS FASHED THEE SO?: What has upset you so much? IV:391

WHERE ELSE WOULD I BE? THE WEST END OF THE WORLD?: This is a Lud saying. III:469

WHY IS A CROOKED LETTER THAT CAN'T BE MADE STRAIGHT . . . NEVER MIND WHY: This is one of Cort's sayings. In other words, don't bother asking. I:149

WILL A STRANGE DOG BITE?: Basically, this is similar to 'your guess is as good as mine.' III:306

WILL YOU DRINK TO THE EARTH, AND TO THE DAYS WHICH HAVE PASSED UPON IT? WILL YOU DRINK TO THE FULLNESS WHICH WAS, AND TO FRIENDS WHO HAVE PASSED ON? WILL YOU DRINK TO GOOD COMPANY, WELL MET?: This toast is made by Roland in River Crossing. III:320

YER A FIERCE TRIM: This is a Lud term for 'you're a tough guy.' III:409

YOU MIGHT AS WELL TRY TO DRINK THE OCEAN WITH A SPOON AS ARGUE WITH A LOVER: II:342

YOU RUN WITHOUT CONSIDERATION AND YOU FALL INTO A HOLE: This is one of Cort's sayings. IV:360

YOUNG EYES SEE FAR: IV:218

YOUTH'S THE WINE WHAT MAKES OLD MEN DRUNK: Nasty old Gasher uses this phrase when he pretends to hump Jake. III:413

LANGUAGE OF THE LITTLE SISTERS OF ELURIA

Roland doesn't hear much of the Little Sisters' language, but what he does hear he cannot identify. It is neither Low Speech nor High Speech, and it sounds like no other language or dialect he has ever heard. Since the Little Sisters are not human, it seems likely that theirs is a demon-tongue. The following phrases are uttered by Sister Mary (Big Sister) when she and the others of her vampiric order feed on the unconscious, unnamed man in the Sisters' hospital tent in Eluria. The words are never translated.

CAN DE LACH, MI HIM EN TOW: E:198
RAS ME! ON! ON!: E:198
HAIS!: E:199

APPENDIX II:
MID-WORLD
MISCELLANY

MID-WORLD DANCES
**Commala (Sowing Night Cotillion or Sowing Night Cotil'): This was the name of Gilead's Spring Dance. The geometric steps of this dance were meant to mimic a courting ritual. I:162

Pol-kam: This dance was popular in Gilead. It was lighter and faster than a waltz. I:150

Quesa: A simple sort of reel. Danced in Hambry. IV:263

Waltz: Waltzing was popular in Gilead. I:150

MID-WORLD DISEASES
Blood-Sickness: This one sounds a bit like blood-poisoning, but it could also be another blood-related illness. III:340

Mandrus: A venereal disease found in Lud. It's also called Whore's Blossoms. III:409

Mutation: Mid-World's many mutations were caused by the Great Poisoning. *See* MUTANTS listed in the CHARACTERS section. *See also* THE GREAT POISONING listed under High Speech and Mid-World Terms.

Rabies: We have this one in Our World too. III:407, IV:535

Radiation Sickness: III:333

Ringworm: III:332

Rot: This disease affects the Border Dwellers of the Mohaine Desert. It is a lot like leprosy. I:9, I:12

Superflu: This one actually affects the alternative Topeka, not Mid-World. It is also known as Captains Trips and Tube-Neck. IV:91

Wasting Disease: IV:388

MID-WORLD DRUGS

Alder-bark: Helps bad breath. II:411

Graf: Strong apple beer. III:319

Mescaline: A hallucinogen that helps gunslingers see and communicate with demons. I:136

Pettibone: An alcoholic drink. IV:315

Sugar: Good for energy bursts. II:111

MID-WORLD GAMES

Castles: A game very much like chess. IV:292

Chancellor's Patience: IV:435

Children's Games: Jacks, tag, Johnny-Jump-My-Pony. IV:459

Croquet and Points: These games were popular among Gilead's ladies. In the new version of *Gunslinger* we find out that Points is played with ninepins. It sounds a bit like bowling. I:65

Faro: This is probably a betting card game, since Sylvia Pittston makes her followers repent playing it. I:54

**Mother Says: This children's game is similar to Simon Says. I:207

**Gran-Points: In this game you hold a bat and wait for a rawhide bird to be pitched. It sounds a bit like baseball. I:187

Watch-Me: This is one of Mid-World's card games. People tend to bet, and the games can get rather dangerous. The two man version of this is called both **Casa Fuerte** and **Hotpatch.** I:54, IV:513

MID-WORLD HOLIDAYS AND CARNIVALS

All-Saints Eve: In the new version of *The Gunslinger*, All-Saints Eve is replaced with Reap. I:28

Barons-Year-End parties: III:68

Easter Night: In the new version of *The Gunslinger*, the Easter Night Dance is replaced by the Sowing Night Cotillion.

Fair-Day Riddling: Riddling was an extremely important game in Mid-World-that-was. Riddling was believed to hold incredible power. A good Fair-Day Riddling contest would ensure that the crops grew well. III:578–79

Fair Days: Here is a list of Mid-World's seasonal Fair Days. III:578

> **Winter**
> **Wide Earth**
> **Sowing (New Earth or Fresh Commala)**
> **Mid-Summer**
> **Full Earth**
> **Reaping**
> **Year's End**

Feast of Joseph Fairtime: In the new version of *The Gunslinger*, this holiday is renamed **Feast of Reaptide.** I:204

Glowing Day: IV:232

MID-WORLD'S MUSICAL INSTRUMENTS

Fiddles: I:47

Guitars: IV:244

Way Gog Music: This instrument, which is a bit like a

bagpipe, isn't actually from Mid-World. It is played on the upper levels of the Tower. III:568

MID-WORLD RELIGIONS
In Mid-World, the Gods almost always seem to drink blood. E:157
Amoco, the Thunder God: I:167–68
Asmodeus: E:157
Baal: E:157
Christian (general): In Mid-World, Christians are called followers of the Jesus-man or of the God o' the Cross. E:157
   Methodism: I:30
Guardian Totems: *See* GUARDIANS OF THE BEAM, located in the CHARACTERS section.

MID-WORLD RHYMES
Ia. Rain in Spain (Found in the original version of *The Gunslinger*)
   The Rain in Spain falls mainly on the plain.
   There is joy and also pain
   but the rain in Spain falls mainly on the plain.

   Pretty-plain, loony-sane
   The ways of the world all will change
   and all the ways remain the same
   but if you're mad or only sane
   the rain in Spain falls mainly on the plain.

   We walk in love but fly in chains
   And the planes in Spain fall mainly in the rain

Ib. Rain in Spain I:75
In the new version of *The Gunslinger*, the second verse is replaced by the following verse:

> Time's a sheet, life's a stain
> All the things we know will change
> and all those things remain the same,
> but be ye mad or only sane,
> the rain in Spain falls mainly on the plain.

**2. Fire Rhyme I:146
In the new version of *The Gunslinger*, Roland says this rhyme before lighting his devil grass fire:
'Spark-a-dark, where's my sire? Will I lay me? Will I stay me? Bless this camp with fire.'

**3. Baby Bunting I:86, I:234
Baby bunting, baby dear, baby bring your basket here.
Chussit, chissit, chassit, bring enough to fill your basket.

4. Turtle Rhyme III:53

> See the TURTLE of enormous girth!
> On his shell he holds the earth.
> His thought is slow but always kind;
> He holds us all within his mind.
> On his back all vows are made;
> He sees the truth but mayn't aid.
> He loves the land and loves the sea,
> And even loves a child like me.

MID-WORLD SIGULS

Christian Medallions: One of these saves Roland from the Little Sisters of Eluria. E:217

Coffins and Blue Coffin Tattoos: These tattoos are worn by the Big Coffin Hunters. Tick-Tock of the Grays wears a coffin-shaped clock around his neck. III:486, IV:194

Dark Bells: The Dark Bells are the *sigul* of the Little Sisters' order. E:219

The Eye: This is the *sigul* of John Farson, but it is actually the *sigul* of the Crimson King. IV:114

Fist and Thunderbolt: This is a lot like Mid-World's version of the swastika. III:377

Jesus-man *Sigul*: A crucifix. E:161

Rose: The Little Sisters of Eluria wear the rose on their habits. It is the *sigul* of the Dark Tower. E:179

MID-WORLD SONGS

'A Hundred Leagues to Banberry Cross' (In the new *Gunslinger*, this is replaced with 'Careless Love') I:130

'Big Bottle Boogie' IV:710

'Careless Love' IV:153

'Captain Mills, You Bastard' IV:640

'Ease on Down the Road' I:130

'Golden Slippers' IV:307

'Hey Jude' I:18, I:130

'I am a Man of the Bright Blue Sea' IV:562

'Onward Christian Soldiers' I:31

'Play Ladies Play' IV:337

'Red Dirt Boogie' IV:588

'Shall We Gather at the River' I:51

'We All Shine On' (cut from the new *Gunslinger*)

'Woman I Love' IV:338

APPENDIX III: POLITICAL AND CULTURAL FIGURES (OUR WORLD)

The Dark Tower series contains many references to the culture, history, and politics of our *where* and *when*. Here is a list of some of the books, films, artists and historical figures mentioned.

ACTORS AND STAGE PERSONALITIES: Humphrey Bogart, Walter Brennan, Gary Cooper, James Dean, Cecil B DeMille, Clint Eastwood, Judy Garland, Robin Leach, Rich Little (comic), Butterfly McQueen, Marilyn Monroe, Paul Newman, Sidney Poitier, Jerry Reed, Burt Reynolds, Adam Sandler (comic), Jean Stapelton, Rod Steiger, Jimmy Stewart, Spencer Tracy, John Travolta, Jack Webb, Raquel Welch

BIBLICAL FIGURES/BIBLICAL STORIES: Adam, Daniel, David and Bathsheba, David and Goliath, Devil (Interloper), Shadrach, Mesach, Abednego, Samson and Delilah, Saint Matthew, Saint Paul, Saint Peter, Mary, Eve and the Serpent, Moses, Jezebel and King Ahaz, Jesus on the Mount, Star Wormwood, Jeremiah, Lazarus, Isaac, Moses

CIVIL RIGHTS FIGURES: Medgar Evers, Freedom Riders, Martin Luther King, Rosa Parks

Appendix III

CULTURAL AND HISTORICAL FIGURES: Alfred Adler (psychiatrist), Attila the Hun, Bonnie and Clyde, Buffalo Bill, Eratosthenes, Incas, Reverend Jim Jones, Christa McAuliffe, Wiley Post, Jack Ruby, Jimmy Swaggart (preacher)

FILM MAKERS: Woody Allen, Federico Fellini, Sergio Leone

FILMS: *The Craft, The Dark Crystal, Dr Jekyll and Mr Hyde, The Exorcist, Halloween, In the Heat of the Night, Gone with the Wind, The Last Starfighter, Mandingo, Old Yeller, One Flew over the Cuckoo's Nest, The Purple Rose of Cairo, Rambo, Robocop, The Shining, Smokey and the Bandit, Star Wars, The Terminator, Three Faces of Eve, War of the Zombies, Zorro***

MAGICIANS: Harry Blackstone, David Copperfield, Doug Henning, Harry Houdini

MUSICIANS: Allman Brothers, Anthrax, Hoagy Carmichael, Johnny Cash, Creedence Clearwater Revival, Bob Dylan, Duke Ellington, Marvin Gaye, Billie Holiday, Megadeth, Wayne Newton, Olivia Newton-John, Kiss, Tony Orlando and Dawn, Elvis Presley, Rolling Stones, David Lee Roth, Sex Pistols, Dodi Stevens, Donna Summer, Barbara Streisand, Led Zeppelin, ZZ Top

SONGS: 'Buffalo Gals,' 'Cinch Mountain Breakdown,' 'Darlin Katy,' 'Dr Love,' 'Double Shot (of My Baby's Love),' 'The Hippy-Hippy Shake,' 'Knock Three Times,' 'Love to Love You Baby,' 'Oxford Town,' 'Paint It Black,' 'Sharp Dressed Man,' 'Tube Snake Boogie,' 'Velcro Fly'

NOVEL, CARTOON, MYTHICAL, FILM AND FOLK-TALE CHARACTERS:
Alice (of Wonderland), Barbara Allen (folksong), Frodo Baggins and Sam Gamgee, Bambi, Bobbsey Twins, Charlie Brown and Lucy, Buckwheat, Edith Bunker, Casper the Friendly Ghost, Cheshire Cat, Claribell the Clown, Donald Duck, Ferdinand the Bull, Hansel and Gretel, Mars Henry, Humpty Dumpty, Icarus, Jack and the Beanstalk and the Giant, Janus, John Henry (folksong), Jove, Clark Kent, Keystone Kops, King Arthur, Little Lord Fauntleroy, Lois Lane, Philip Marlowe, Travis McGee, Merlin the Magician, Ronald McDonald, Narcissus, Oedipus, Old Yeller, Peter Pan and Captain Hook, Popeye, Puck, Rambo, Shane, Speedy Gonzales, Scheherazade, Spiderman, Superman, Thor, Tin Woodman, Ulysses, William Wilson

POLITICAL FIGURES
CUBA: Fidel Castro
GERMANY: Adolf Hitler
HAITI: Papa (Poppa) Doc Duvalier
USA: President Jimmy Carter, Barry Goldwater, President Lyndon B. Johnson, President John F. Kennedy, General MacArthur, Lee Harvey Oswald, President Ronald Reagan, President Harry S. Truman, Vice-President George Bush Sr.
USSR: Nikita Khrushchev
VIETNAM: Diem Brothers

RADIO, TELEVISION AND SPORTS PERSNALITIES:
Mel Allen (sports announcer), Athletics, Braves, George Brett, David Brinkley (news), Walter Cronkite (news), Dwight Gooden (baseball), Chet Huntley (news), Sugar Ray Leonard, Mets, Walter Payton (football), Royals, Yankees

TV PROGRAMS: *All in the Family, Brady Bunch, The Little Rascals, The Twilight Zone, Cheyenne, Dragnet, Gunsmoke, Hollywood Squares, Miami Vice, Peter Gunn, Journey to the Center of the Earth, The Rifleman, Three Faces of Eve*

WRITERS AND ARTISTS: Richard Adams, Thomas Hart Benton (painter), Clay Blaisdell, William Blake, William Peter Blatty (screenwriter), Robert Browning, Edgar Rice Burroughs, Raymond Chandler, William Cowper, Salvador Dali, Dante, Walt Disney, T.S. Eliot, William Faulkner, Chester Gould (cartoonist), Donald M. Grant (publisher), Alex Haley, Nathaniel Hawthorne, Robert E. Howard, Shirley Jackson, Roy Krenkel (artist), Michelangelo, George Orwell, Wayne D. Overholser, John D. MacDonald, Edgar Allan Poe, Frederick Remington (painter), Charles Schultz (cartoonist), William Shakespeare, Thomas Wolfe

BOOKS, STORIES AND POEMS: *Alice's Adventures in Wonderland, The Bridge of San Louis Rey, Catch-22, The Hobbit, King James Bible, Little Lord Fauntleroy, Look Homeward, Angel, Lord of the Flies,* 'The Lottery,' 'Love Song of J. Alfred Prufrock' (quoted by Blaine), *Mike Mulligan and his Steam Shovel, Peter Pan, The Plague, Punch* (magazine), *Roots, A Thousand and One Nights,* Tom Sawyer, *Shardik,* 'The Waste Land,' *Watership Down, Wizard of Oz, You Can't Go Home Again*

APPENDIX IV
MID-WORLD MAPS

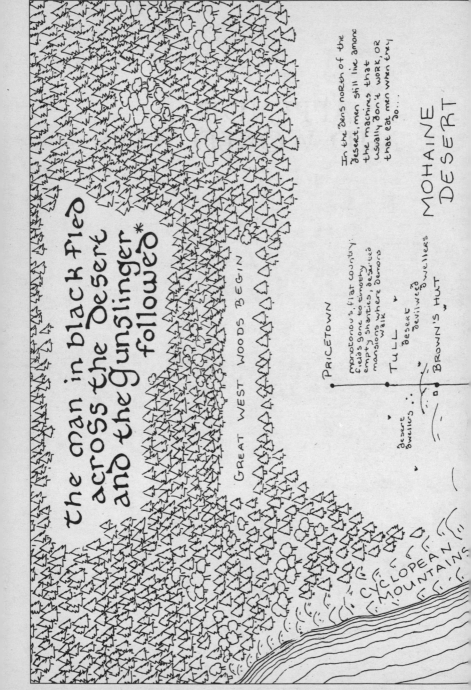

the man in black fled
across the Desert
and the gunslinger
followed*

GREAT WEST WOODS BEGIN

PRICETOWN

monotonous, flat country.
fields gone to timothy.
empty shanties, deserted
mansions where demons
walk

TULL

desert   Desert
Dwellers   Dwellers

BROWN'S HUT

In the Dens north of the
Desert, men still live among
the machines that
usually Don't WORK, OR
that eat men when they
Do......

MOHAINE
DESERT

CYCLOPEAN
MOUNTAINS

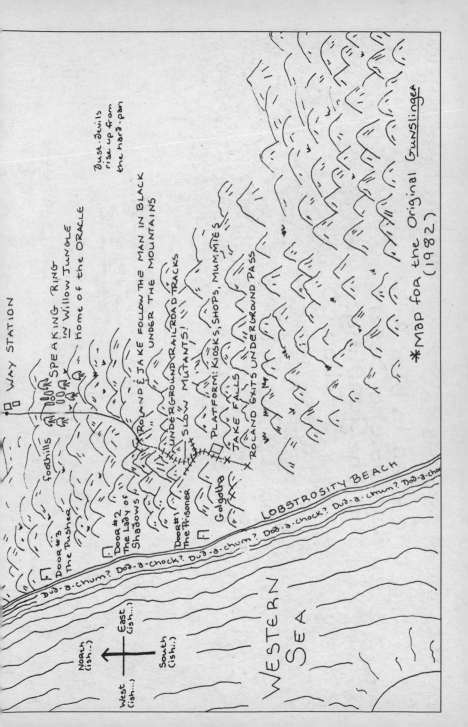

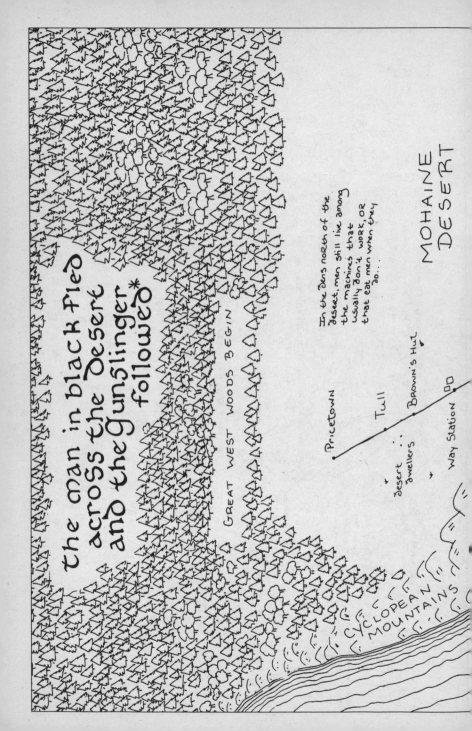

the man in black fled across the Desert and the gunslinger followed*

GREAT WEST WOODS BEGIN

In the Dens north of the desert, men still live among the machines that usually don't work, OR that eat men when they do....

MOHAINE DESERT

Pricetown

Tull

Desert dwellers

Brown's Hut

Way Station

CYCLOPEAN MOUNTAINS

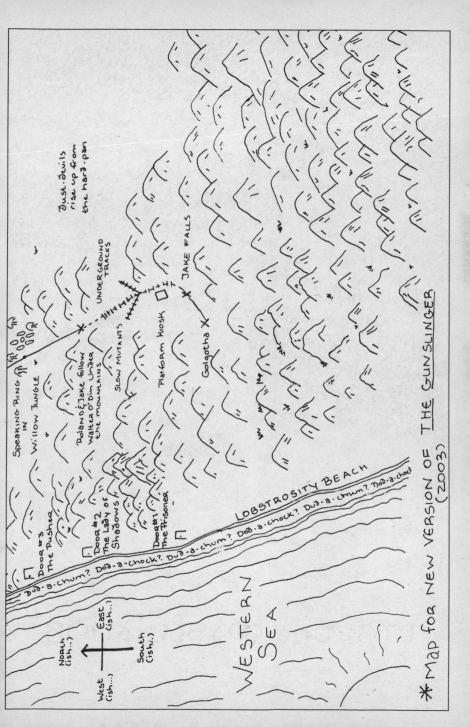

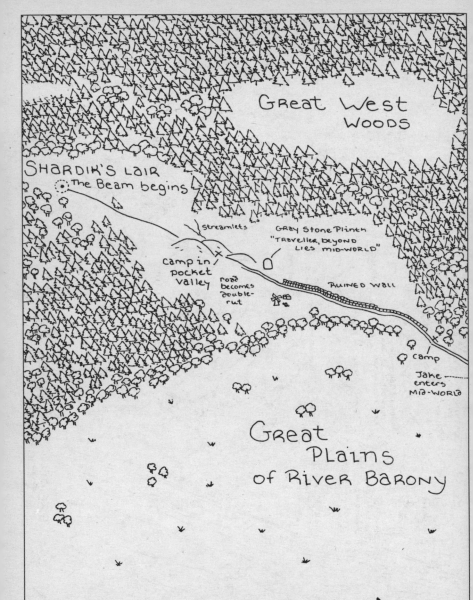

GREAT WEST WOODS

SHARDIK'S LAIR
• The Beam begins

streamlets

GRAY Stone Plinth
"TRAVELLER, BEYOND
LIES MID-WORLD"

Camp in
pocket
Valley

road
becomes
double-
rut

RUINED WALL

camp

Jake
enters
MID-WORLD

GReAT
PLAINS
of RIVER BARONY

DT3: the wastelands

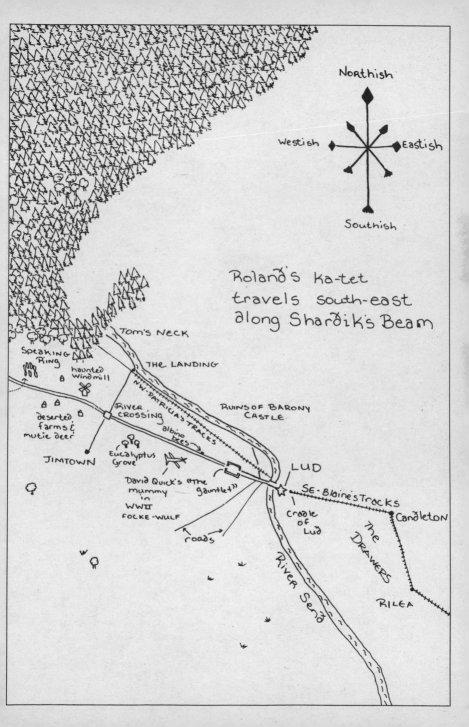

APPENDIX V:
READING GROUP
GUIDES

The Dark Tower I: The Gunslinger, Revised Edition, 2003

1. Who is Roland of Gilead? What is his ancestry? How does his personal history reflect the history of his land?

2. In many ways, Roland reminds us of the semimythical gunslingers of the late-nineteenth-century American West. Like them, he is simultaneously part lawman and part outlaw. Are there any figures from folklore, history, or film that remind you of Roland? How is he similar to them and how is he different? Would you call Roland a hero or an antihero?

3. Why does the term *man in black* have such emotional impact? What images do we automatically associate with such a figure? Do you believe that Walter is actually human? Is he demonic? What role does the demonic play in Roland's world?

4. One of Roland's favorite phrases is 'the world has moved on.' What does this mean? What do you think Roland's world was like before it moved on?

5. Throughout *The Gunslinger*, we are struck by the number of similarities between our world and Roland's world. The towns-folk of Tull know the words to the Beatles' song 'Hey Jude,' and they use *bocks* (bucks, or dollars) as their currency. Jake's description of New York (recounted while he is under hypnosis) reminds Roland of the mythical city of Lud, and

the tunnels beneath the Cyclopean Mountains contain the ruins of a subway system that remind Jake of home. How do you explain these similarities? What is the relationship between Roland's world and our world?

6. Although Sylvia Pittston claims to be a woman of God, she is actually one of the most actively destructive characters found in *The Gunslinger*. As Roland's lover Allie says, Pittston's religion is poison. What role does Pittston play in the novel? Have you come across Pittston-like characters in any of King's other fiction? How do you explain the discrepancy between Pittston's professed role as a preacher and her actual allegiance to the man in black and the Crimson King? What are the divisions between good and evil in Roland's world?

7. Nort, the weed-eater Roland meets in Tull, suffers a terrible fate. After being poisoned by the addictive devil grass, he is resurrected by the sinister Man in Black, only to be later crucified by Sylvia Pittston and her followers. The terms *resurrection* and *crucifixion* automatically make us reflect upon the biblical account of Jesus' crucifixion and resurrection, and the belief that, come Judgment Day, the dead will rise and be held accountable for the good and evil of their lives. Why do you think King includes these references? Why do you think Nort is crucified *after* being resurrected, a direct reversal of the biblical events?

8. Nort is not the only sacrificial figure found in *The Gunslinger*. Why does the Man in Black call Jake Roland's 'Isaac'? What does this tell us about Roland, about his relationship to the man in black, and his relationship to the Dark Tower?

9. When do the characters of *The Gunslinger* use High Speech? Would it be justified to call this a sacred language? What languages, in our world, are associated with religious ceremonies, ritual, and magic? What makes them special? Can these same attributes be said to belong to High Speech?

10. In literature, settings often serve a symbolic purpose. Throughout *The Gunslinger*, the landscapes Roland traverses are

described as hostile, dry 'purgatorial wastes.' Even relatively lush environments, such as the willow jungle, are full of dangerous forces, both mortal and demonic. In terms of its history, why is Roland's land so dangerous and desolate? What is the symbolic significance of this harshness?

11. Although the setting of the Dark Tower series reminds us of a cowboy western, King's Tower novels draw from many other literary genres, including gothic fiction, science fiction, horror, and medieval Romance. Can you identify these elements in *The Gunslinger*?

12. One of Stephen King's central inspirations for writing *The Gunslinger* was Robert Browning's poem 'Childe Roland to the Dark Tower Came.' The Victorians who first read 'Childe Roland' saw it as a story of heroism and duty. For them, it was a Romance in which a brave knight attempted to make a pilgrimage even though all before him had failed. More recent critics, however, have read the poem in much more psychological terms. They interpret the landscape that Browning's Roland traverses as a reflection of the character's fears, terrors, and preoccupations – in other words, as a reflection of his internal state. In this interpretation, the knight's search for the Dark Tower ultimately leads him to the center of himself, and to the truth of self-awareness. Do you think that either of these interpretations can be applied to *The Gunslinger*, in all or in part? Is Roland's story a heroic tale of a knight on a quest, or can Roland's travails be read as an allegory for the decisions, strivings, successes, failures, and personal betrayals we all face?

13. Ancient warrior cultures developed strict codes of honor and duty, which we now refer to as *heroic codes*. Great heroes were expected to be courageous, fearless, and headstrong. They had little or no regard for personal safety and in fact often acted rashly. What a warrior's peers thought of him mattered above all else, and he thought little or nothing about personal conscience (in the modern sense) or the well-being of the soul.

The warrior did not aim to enter Heaven, but to become legendary. Personal honor, family honor, and/or loyalty to the king or chieftain were what made a man worthwhile. Did the gunslingers of Gilead obey a Christian code or a heroic code? What about Roland? Is there a shift between these two codes as the novel progresses?

14. Judeo-Christian culture is primarily a guilt-based culture. In other words, people believe that God alone has the right to judge sins, and that He knows our guilt or our innocence, no matter what the world thinks of us. If an individual is innocent, he (in theory at least) can hold his head high, even though his reputation has been ruined. What matters is personal conscience. Hence, by the same token, if an individual believes he has committed a crime, he will be consumed by guilt, even if no one else ever discovers what has been done. Warrior cultures, on the other hand, were often shame-based cultures. In shame-based cultures, an individual must avoid 'losing face,' since the disgrace he or she accrues reflects not only on the individual, but upon the family and the lineage. What a person thinks of himself matters less than what society thinks of him. Did Cort train apprentice gunslingers using guilt or shame? What does this tell us about gunslinger culture? At his hanging, does Hax show either guilt or shame? Why? What kind of culture does he seem to reflect? Does Roland primarily experience guilt or shame? Does this change over the course of the novel? Why, in terms of Roland's personal development (or lack of it), might this happen?

15. Take a look at the tarot reading Walter does for Roland in the golgotha. How many of these cards are from the traditional tarot deck? Are there any others that seem to be versions of traditional cards? Which cards did King create anew? Which ones actually come from other sources? (Hint: Take a look at T. S. Eliot's poem *The Waste Land*.) What is your interpretation of this reading? Why do you think Walter burns the card of Life?

16. At the front of the revised edition of *The Gunslinger* (2003), King

adds a quote from Thomas Wolfe's novel *Look Homeward, Angel.* (This quote did not appear at the front of the previous edition.) What emotions does this quote arouse in us? Why do you think King added it? Does it affect your interpretation of the novel?

The Dark Tower II: The Drawing of the Three

1. How does King's writing style change between *The Gunslinger* and *The Drawing of the Three*? What about his storytelling process? What are the strengths of each approach?

2. In the prologue of *The Drawing of the Three,* Roland has a dream in which he becomes the human embodiment of Walter's tarot card the Sailor. Why does he consider this a good dream? What is actually happening to him, and with what results? Do you believe that this is an existential punishment for his previous actions, a violent joke played upon him by the Man in Black, or simply a chance event?

3. What is ka, and how does it affect Roland's life? Does it seem to imply predestination? Are human beings trapped by ka, or do we retain free will?

4. Describe the three magic doors. How do they work? Does ka have anything to do with their existence?

5. What disembodied voices echo inside Roland's mind? What part do they play in Roland's internal monologue/dialogue? Are they forces for good or for ill? In turn, how does Roland *become* a voice in the minds of other people? Does this affect your interpretation of the voices inside Roland's consciousness?

6. Unlike the action of *The Gunslinger*, which takes place in Roland's world, much of the action of *The Drawing of the Three* takes place in our world. In fact, many of Eddie's problems, and most of Detta/Odetta's problems, have their roots in U.S. culture and U.S. history. What social, economic, and cultural problems of 1980s America touched Eddie Dean's life? What long-range

effect did the Vietnam War have upon Henry Dean and, in turn, upon Eddie? How did racial hatred, segregation, and then the Civil Rights Movement affect Odetta Holmes's life? What about Detta Walker's?

7. Why is Eddie Dean willing to put his life at risk for his brother, Henry? Does Henry deserve this kind of loyalty?

8. What, in Roland's treatment of Eddie, shows that Roland comes from a warrior culture, not our culture? What part does patriarchal lineage play in gunslinger culture? Why would this be especially alien to Eddie?

9. Some warriors cultivate battle frenzy, using this altered state of consciousness to achieve feats that would otherwise be almost impossible. A famous historical example of this phenomenon can be found in the Norse berserkers. What is Roland's battle frenzy like? What about Eddie's? Is *frenzy* the right word?

10. Why did Odetta's father refuse to tell her about his past? What metaphor does King use to describe Dan Holmes's protective silence? How does Dan Holmes's treatment of his past contribute to Odetta's fragmentation?

11. How does Roland help to cure Odetta? Why is his timing so significant?

12. Were Jack Mort's attacks upon Odetta racially motivated?

13. How does Roland assess the people of our world – both those he sees on the plane and those he deals with while controlling Jack Mort's body? What does this say about the difference between a world that has 'moved on' and one that has not?

14. The second section of *The Drawing of the Three* (the one immediately following 'The Prisoner') is entitled 'Shuffle.' One of the images that King is conjuring is that of a cardsharp, shuffling a deck of cards. Why does King use this image? What kind of deck is being shuffled? What event, from *The Gunslinger*, does this remind us of? Why is the final section of the book entitled 'Final Shuffle'?

15. The verb *to draw* has many meanings and can be used in many contexts. Roland, Eddie, and Detta all draw guns. Roland draws his two companions into his world. However, the verb *to draw* can also be used to describe the action of drawing poison from a wound so that the wound can heal. What role does this kind of drawing play in *The Drawing of the Three*?

16. What role does Jake play in this novel? Why is this so significant in terms of Roland's development?

The Dark Tower III: The Waste Lands

1. Between the end of *The Drawing of the Three* and the beginning of *The Waste Lands*, the relationships among Roland, Susannah, and Eddie shift. Describe these changes. What causes them? Does Eddie now trust Roland? Does Susannah?

2. What is the gunslinger litany? What worldview does it imply – from what a gunslinger should honor to how he/she should attack his/her enemies?

3. In what ways are Roland's new friends much like his deadly old friends? What happened to those old friends? Do you think the same fate awaits Roland's new friends?

4. What is ka-tet? How do the forces of ka-tet bind individuals together, and how do they ultimately bind a society together?

5. Describe the metaphysical map that Roland draws at the beginning of the novel. What is its linchpin? What sits upon its circumference? What forces hold the world together? What part did the Great Old Ones play in the devising of this map? Do you think that the forces described there predate them? Why or why not? Does this map describe the actual origins of the world or of the linked worlds? What role did North Central Positronics play in the making of this world, or in the remaking of it?

6. What are the Drawers? Are they objective places – places that you could find on a map – or is their existence more subjective?

Have you encountered any such places in your life? If so, what are they? Do you have a special term for such places?

7. What paradox tears Roland's mind apart at the outset of the novel? What causes it? What eases his suffering? Why is this significant?

8. What voices does Jake hear in the Vacant Lot, just before he sees the Rose? What happens to him when he actually sees this flower? How does Jake's vision of the Rose differ from Eddie's vision of the Tower amid its sea of roses?

9. What is the White?

10. While contemplating the rose, Jake sees that it grows out of alien purple grass. Roland sees the same purple grass during his vision in the golgotha, at the end of *The Gunslinger*. Why does King seem to want us to compare these otherwise dissimilar visions? What is he telling us about the nature of the Rose?

11. What is the difference between Jake's door, labeled *The Boy*, and the beach doors?

12. The scene in which Roland and his new ka-tet cross the bridge into Lud eerily echoes the passage in *The Gunslinger* where Jake falls to his death. Compare these two scenes. What do they tell us about the changes happening within Roland?

13. The third book of the Dark Tower series takes its title from T. S. Eliot's long poem 'The Waste Land.' Two themes that thread through Eliot's poem are fragmentation and alienation — the fragmentation of modern culture and its inevitable loss of meaning, and the sense of alienation that individuals experience in reaction to this. (It must be remembered that 'The Waste Land' was written in the aftermath of World War I, when Europe was still in shock over the death and destruction caused by modern weaponry.) How does King's novel reflect these themes? How does this fragmentation extend to the psyches of the characters themselves, and even to the computerized personalities of machines?

14. In his notes on 'The Waste Land,' T. S. Eliot stated that he

was extremely influenced by the Grail legend. What is the legend of the Grail? Do you think it influenced Stephen King when he wrote *The Waste Lands*?

15. Eleven dimensions, worlds made out of vibrating strings, parallel universes that contain alternative versions of you . . . Sounds like another Dark Tower book? It's not, but it does seem as though the scientific community is finally taking Jake Chambers seriously. There *are* other worlds than these. For a fascinating description of string theory (and as a way to begin discussing the similarities between contemporary physics and the multiple worlds of the Dark Tower series), visit the following Web sites: www.pbs.org/nova/ elegant (a terrific introduction) www.bbc.co.uk/science/ horizon/2001/parallelunitrans.shtml (another great introduction) http://superstringtheory.com (for brave folks who are used to technical language) www.scientificamerican.com (in the 'search' section, type *Parallel Universes*)

The Dark Tower IV: Wizard and Glass

1. Why, do you think, did the Great Old Ones build Blaine? What purpose did he serve in their world? What do you imagine the Old Ones' world was like?

2. While riding in Blaine, Eddie thinks to himself, *Not all is silent in the halls of the dead and the rooms of ruin. Even now some of the stuff the Old Ones left behind still works. Ant that's really the horror of it, wouldn't you say? Yes. The exact horror of it.* How does Eddie's statement prefigure the coming action? Does his observation hold true for the first three novels of the series?

3. What is a thinny? What effect does it have on those near it? Is it alive? How does the image of the thinny help to bridge the two parts of *Wizard and Glass* — the section that takes place in Topeka and the one that takes place in Hambry?

4. Why does Roland say that in Hambry 'the waters on top and the waters down below seemed to run in different directions'?

5. Ka is a wheel; its one purpose is to turn and (inevitably) repeat. In what ways have we seen the wheel of ka turn so far in the series?

6. What is the story of Lord Perth, which we learned about in *The Waste Lands*? How did that myth play out in the novel? How does it continue to resonate throughout *Wizard and Glass*? Do you think the theme of the Lord Perth tale is also one of the themes of the Dark Tower series?

7. Who is Rhea of the Cöos? What role does she play in the novel? How does she compare to Roland's other major enemies – the Man in Black and Sylvia Pittston? If Rhea had been a male character, would she have been as convincing or as formidable? Why or why not?

8. What is the Wizard's Rainbow? What do we know about it? How many of the balls are still in existence, and why are they said to be alive and hungry? What is the relationship between the White, which Roland and the other gunslingers serve, and the spectrum of colors that make up the Wizard's Rainbow?

9. The imagery surrounding Maerlyn's Grapefruit is often sexual; even its color is described as 'labial pink.' Why does King use this imagery? What is the relationship between the Grapefruit and emotions such as desire, jealousy, and vengeance? How do these emotions drive the action of Roland's Hambry adventure? How did they begin his journey into manhood, even down to the early winning of his guns?

10. How is Roland's experience of Maerlyn's Grapefruit different from those of the other people who have it in their possession? Why do you think this is so? What visions does Roland have while the ball is in his possession? How does the ball lead to his downfall?

11. The tale of Hambry begins under a Kissing Moon and ends under a Demon Moon. Why is this significant? How does the transition from one of these moons to the other reflect the darkening of the novel's atmosphere?

12. At the beginning of the Hambry portion of *Wizard and Glass,* Susan Delgado must 'prove' her honesty. What does this mean? In what other ways does Susan continue to prove her honesty throughout the book? What other characters prove themselves to be honest? Which characters prove to be dishonest?

13. *For if it is ka, it'll come like a wind, and your plans will stand before it no more than a barn before a cyclone.* In what ways have we seen Pat Delgado's description of ka hold true, both in this novel and in the three preceding ones?

14. How would you describe Cuthbert Allgood? What does Roland love about him? What about him angers Roland? In what ways is he like Eddie? Is this similarity also ka?

15. What do you think the relationship is between Walter (also known as the Man in Black), Marten, Flagg, Fannin, and Maerlyn? What part do these nasty characters play in this novel?

16. In what ways does gunslinger culture actually inflame the rebellion led by Farson?

17. When Roland first meets Susan Delgado, King tells us, 'Roland was far from the relentless creature he would eventually become, but the seeds of that relentlessness were there – small, stony things that would, in their time, grow to trees with deep roots . . . and bitter fruit.' Why does King tell us this? Do you agree with this assessment of Roland's character?

18. Where do we see the sigul of the open, staring eye? Why is it so sinister? How does it connect Hambry, Topeka, and the Green Palace? What does it tell us about Roland's world?

The Dark Tower V: Wolves of the Calla

1. In his author's note, Stephen King acknowledges the influence that several films and film directors have had upon the Dark Tower series. Most notably, he mentions Sergio Leone's spaghetti westerns starving Clint Eastwood (*A Fistful of Dollars;*

For a Few Dollars More; The Good, the Bad, and the Ugly), and Akira
Kurosawa's classic *The Seven Samurai*. He also gives credit to
John Sturges's 1960 western (a remake of the Kurosawa film),
The Magnificent Seven. Can you describe the influence that any or
all of these films have had upon the Dark Tower series as a
whole and upon *Wolves of the Calla* in particular?

2. At the beginning of Chapter I of *Wolves of the Calla*, Eddie Dean
reflects upon the old Mejis saying *Time is a face on the water*. Do his
theories explain why time passes differently in our world and in
the borderlands? Why or why not? Do his observations hold true
for you, personally? Have you ever experienced such time-dilation
or time-contraction?

3. Why are Eddie, Jake, Susannah, and Roland so wary of Andy
when they first meet him? Why is this significant, both in
terms of our ka-tet's history and in terms of the history of
Roland's world?

4. What is happening to Susannah Dean's personality? How did
this come to pass? Do you think this process is part of her
ka? Given her condition, what do you think will happen to
our ka-tet in the final two books of the series?

5. Who are the roonts? How did they become roont? Do you
think that the roonts understand what has happened to them?
What, from the text, makes you say this?

6. What power do the Wolves ultimately serve? Why are the
people of the Calla so afraid to fight them? Can you understand their fear?

7. What mythical event do the Sisters of Oriza honor? What
purpose do they serve in terms of plot? Do you think that
King is trying to make us reexamine traditional ideas about
men and women?

8. Describe Black Thirteen. What is its history? What role does
it play in the book? How does it compare to Maerlyn's
Grapefruit, which figured prominently in *Wizard and Glass*?

9. What is todash? Why is it dangerous to travel todash? Who

are the Manni? Why do they believe that todash is 'the holiest of rites and most exalted of states'?

10. What role does the number 19 play in *Wolves of the Calla*? Where have we seen it before? (Hint: You'll need a 2003 edition of *The Gunslinger* to answer the second part of this question.)

11. Describe the Cave of Voices (also known as Doorway Cave). What is its function? Is it magical or mechanical? What voices do the various characters hear when they are inside the cave? In what way does the 'demon' or 'mechanism' of this cave expose unconscious fear or guilt? If you were suddenly transported to the Cave of Voices, who would come to speak to you?

12. What is the meaning of the term *commala*? Why would the Commala Song be so important in a rice-growing community? Does the Commala Song – and its accompanying dance – remind you of any ceremonies from our world?

13. Compare the tale of Lady Oriza to the story of Lord Perth, which we learned about in *The Waste Lands*. What do they have in common? How do they differ? What themes do they share with the Dark Tower series as a whole?

14. Where, in King's fiction, have we met Father Callahan before? Why do you think King decided to link a non–Dark Tower book so closely to the Dark Tower series?

15. As we all know from experience, few people are completely good or completely evil. Even the most annoying individual can surprise us with a selfless act, and an otherwise admirable person can sometimes shock us with an angry word or an unfair judgment. The same goes for well-drawn, believable characters. Make a list of the most important characters we meet in Calla Bryn Sturgis. Who is 'good'? Who is 'bad'? Who would you say is 'brave' and whom would you call 'cowardly'? Now take a look at any scenes where these characters exhibit unexpected, opposite tendencies. How does the author make us sympathize with the wicked or feel disappointment with the opinions and actions of the 'good'? How does King let us see both the savory and unsavory traits of each character?

16. Roland's world contains both machinery and magic. Most of the machinery we've encountered so far has been hostile, but the magic is more ambiguous. In *Wolves of the Calla*, the most potent magical objects are the Rose and Black Thirteen. Is one completely good and the other completely evil? Why or why not? What greater forces do these objects represent? Do you think that they symbolize a struggle found in our world as well?

17. Both fans and reviewers often refer to King's large body of work as 'the Stephen King Universe' or 'the Stephen King Multiverse.' How do you interpret these terms? What part does the Dark Tower play in this universe? What part does our world play in this universe? Do you think that Stephen King's realistic fiction should also be classed as part of the 'Stephen King Universe'?

18. Human beings have always craved magical, supernatural tales. In fact, many of the earliest and greatest of our stories — *The Epic of Gilgamesh, Beowulf,* and *The Odyssey,* to name just a few — tell about man's interaction with the unseen worlds. Although 'official' culture denies that telepathy, spirit worlds, and magic exist, such ideas still thrive as part of modern folklore. Why do you think that magical and supernatural tales are still popular? Do you think their appeal has grown over the past few years? Why? Do these kinds of tales serve a particular purpose, either socially or personally? Do you think the appeal of the Dark Tower series lies in the way it successfully weaves together both technology and magic?

The Dark Tower VI: Song of Susannah

1. Stephen King placed two unusual facing pages at the beginning of *Song of Susannah.* At the center of the left-hand page (which is otherwise blank) is the word *REPRODUCTION.* At the center of the right-hand page is one large number — *19.* However, in the bottom left-hand corner of the right-hand page is the tiny number *99.* What effect is King striving for? What effect do these pages have upon you as a reader?

2. How does King shift our mood from one of elation, when the Wolves are defeated near the end of *Wolves of the Calla*, to one of anxiety at the beginning of *Song of Susannah*? What series of tragedies – and inexplicable events – takes place?

3. What is a Beamquake? What effect does it have on the borderlands? What is its significance, as far as our characters' quest is concerned?

4. Who, or what, is Mia? How does her appearance (and disappearance) drive the action of *Song of Susannah*? In what ways does her history intertwine with Roland's?

5. When the Manni help Roland, Eddie, Jake, and Callahan open the Unfound Door, they all expect that it will open onto New York City in 1999, and then onto Stoneham, Maine, in 1977. Eddie and Roland are supposed to follow Susannah into the Big Apple, and Jake and Callahan are supposed to pursue Calvin Tower in Maine. What goes wrong? What series of unexpected events takes place? In your opinion, who or what is behind this change of plan?

6. What is Susannah's can-tah? How do you think it came to Susannah? With what force is it aligned? Have you ever encountered a similar type of object in any of King's other fiction? (Hint: Take a look at the novel *Desperation.*) If so, how does it differ from Susannah's can-tah? What does this say about the forces of the White and the Outer Dark in the Stephen King universe?

7. What is Susannah's Dogan? What part does it play in *Song of Susannah*? How does it link this novel with *Wolves of the Calla*? Is Susannah's Dogan completely imaginary? Is the machinery within it completely under Susannah's control? Why or why not?

8. What are Demon Elementals? What role do they play in our tet's adventures? Why do you think that King waited until *Song of Susannah* to tell us about them? How do they affect your view of the Guardians? How do they affect your vision of Roland's world?

9. What role does John Cullum play in *Song of Susannah*? Do you think that his appearance is linked to ka? If so, what part does ka play in the battle between the White and the Outer Dark? Does it always play the same role?

10. Unlike most novels, *Song of Susannah* is divided not into chapters but into stanzas, a term we usually associate with songs and poems. Does this name change affect how we read the novel? Does it affect our expectations? At the end of each chapter/stanza, King includes a short rhymed section containing a stave and a response. What do these terms mean, both in and of themselves and in the context of the novel?

11. What is the significance of Susannah's dream at the beginning of the tenth stanza? What visions does she have? What future do they foretell? Can this future be altered, even though the visions show future events in the Keystone World?

12. In stanza eleven, Roland says that Stephen King is the twin of the Rose. Earlier in the Dark Tower series, we were told that the Rose is the twin of the Dark Tower. How do you explain the relationship between King, the Rose, and the Tower?

13. What is the nature of the black shadow that Eddie Dean sees hovering around sai King? What is its possible significance, both in terms of King's life and our tet's quest?

14. Why — according to sai King — did he stop writing the Dark Tower series? What about Roland, in particular, disturbed him? Do you agree or disagree with his assessment of our gunslinger? In your opinion, has Roland changed since King first started writing about him? Were there any other forces that contributed to King's ceasing work on the Dark Tower series?

15. In stanza eleven, King describes his writing process. Does this description surprise you? Why or why not?

16. At the end of *Song of Susannah*, Stephen King includes a section entitled 'Coda: Pages from a Writer's Journal.' According to the *Oxford English Reference Dictionary*, a coda is a concluding event or series of events. More specifically, it tends to refer to the

concluding passage of a piece of music (or of a movement within a piece of music), usually one that acts as an addition to the basic structure. In ballet, the term *coda* refers to the concluding section of a dance. Why do you think King chose to call this section a coda? What does this say about the structure of *Song of Susannah*? What specific event in *Wolves of the Calla* is King consciously echoing?

The Dark Tower VII: The Dark Tower

1. Of all the books in the Dark Tower series, *The Dark Tower* is probably the most action-packed. What are the major crisis points within the novel? How does King create this dramatic tension? How do you think King goes about planning such a plot? Does the story line just evolve naturally from the characters he imagines?

2. What do Jake and Callahan find in the Dixie Pig? In what ways do the forces of the Outer Dark mock the White? Since the Crimson King is also descended from Arthur Eld, is there some hidden significance in this mockery? If so, what does this say about the nature of the White? What about the nature of the Tower?

3. How does Pere Callahan's death, at the beginning of *The Dark Tower*, refer back to his experiences in *'Salem's Lot*? What does this say about Callahan's ka?

4. What is an aven kal? How is it similar to, or different from, todash?

5. What kind of 'walk-in' do Eddie and Roland meet along Route 7 in Lovell? How did this creature enter our world? What connection does King make between walk-ins, the Prim, and the creative imagination?

6. What is the difference between a magical door, which links worlds, and a mechanical one? Where do the different types come from? Is one aligned with the White and one with the Outer Dark? Can such simple labels be put on them? Why?

7. The Breaker prison in Thunderclap is known as the Devar-
Toi to the prisoners and Algul Siento to the can-toi and taheen
guards. How do these two names express different perspec-
tives on the duties being performed there?

8. The three Breakers who initially aid Roland, Eddie, Susannah, and
Jake all come from other places in King's fiction — either from
earlier parts of the Dark Tower series or from other stories or
novels. Where do these characters come from? Why does King
choose these characters? What does this say about the Dark
Tower itself, and about the interconnectedness of the 'Stephen
King Universe'?

9. To describe Pimli Prentiss, Master of the Devar-Toi, Stephen
King compares him to Jim Jones, the leader of the People's
Temple in Guyana, who convinced his followers to commit
mass suicide. What effect does this have upon us? Is King
making a wider social statement when he draws this comparison?

10. What is ka-shume? How does this force manifest in the ka of
our ka-tet? Can a person escape ka-shume?

11. Although it has its own stark beauty, Roland's world has been
devastated by mutations, plagues, and ruinous technology. Now
that you've finished the series, how do you think Mid-World
relates to our world? Does the company North Central
Positronics have any symbolic significance? Is King
commenting on contemporary culture? If so, what is he saying?
Is his vision completely positive, completely negative, or something in between?

12. In the final two books of the Dark Tower series, King enters
the tale directly. In fact, at one point King calls himself the
deus ex machina, or the 'god out of a machine.' What is your
reaction to King's appearance in the Dark Tower series? What
place does the fictional Stephen King have in the Dark Tower
universe? What about the real Stephen King?

13. According to the people of the Tet Corporation, there is a
direct link between the Dark Tower series and King's other fiction.

What is it? Do you view King's various novels as pieces of a giant jigsaw puzzle, with the Dark Tower novels at the center? Why or why not? If you don't see King's fiction in this way (or if you haven't read many of King's other books), think about any King films you've seen, or any episodes of his various TV series. Are there any themes that seem to repeat?

14. What are the can-toi? What are the taheen? How are they the same and how are they different? King compares the taheen to the monstrous figures found in Hieronymus Bosch's famous triptych, *The Garden of Earthly Delights,* painted circa AD 1500. Take a look at this painting. (It's fairly easy to find. Just type *Hieronymus Bosch,* and *Garden of Earthly Delights,* into your search engine.) As you will see, when the triptych is closed, its outer shutters depict the creation of the world. When the triptych is open, the left panel depicts Adam and Eve and the earthly paradise, the center panel illustrates the world engaged in sinful pleasures, and the right panel (where our taheenlike creatures appear) represents Hell. How are King's creations similar to these painted figures? By drawing this comparison, what other, unspoken comments is King making about End-World, the Devar-Toi, and the Crimson King?

15. At the beginning of *The Dark Tower,* Jake reflects upon one of Roland's sayings. According to our gunslinger, 'You needn't die happy when your day comes, but you must die satisfied, for you have lived your life from beginning to end and ka is always served.' What does this statement mean? Do you agree or disagree with the philosophy it expresses? Take a look at each member of Roland's ka-tet: Eddie, Susannah, Jake, Oy, Callahan, and even Roland himself. Do any or all of them remain true to this vision?

16. At the beginning of *Wolves of the Calla,* Stephen King includes a section entitled 'The Final Argument.' According to this introductory piece, each of the seven novels of the Dark Tower series has a subtitle. Moving, in order, from *The Gunslinger* to

Song of Susannah, these subtitles are 'Resumption,' 'Renewal,' 'Redemption,' 'Regard,' 'Resistance,' and 'Reproduction.' In terms of Roland's quest, what is the meaning of each of these subtitles?

17. Although each of the first six novels of the Dark Tower series has a single-word subtitle, *The Dark Tower* (the final book of the series) has a four-word subtitle. It is 'Reproduction, Revelation, Redemption, Resumption.' How does this subtitle reflect the action of the novel? How does it interact with the subtitles of the previous novels? If you sit and contemplate the meaning of each of the words in *The Dark Tower*'s subtitle, does it affect your interpretation of the novel's ending? How does it affect your interpretation of Roland's quest?